D1171582

IT's ABOUT TIME®

HERFF JONES EDUCATION DIVISION

84 Business Park Drive

Armonk, NY 10504

Phone (914) 273-2233

Fax (914) 273-2227

Program Components

Student Edition

Teacher Edition

Practice Problems

Reinforcement Problems

Key Concept Sheets

Enrichments in Algebra and Geometry

Media

Teacher Resources CD

Appendix CD

Test Generator CD

Professional Development Videos

MATH *Connections: A Secondary Mathematics Core Curriculum* was developed under the National Science Foundation.

Grant No. ESI-9255251 awarded to the Connecticut Business and Industry Association.

ISBN 978-1-58591-701-3

ISBN 978-1-58591-702-0 (Year 1, 2 Book Set)

1 2 3 4 5   12 11 10 09 08

This project was supported, in part,
by the
National Science Foundation
Opinions expressed are those of the authors
and not necessarily those of the Foundation.

Welcome to **MATH** *Connections*®

This book was written for you. It is designed to provide you with mathematical experiences that will excite your curiosity, stimulate your imagination, and challenge your skills. It bridges mathematics with the real world of people, business, and everyday life. It isn't finished until you take an active part in the interesting problems and projects that invite you to explore important mathematical ideas. You'll want to discuss these ideas with other students, your teacher, and your family. You might find that not all your ideas work, but try again, perhaps a different approach will work—that is all part of learning. And the learning is up to you!

In this new Second Edition, changes have been made to the text to make it easier to read, understand, and learn the material. Activities and sections have been added that cover topics you may find on state exams. There is now an expanded review at the end of each section, called **Looking Back**, where you can see all the important laws, facts, and ideas of the section summarized, followed by exercises where you can practice what you've learned. Those questions will be similar to those you'll find on the state tests.

<u>In the Margins</u> **The Learning Outcomes** are in the margins of the first page of each section. These will alert you to the major topic. The **Thinking Tip** in the margins will help you in gathering your ideas and in solving problems. **About Words** will show you how some words we use in mathematics relate to words you already know and use every day. **About Symbols** will explain particular notations and their use in mathematics.

<u>In the Text</u> **A Word to Know** and **A Phrase to Know** appear in the text and signal particularly important definitions. Similarly, **A Fact to Know** signals an important mathematical result.

<u>In the Profiles</u> You will meet people in various careers and professions who use mathematics in their everyday work.

At the back of the book, you will find a Glossary and Index.

To assist with your learning and problem solving, you will also find a CD attached to the inside back cover of the book that contains the following:

- Appendix A: Using a TI-84 Plus Graphing Calculator
- Appendix B: Using TI-Nspire Software
- Appendix C: Using Cabri II Plus and Cabri 3D Software
- Appendix D: Using Autograph Dynamic Software

From time to time you'll see these graphic icons that call you to action:

Do This Now
Identifies questions for you to answer.

Discuss This
Identifies questions for you to discuss as a class or in groups.

Write This
Usually requires you to gather information or reflect on a particular topic.

How **MATH** *Connections* takes you to the real world.

MATH *Connections* begins with you!
Each **MATH** *Connections* chapter introduces a concept by asking you to think about what you already know. You bring a lot of your life experiences into the classroom and with **MATH** *Connections* those experiences are strengths.

Provides a solid foundation in mathematics.
Building on your knowledge, **MATH** *Connections* connects your experiences with comprehensive mathematics. You'll learn algebra, geometry, statistics, probability, trigonometry, discrete mathematics, plus linear programming, and optimization techniques.

Relates the mathematics to real situations.
As you learn the mathematics, you will apply it to real situations from hundreds of professions and careers ranging from architecture to microsurgery to managing a grocery store. Whether it is at home, in games, in sports or at work, **MATH** *Connections* connects mathematics to the real world of science, literature, art, and the things you do every day.

Think math.

Do math.

Talk math.

Write math.
Ultimately, math is a language that can help you in every aspect of your life. And with **MATH** *Connections*, you really make mathematics your own by exploring, looking for patterns, and reasoning things out. Whether you are working on your own, in small groups, or as a class to solve problems, with **MATH** *Connections*, you will achieve a real understanding of mathematics.

Classroom tested for excellence.
MATH *Connections* works! **MATH** *Connections* was field tested by more than 5000 students like yourself, in more than 100 high school classrooms. During the four-year field test, it was continuously refined by its developers and high school teachers. And year after year it has proven to make the learning of mathematics more effective and more enjoyable. Plus, bottom line, **MATH** *Connections* students score higher on state and national tests.

Prepares you for your future.
Whether you plan to pursue a career in the sciences, the fine arts, or sports, **MATH** *Connections* prepares you for the real world and for your future.

Algebra, geometry, probability, trigonometry, statistics, discrete mathematics, linear programming, optimization...

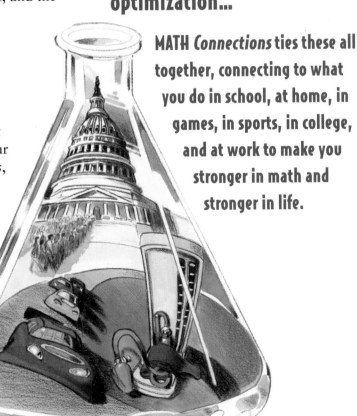

MATH *Connections* ties these all together, connecting to what you do in school, at home, in games, in sports, in college, and at work to make you stronger in math and stronger in life.

Original MATH *Connections*® Team

Contents

Chapter 7 Counting and Probability

Chapter 8 Quadratic Functions and Equations

Technology and MATH *Connections*

MATH *Connections*, a three-year program, has a great deal of technology integrated and applied throughout it. However, you will only need a graphing calculator and a computer graphing utility, if your school has the software, to use this program.

Four appendices found in the **MATH** *Connections* program, will help you learn how to use the different kinds of technology available to you. Two of the appendices, which can be found at the back of this book, will give you instructions on the use of the TI-84 Plus graphing calculator and the TI-Nspire handheld. The two remaining appendices, which can be found on a CD that your teacher has, can be printed out and given to you when needed. The first appendix on the CD is Cabri II Plus and Cabri 3D, two geometry programs. The other appendix is Autograph Dynamic Software, a computer graphing program. All four appendices are wonderful tools that will help you to better understand and learn the mathematics being presented.

Beginning in Chapter 1 of Year 1, you will begin to use the TI-84 graphing calculator. The TI-84 is a tool that not only allows you to calculate solutions, but also allows you to investigate concepts and develop your own mathematical understanding of these concepts. To let you know that a problem or concept being presented involves the use of a calculator, the following icon will appear:

If you are unsure about how to use the calculator with a particular concept, you can read the appendices in the back of your textbook to get step-by-step instructions.

Your school may also have one or more computer software programs that can help you solve many of the problems in your textbook. To let you know when one of the computer graphing programs would be helpful in your investigation of the concept, you will see the following icon:

One of the major advantages of a computer graphing utility is that you can print out the results of your work to include in your notes. You can also produce a typed report based on your findings.

These different kinds of technology are just a few of the tools in **MATH** *Connections* that help you understand mathematics. Working together, sharing ideas with classmates, asking questions, reading, note taking, and experimenting with ideas are other tools that, when practiced every day, make learning mathematics with the **MATH** *Connections* program easy and fun.

Deirdre Lord
Reducing Electricity Costs

Deirdre Lord works for Citizens Energy Corporation in Boston, Massachusetts. Joe Kennedy founded this nonprofit energy company. Its goal is to use industry to provide low-income communities with energy education and assistance programs.

As a project manager, Deirdre helps people understand and take advantage of new utility regulations. "Deregulation is very confusing," she explains. "It means that utilities can now compete with each other, just like any other business. My big challenge is to get low-income customers to join an energy pool. As a pool, they can get better rates from the electric companies."

Deirdre has a Masters Degree from the University of Delaware.

As a student, she saw the need for mathematics, so she studied statistics as well as economics.

"I now use these tools all the time," she says. "They are very important to my work."

Deirdre often uses bar charts and graphs to show her clients why they should join an energy pool. "I put the mathematics of the utility bills into something visual. This helps my clients understand what they can save. There are a number of dependent and independent variables in these calculations. I use estimation techniques to explain the savings.

"By putting our group with other groups, say large community centers or public housing complexes, we can do even better," Deirdre adds. "I'd like to see this program expand and become an example for the entire country."

Using Lines and Equations

5.1 A Guessing Game

Learning Outcomes

After studying this section you will be able to:

Develop strategies for a simple guessing game

Read a tree diagram that describes an algorithm

Compare different algorithms for the same problem.

In this program, you have already learned how to solve many mathematical problems. In Chapter 1 of Book 1a you learned how to display and interpret data. In Chapter 2 you learned how to set up and solve equations, and in Chapter 3 you learned how to graph them. In Chapter 4 you learned how to find a line and equation to fit some data. In this chapter we will tie these ideas together to solve new types of problems.

For some of the problems you solved, you used a definite algorithm. There was a sequence of steps that always led to an answer. In other cases you used strategies like guessing, estimating, or trial and error. In this chapter you will learn algorithms for solving those problems more easily and accurately.

Algorithms are also important for computers. Before you can program a computer to do something, you must have an algorithm in mind. In some cases, several algorithms must be analyzed to find the best one.

As an example of how to develop an algorithm, we will analyze a simple game where one person picks a whole number from 1 to 100. Another person tries to guess the number by asking only questions that can be answered Yes or No, such as, "Is it 53?" or "Is it more than 9?" or "Is it less than 88?" etc.

Pair off with one of your classmates and play the game four times. Take turns being the guesser. Record the number of questions the guesser asks before he or she guesses the number.

After playing this game, you and your partner should have four pieces of data. If either of you guessed the number with eight or fewer questions, you did a very good job! (Did you have a strategy or did you just guess at random?) How did your classmates do?

5.2

Gather data from the entire class. Use some data analysis techniques to summarize and display it.

Did anyone find the number after very few questions? Did they have a strategy or were they just lucky? (You can check this out by having the good guessers repeat the game with several different partners.) Was anyone consistently a good guesser? If so, what was their strategy? Discuss possible strategies with your classmates and try to find a good one. See if you can predict the fewest questions needed to guess the number.

Here is a simple algorithm for playing this game. The guesser asks:

1. Is the number 1?
2. Is the number 2?
3. Is the number 3?
4. Is the number 4?

and so forth.

5.3

Does this algorithm work? That is, if you are the guesser, will you eventually find the number if you use it? How many questions would you have to ask if the number is 25? What if it is 95? What would be the fewest questions that you might have to ask? What would be the most? How could your partner make you ask a lot of questions?

As you can see, this algorithm is not very efficient. You might have to ask a lot of questions before you find the correct number. We can do better. Here's a way to approach this problem (and many others like it) more efficiently.

We will start with a smaller version of the game—guessing a number from 1 to 8—so that we can easily look at all the possible ways of playing it. Once we find a better algorithm for that case, we will see if it works for guessing a number from 1 to 100. First, to be sure that we understand the problem clearly, we will write it in mathematical language.

Thinking Tip

Solve a simpler problem.
Sometimes you can see how to solve a problem if you try a simpler version of it first.

The guesser must guess the value of a whole number x where $1 \le x \le 8$. Earlier, you learned that $1 \le x \le 8$ means "x is between 1 and 8, inclusive." In other words, "1 is less than or equal to x and x is less than or equal to 8."

The basic idea of our new algorithm is to cut the number of possibilities (roughly) in half with each question. For example, if $1 \le x \le 8$, a good first question to ask is, "Is x more than 4?" If the answer is Yes, then x must be 5, 6, 7, or 8. If the answer is No, then x must be 1, 2, 3, or 4. In either case, you have reduced the problem to one of guessing one of four numbers, a much shorter problem.

If your partner says x is greater than 4, the next question would be, "Is it greater than 6?" This again divides the possibilities in half.

1. **What is the next question if your partner says x is not bigger than 6?**

2. **If your partner answers your first question by saying that x is *not* more than 4, what is a good next question?**

5.4

All possibilities for this algorithm are represented by the *tree diagram* in Display 5.1. (You will learn more about tree diagrams in Chapter 7.) Read it starting from the left, where

Thinking Tip

Draw a diagram. Often, looking at a simple drawing will help you understand and remember how a process works. Drawing the diagram yourself is even better because it makes you focus on details you might otherwise overlook.

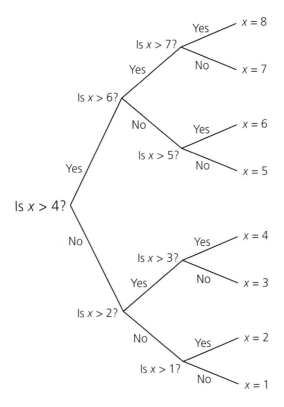

Display 5.1

it says "Is $x > 4$?" If the answer is Yes, then follow the line going up to the next question ("Is $x > 6$?"). If the answer is No, then follow the line going down to the next question ("Is $x > 2$?"). Then start again with the new question and continue as before.

5.5 Does the algorithm in Display 5.1 work? That is, will a guesser using this algorithm eventually find x? If you are the guesser, how many questions will you need if your partner picks the number 2? What if your partner picks 5? What is the least number of questions you might need? What is the greatest number of questions you might need? Can your partner make you ask a lot of questions?

5.6
1. Create an algorithm like the one in Display 5.1 for guessing a whole number x with $1 \leq x \leq 16$. Ask your teacher for a copy of Display 5.1 and expand it to fit your algorithm. How many questions are needed to guess x?

2. Create a similar algorithm for guessing a whole number x with $1 \leq x \leq 4$. How many questions are needed to guess x? Make a tree. (*Hint:* Save a tree by covering up a part of the one you already have.)

3. Create a similar algorithm for guessing a whole number x with $1 \leq x \leq 2$. How many questions are needed to guess x? Make a tree. (*Hint:* Save a tree by covering up a part of the one you already have.)

4. Copy and complete Display 5.2. Look for a pattern.

Guess a Number from 1 to...	Number of Questions Needed
2	
4	
8	
16	

Display 5.2

In the examples we have looked at, we could always divide the possibilities exactly in half. We cannot do that if we want to guess numbers from 1 to 5 (or from 1 to 93 or ...). In cases like this, we come as close as we can. We might ask if x is greater than 2 and divide the possibilities into {1, 2} and {3, 4, 5}, or we might ask if x is greater than 3 and divide the possibilities into {1, 2, 3} and {4, 5}. In any case, the goal is to divide the possibilities into two sets that are both as large as possible. That way, no matter what the answer is, we eliminate nearly half of the possibilities.

Make a tree diagram for the guessing game for $1 \le x \le 11$. If you use an algorithm similar to the one we have been describing, what would your first question be? How many guesses are needed to find x? Is the number of guesses you need always the same?

5.7

Pair off with a classmate and play the guessing game four times for $1 \le x \le 100$. Use the algorithm you learned in this section. Take turns being the guesser. Record the number of questions the guesser has to ask before finding x. Pool data from the entire class. Use data analysis techniques to summarize and display the data. Are the results better than the first time you played the game?

5.8

Problem Set: 5.1

1. Continue the table of Display 5.2. Add four more rows, using the pattern you found. Describe the general pattern of this table in terms of exponents.

   (a) Use your completed table to estimate the number of questions needed to find a whole number x, when $1 \le x \le 100$. Explain your thinking.

   (b) Look at the data you compiled when your class played this game. How well did your class do in relation to your answer to part (a)?

   (c) Using this algorithm, would you guarantee that you could find a whole number x, when $1 \le x \le 1000$, using no more than ten questions? Why or why not?

2. Suppose that you are guessing a whole number x where $101 \le x \le 200$. If you used an algorithm like the one described in this section, what question would you ask first? What if you were guessing a whole number between 368 and 593, inclusive? How many questions would you need in each case?

3. A dealer in rare coins has a bag of 100 silver dollars. She knows that there is one counterfeit coin that was mixed in with the good ones by mistake. It is hard to tell a real coin from a fake one by looking at them. She does know that the fake coin weighs less than a real one. The coin dealer asked a nearby laboratory if she could use their accurate balance scale. They will let her use it, but they charge for each weighing. She could weigh each coin one by one, but this method might take 100 weighings to find the fake coin. She cannot afford to pay for a lot of weighings. She has figured out a way to find the fake coin with fewer than 10 weighings.

   (a) How do you think she did it?

   (b) Would your method change if you knew that the fake coin does not weigh the same as a real one, but you did not know if it weighs more or less? Explain your answer.

5.2 Organizing Trial and Error

Learning Outcomes

After studying this section you will be able to:

Use the guessing game algorithm and tables to solve applied problems

Estimate roots of numbers.

In the previous section, we played an old guessing game. We saw that making wild, random guesses was not a good way to find the answer, so we found an algorithm for playing the game. By choosing our guesses carefully we could "zoom in" on the answer more quickly. In this section, we will use the basic ideas from that algorithm to find answers to some real-life problems. Tables will help us display and organize the data we get. Sometimes our guesses do not give us the exact answer, but can get us as close as we want. An approximate answer is often close enough for what you need.

Earlier in **MATH** *Connections*, we were comparing two rate schedules for the Central Connecticut Electric Company. That was one place where you had to guess. The electric company had been charging a monthly customer service charge of $8.50 plus 9 cents per kilowatt-hour (kWh). Then the electric company asked the Public Utility Commission (PUC) for an increase to 10 cents per kWh. The PUC agreed to the rate increase if the customer service charge was reduced to $6.00.

5.9

1. **Write equations that express the total charge (T) in terms of the number of kilowatt-hours used (u), for each of the two rate schedules.**

2. **You were asked to see if you could find a usage for which the two rate schedules charge the same amount. Were you able to solve this problem? If so, how did you do it?**

One way to solve this problem would be to try successive values of u — 0, 1, 2, 3, ...— until we find a solution.

5.10

Does this algorithm work? That is, will you eventually find the answer if you use this algorithm? How long do you think it will take? What will happen if there is no value of u for which the two schedules give the same bill?

We will start with this algorithm, even though it is not very efficient. Then we will try to improve it.

5.11

Make a table like Display 5.3. We have done the first two lines for you. Leave lots of extra space so that you can add additional lines later.

Usage u (kWh)	Old Rate Schedule Total charge T (dollars)	New Rate Schedule Total charge T (dollars)
0	8.50	6.00
1	8.59	6.10
2		
3		

Display 5.3

One difference between this problem and the guessing game problem is that we knew there was an answer to the guessing game problem.

5.12

Using Technology

Which rate schedule gives the larger bills for the usages you have in your table? Based on your table, do you think there will be a usage for which the other rate schedule gives larger bills? Explain. Do you think the two rates will ever give the same bill?

The next four values in the table would be for $u = 4$, 5, and 6 kWh. From the table we have so far, it does not look like we are very close to a solution. Maybe we should try some larger values for u.

5.13

Add rows for $u = 100$, 200, 300 and 400 kWh to your table. We will be adding more values of u later, so leave a blank line before each new line. Do you find any values of u for which the new rate schedule gives a larger bill? If not, what do you need to do next?

We are now going to adapt our guessing game algorithm to solve the usage rate problem. Eventually, we shall see how that algorithm may be applied to many different problems. If you solved this problem earlier, you should compare your solution to this method.

Based on the table you completed, we will make certain assumptions. Because they are assumptions, we cannot be sure that they are true, but they are reasonable guesses that allow us to get started. Later, if we do not find a usage at which both rate schedules charge the same amount, we will come back and recheck our assumptions.

After you completed your table, you should have found that the new rate is less expensive for usages of 100 and 200 kWh. Therefore, our first assumption will be that the new rate is less expensive for usages of 200 kWh or less. That is, the new rate is less expensive when $u \le 200$.

From the table you made, it appears that any usage for which both rates are the same will probably be between 200 and 300 kWh. We could guess at numbers in the 200 to 300 range, but the algorithm is a more efficient approach. The idea is to use a guess halfway between 200 kWh and 300 kWh, just as you did in the guessing game. (Remember that the mean of two values is always halfway between the two numbers.)

1. What number is halfway between 200 and 300?
2. Add a new row for the usage that is halfway between. What do you find?

5.14

The algorithm we just used is like the one for the guessing game. At each step, we went halfway between two previous guesses. Before we could do this, we had to have a value of u for which the old rate costs more than the new rate and a value for which the new rate costs more than the old rate. Then we looked between those two values. In this example, our algorithm found the correct answer ($u = 250$ kWh) very quickly. It was certainly a big improvement over trying $u = 1, 2, 3, \ldots$ up to $u = 250$! In other situations, we may not be so lucky.

You may recall that in an earlier problem about simple and compound interest, Alfredo was saving money for a trip to Central America. He had a gift of $1,000 and needed a total of $2,400. We wanted to know how long he would have to save before he had $2,400 if he earned 7% compound interest. You solved the problem using

$$T = 1000 \cdot (1.07)^n$$

where T is the total amount Alfredo has after n years.

See how much money Alfredo would have after 0, 8, and 16 years at 7% annual compound interest. Apply the methods of this section to find out when he has $2,400.

5.15

You solved this same problem by trial and error back in Chapter 2 of Book 1a. That algorithm took a long time and a lot of work.

If Alfredo's aunt paid him simple interest instead of compound interest, the total amount T that he would have after n years at 7% interest would be given by

$$T = 1000 + 1000 \cdot (0.07) \cdot n$$

so, by the Distributive Law,

$$T = 1000 \cdot (1 + 0.07)n = 1000 \cdot 1.07n$$

Apply the methods of this section to find out when Alfredo will have $2,400 using a simple interest of 7%.

5.16

Some practical problems may come up in the compound interest case. One is that there may not be an exact answer. However, we can find out when Alfredo has more than $2,400, and that is good enough.

Here is a slightly different example where we can never get an exact answer. In the beginning of **MATH** *Connections*, you found the standard deviation by taking the square root of the variance. You probably did that with a square root key on your calculator. Here is a way to find a square root using the algorithm we have been studying.

What is the square root of 3? We know 1 is too small because $1^2 = 1$, and 2 is too large because $2^2 = 4$. Guess halfway between. Keep on going and see how accurate a value you can get. Use the square root key on your calculator to check your accuracy.

5.17

Thinking Tip

Make approximations. Sometimes an approximate result is much easier to find than an exact one and is close enough to answer the question.

Take our word for it: You will *never* get an exact decimal value for the square root of 3 using this (or any other) algorithim. However, you can get answers that are as close as you want.

In trying to find the square root of 3, you may have found that going halfway between two numbers was not always convenient. For example, halfway between 1.75 and 1.625 is 1.6875. In the guessing game, you need not go exactly halfway between the two numbers. You may take any number in between. In picking a number, notice whether one of the earlier guesses is closer than the other. At one point in finding the square root of 3, you wanted to go between 1.5 and 1.75. You can compute that $1.5^2 = 2.25$ and $1.75^2 = 3.0625$. It looks like 1.75^2 is much closer to 3 than 1.5^2. You might make your task easier and quicker by guessing 1.7 next rather than using the number that is exactly halfway between 1.5 and 1.75.

Try to find the square root of 3 using our algorithm, but pick convenient in-between values. At each step, discuss with your classmates what the next step should be. When you agree, try the guess. See if this is faster or easier than what you did before.

5.18

Of course, this algorithm may not be too impressive if your calculator has a square root key, so let's try fifth roots. We say x is a fifth root of y if $x^5 = y$. For example, 2 is a fifth root of 32 because $2^5 = 32$. A small number in the radical sign signals a root other than a square root, like this:

$$\sqrt[5]{32} = 2$$

Using Technology

5.19

Use our algorithm to find $\sqrt[5]{100}$, correct to two decimal places. We'll help you by asking some questions.

1. What two successive whole numbers is $\sqrt[5]{100}$ between? How do you know? Which one do you think it's closer to?

2. What number will you try next? What does "try" mean here? Is $\sqrt[5]{100}$ larger or smaller than the number you chose? How do you know?

3. Trap $\sqrt[5]{100}$ between two successive tenths.

4. Now trap $\sqrt[5]{100}$ between two successive hundredths.

5. Use your answer to question 4 to find $\sqrt[5]{100}$, correct to two decimal places. Explain your reasoning.

Problem Set: 5.2

1. Use the algorithm method described by the questions just before this problem set to find the following roots, correct to two decimal places:

   (a) $\sqrt{2}$

   (b) $\sqrt[3]{3}$

   (c) $\sqrt[4]{4}$

   (d) $\sqrt[5]{5}$

   (e) $\sqrt[5]{1000}$

2. If you did problem 1, you probably noticed that the answers to parts (a) and (c) are the same, at least to two decimal places. Are they really exactly the same?

   (a) Calculate $(\sqrt{2})^4$. How does this tell you that the answers to 1(a) and 1(c) are exactly the same?

   (b) Recall that $\sqrt{2}$ is just the common shorthand for $\sqrt[2]{2}$. With this in mind, part (a) tells you that $\sqrt[2]{2} = \sqrt[4]{4}$. This seems to be the beginning of a pattern. What do you think comes next? Does it work the way you think it should? Justify your answer.

(c) Extend part (b) to find a general pattern that begins with $\sqrt[2]{2} = \sqrt[4]{4} = \ldots$. Write your pattern in words and then in symbols, if you can.

3. You saw the following data set in Chapter 2:

A bacterial culture is being treated with ultraviolet rays in an attempt to kill the bacteria. The following table shows the percentage of bacteria surviving after t hours of treatment.

Length of Treatment (t hours)	% Surviving (S)
0	100
1	91
2	82
3	73

Display 5.4

(a) Write an equation that gives the percentage of bacteria surviving (S) in terms of the number of hours of treatment (t).

(b) Copy the table and add rows for 8, 10, 12, and 15 hours of treatment.

(c) Use the algorithm you studied in this section to estimate how long it will take for all of the bacteria to be killed.

4. Claire just began working for the Chesapeake Company. She is earning $18,000 a year right now. She has been told that each year she will get a raise equal to 5% of her previous year's salary.

(a) How much will she be earning next year?

(b) Write an equation you can use to calculate the total amount T that Claire will be earning after n years.

(c) How much will she be earning after 16 years?

(d) Use the algorithm studied in this section to estimate how long it will take before she earns $30,000 per year.

5. Linda's science class is studying falling objects. Her science teacher says that if you drop a golf ball from 400 feet above the ground, it will take 5 seconds to hit the ground.

(a) How many seconds do you think it will take for the ball to fall halfway to the ground?

(b) The height of the ball in feet H can be expressed in terms of the number of seconds t (time) after the ball is dropped. The equation that describes this is $H = 400 - 16t^2$. Set up a table to display the time falling, t (in seconds), and the height above the ground, H (in feet). Use it with the algorithm studied in this section to estimate how long it takes for the ball to fall halfway to the ground.

(c) Write a paragraph about these questions: How did your answer from part (b) compare to the estimate you made in part (a)? Were you surprised? Why or why not? Is the rate of speed of a falling object linear? How do you know?

5.3 A Picture Is Worth…

Earlier in **MATH** *Connections* you learned how to make graphs of equations and of data. A graph of data often helps you to see how two variables are related. It may not be as detailed as a data table, but it can bring out patterns better. When we want to investigate the relationship of two variables, we have to decide which method to use. Let's look at the two methods.

In the previous section, you used tables to compare two electric utility rates. Some of the values you calculated for the table in Display 5.3 are shown in Display 5.5.

Usage u (kWh)	Old Rate Schedule Total charge T (dollars)	New Rate Schedule Total charge T (dollars)
0	$8.50	$6.00
100	$17.50	$16.00
200	$26.50	$26.00
300	$35.50	$36.00
400	$44.50	$46.00

Display 5.5

Display 5.6 is a graph of the data from the old rate schedule.

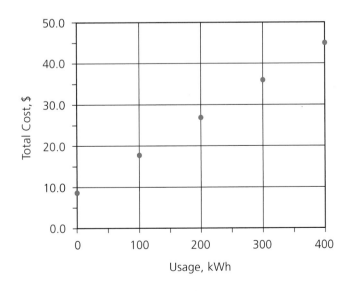

Display 5.6

Notice that we chose scales on the axes to match the table. Usages go from 0 to 400 kWh in the table and on the graph. For the cost axis, we rounded and let the scale go from 0 to 50 dollars. It is convenient to include the origin (0, 0) if it is not too far from the rest of the graph. We put tick marks every 50 units on the usage axis and every 5 units on the cost axis. Alternate tick marks are labeled.

5.20

Put a ruler on Display 5.6 and see if the points fall close to a straight line. Do they? Recall that equations in the form $y = ax + b$, where a and b are constants, form a straight line. Is the equation $T = 0.09 \cdot u + 8.50$ in this form?

In Display 5.7, we have added the line that fits the old rate schedule data.

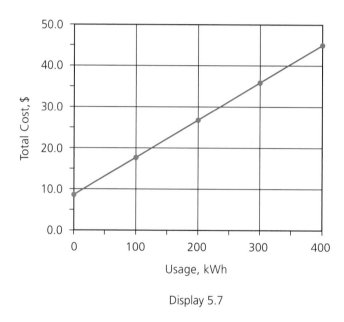

Display 5.7

To compare the two rate schedules, we plot the data for the new rate schedule on the same graph.

When you graph data, you usually want the individual points to stand out. When you graph a straight line, you usually want the line to stand out. Once we have the line for the old rate schedule, we do not need to keep the points used to get it. Display 5.8 shows the line for the old rate schedule and the points for the new rate schedule.

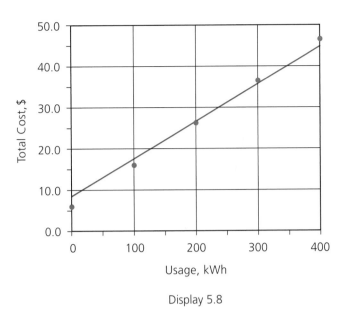

Display 5.8

How can you tell from the graph when the new rate schedule gives a higher cost than the old rate schedule?

5.21

Now we will put in the line for the new rate schedule and eliminate the points we used to get it. See Display 5.9.

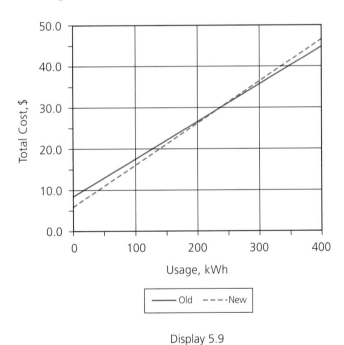

Display 5.9

Here we have used a dashed line for the new rate schedule to distinguish it from the old. Comparing two lines is easier if you graph both of them using the same scale. It is even better if you put them both on the same graph.

5.22

Look at the graph in Display 5.9 and answer the following questions:

1. Which rate schedule charges more for usages less than 200 kWh? How did the graph help you to answer this?

2. Which rate schedule charges more for usages greater than 300 kWh? How did the graph help you to answer this?

3. Where do the two lines seem to intersect? What does this point of intersection tell you about the two rate schedules? How does this compare to the solution to the problem you solved in the previous section?

In Section 5.2, we guessed at the answers to questions 1 and 2 above when we began using the algorithm. The graph shows us that those assumptions are true.

The two straight lines intersect exactly once and will never intersect again. To the left of the point of intersection, one rate schedule will *always* charge more; to the right of the point of intersection, the other rate schedule will *always* charge more. Since usage can never be negative, we can see all the points to the left of the point of intersection in Display 5.9. We cannot see past 400 kWh to the right, but we can see that the lines are getting further apart.

The coordinates of the intersection point are the usage and total cost at which the two rate schedules are the same. In Section 5.2 we used a form of the guessing game algorithm to find this point. We can also use a graph.

Any points that the lines have in common satisfy *both* equations. When we have two or more equations, we say we have a **system of equations**. Finding values of the variables that satisfy *all* the equations is called **solving the system**.

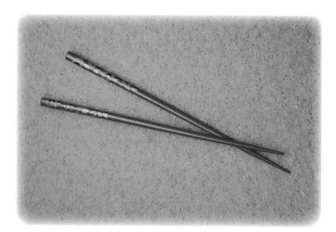

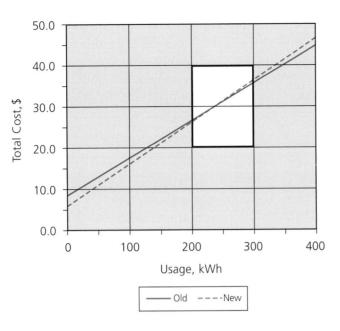

Display 5.10

In Display 5.9, the coordinates of the crossing point solve the two-equation system $T = 0.09u + 8.50$ and $T = 0.10u + 6.00$. But that graph gives us only a rough idea of where the lines intersect. We can get a better idea by magnifying the area around the intersection. We do this by making a new graph that shows only a region closer to where the lines cross. We chose a "window" of $200 \le u \le 300$ and $20 \le T \le 40$, the unshaded box in Display 5.10. That part of the graph is redrawn larger in Display 5.11.

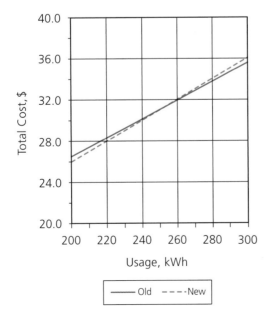

Display 5.11

Display 5.11 should look about the same as Display 5.9, until you look at the scale. You should be able to read the intersection point more accurately from this new graph. We can keep zooming in like this and find the coordinates of the point of intersection as accurately as we want. Display 5.12 has another scale, giving you an even closer look at the intersection.

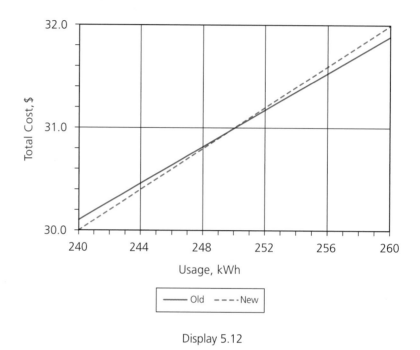

Display 5.12

5.23

1. (a) What is the "window" in Display 5.12?

   (b) What is the "window" in Display 5.11?

   (c) Where in Display 5.11 is Display 5.12 located?

2. Use Display 5.12 to estimate the coordinates of the intersection point. Explain the meanings of the values of T and u that you find. Comparing your estimates with the ones you made earlier using the graph in Display 5.9, which do you think are better? Why?

Using Technology

A disadvantage of the graphical method is that it takes a great deal of time to draw all of the graphs by hand. The graphs must be made carefully to have accurate results. You can make accurate graphs very quickly with a spreadsheet program. Using a spreadsheet program, these graphs can be made to look professional for use in a presentation. If you only need to find an intersection point, you can use a graphing calculator. The graphs will not be as attractive, but the calculator can zoom in much more quickly.

Problem Set: 5.3

1. Use graphs to solve each pair of equations.

   (a) $y = 0.5x + 1$
   $y = 1.0x + 4$

   (b) $m = 2p + 3.5$
   $m = 1.8p + 5$

   (c) $y = 2x + 7$
   $y = 2(x + 7)$

   (d) $y = 2x + 8$
   $y = 2(x + 4)$

2. All new appliances have an energy cost sticker. This sticker displays the average cost of using the appliance for one year. Kara is looking at refrigerators at the Huge Appliance Store. She finds two models that are the right size and have the features that she wants. Kara wants to keep this refrigerator for a long time, so she is concerned about how much it will cost to use it. She decides to calculate the total cost of owning each model, its price, plus its cost for energy, and then use this information to decide which one is more economical. Display 5.13 shows the information she copied from the energy cost stickers.

Model	Cost	Average Yearly Energy Cost
Cool Air	$575	$47
Arctic Blast	$500	$55

Display 5.13

   (a) For each model, write an equation that gives the average total cost, T dollars, after y years.

   (b) The average life of a refrigerator is 15 years. Draw a graph of each equation on the same coordinate axes to display at least 15 years of use.

   (c) If Kara plans to keep her refrigerator for less than 4 years, which model should she buy?

   (d) If Kara plans to keep her refrigerator for more than 13 years, which model should she buy?

   (e) Use the method described in this section to determine the coordinates of the point where the two lines intersect. How are the coordinates of this point related to the total cost of owning a refrigerator?

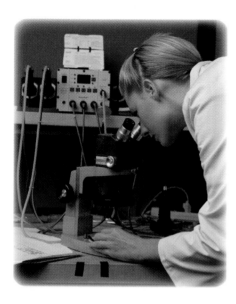

(f) If you were Kara, which refrigerator would you buy? Explain your answer.

3. Insulin is a drug that allows your body to use the sugar that you eat. Many people have a condition called *diabetes mellitus*. Their pancreas doesn't produce enough insulin, so their body must get it from other sources. In the past, insulin has been harvested from animals.

Scientists are now looking at faster and better ways of producing insulin. One way they do this is by splicing the appropriate human gene to the gene of common yeast and then growing the yeast in a culture. As the yeast makes the chemicals it needs to live, it also manufactures insulin, based on instructions from the "hitchhiking" gene. Then the yeast and all of the other compounds can be filtered away, leaving a solution of human insulin.

Different strains of yeast will produce the insulin at different rates. Display 5.14 is a table of expected results for two strains. For each strain, the table shows the number of hours the yeast was cultured and the amount of insulin harvested.

	Insulin Yield (grams)	
Hours	Strain 1	Strain 2
4	19.44	10.2
8	23.88	19.4
12	28.32	28.6
16	32.76	37.8
20	37.20	47.0
24	41.64	56.2
28	46.08	65.4
32	50.52	74.6
36	54.96	83.8
40	59.40	93.0
48	68.28	111.4

Display 5.14

(a) Graph both sets of data on the same coordinate axes. Do the relationships appear to be linear? If they are, draw a straight line for each strain of yeast.

(b) Which strain would be best if you have to harvest the yeast after 8 hours? After 10 hours? After 30 hours? Which of these questions are best answered from the graph and which are best answered from the table?

(c) In determining which strain of yeast to use, a scientist must consider various other factors, such as the cost and size of equipment. As a first step, one needs to find the point at which the production of insulin is the same no matter which strain is used. Estimate this from your graph.

4. The Rent & Roll car rental agency charges $225 per week and 25¢ per mile for its small cars.

   (a) What would be the cost to rent a small car from Rent & Roll for a week, if you drove it 150 miles?

   (b) Write an equation to find the total cost, C dollars, of renting a small car from Rent & Roll for a week and driving it m miles.

   (c) What kind of equation did you write in part (b)?

   (d) What is the slope of the equation you found in part (b)? What is its y-intercept?

   (e) Graph the equation you found in part (b).

5. The Save-A-Buck car rental agency charges $175 per week and 50¢ per mile for its small cars.

   (a) What would be the cost to rent a small car for a week from Save-A-Buck if you drove it 150 miles?

   (b) Write an equation to find the total cost, T dollars, of renting a small car from Save-A-Buck for a week and driving it m miles.

   (c) What is the slope of the equation you found in part (b)? What is its y-intercept?

   (d) Graph the equation you found in part (b).

6. Use your results from problems 4 and 5 to answer the following questions:

   (a) Graph the equations you found in problems 4(b) and 5(b) on one set of axes.

   (b) Look at the graph you drew in part (a). Would it cost more to rent a small car from the Rent & Roll agency than from the Save-A-Buck agency? Would it ever be the same? Less?

   (c) What does the point where the lines intersect represent? What are the coordinates of that point?

   (d) Mr. Washington wants to rent a small car for a weeklong trip. Under what conditions should he rent from Rent & Roll? Under what conditions would it be better to rent from Save-A-Buck?

7. Mary's house is 5 miles from Juan's.

   (a) If Mary begins bicycling toward Juan's house at 3:00, and she bicycles at an average of 6 mph, how many miles will she go in 2 hours? In 15 minutes? Explain how you figured this out.

   (b) Let t be the number of hours since 3:00. Write an equation for the distance M in miles Mary is from her house in t hours. What is the slope of this line?

   (c) At the same time Mary leaves her house, Juan begins bicycling from his house toward Mary's. Juan bicycles at an average rate of 4 mph. Draw a diagram representing the situation.

   (d) How far from Mary's house will Juan be half an hour after he leaves his house?

   (e) Again let t be the number of hours since 3:00. Write an equation for the distance J in miles Juan is from Mary's house in t hours. What is the slope of this line?

   (f) Graph the two equations on one set of axes to represent Mary's and Juan's trips. Do the two lines intersect? At that point, Mary and Juan are both the same distance from Mary's house. What is that distance? At what time does that happen?

8. Tommy Kaye's Video charges a $10.00 membership fee and $3.00 per video rental.

   (a) What is the total cost for renting 16 videos (including the membership fee) at Tommy Kaye's?

   (b) Write an equation that gives the total cost T for r rentals at Tommy Kaye's. Is this equation linear?

   (c) Graph the equation you found in part (b) on your graphing calculator. Is the graph a line?

9. The Shop Quick video store has no membership fee but charges $3.25 per video rental.

   (a) What is the total cost for renting 16 videos at Shop Quick?

   (b) Write an equation that gives the total cost S for r rentals at Shop Quick. Is this equation linear?

   (c) Graph the equation you found in part (b).

10. This problem refers to problems 8 and 9.

    (a) Graph the equations you found for the total cost of rentals at Tommy Kaye's and Shop Quick on one set of axes.

    (b) Should the two graphs intersect? (*Hint:* Think about the slopes of the graphs.) If they should, find the point of intersection. What would this point represent?

    (c) Under what conditions will the total cost at Tommy Kaye's be the same as the total cost at Shop Quick? Under what conditions will it be less? More? Use your graph to explain your answers.

5.4 Pictures on Your Calculator

Learning Outcomes

After studying this section you will be able to:

Solve a linear equation for one of its variables

Use a graphing calculator to solve a system of equations.

You can use a graphing calculator or spreadsheet to graph systems of equations. This technology can make our work easier in some ways, but harder in others. Most computers and calculators require you to enter the equations in a particular way, and they may limit your variable names to x and y. In order to get these electronic tools to work for you, you have to "talk" to them in their language and interpret what they tell you.

For instance, in Section 5.3 we described the Electric Company rate data by the equations $T = 0.09u + 8.5$ and $T = 0.10u + 6$. Because we graphed T on the vertical axis, it acts like y. Because we graphed u on the horizontal axis, it acts like x. We say that T is the dependent variable because the total charge for the electricity depends on the number of kilowatt-hours used. Like y, the *dependent* variable is usually graphed on the vertical axis. The other variable here, u, is called the *independent* variable. It is plotted on the horizontal axis, like x. Mathematically, it does not matter whether we call our variables x and y or u and T. The graph of the equations

$$T = 0.09u + 8.5$$
$$T = 0.10u + 6$$

with u on the horizontal axis and T on the vertical axis, looks exactly like the graph of the equations

$$y = 0.09x + 8.5$$
$$y = 0.10x + 6$$

with x as the horizontal axis and y as the vertical axis.

Using u and T as our variables has the advantage of reminding us that they stand for the Usage and the Total charge, while x and y have the advantage that they are the labels used by many graphing calculators.

Often you will need to input equations in a particular form. For example,

$$0.8h + 3.2v = 16,000$$

is a perfectly good equation, but it cannot be put into most spreadsheets or graphing calculators in that form. The following example illustrates where such an equation might appear in real life. You will see how to graph the equation by hand and how to put it into a form that a spreadsheet or graphing calculator can use.

Webbfoot.com sells Internet access and helps its customers set up home pages on the World Wide Web. They offer two kinds of accounts. The less expensive one, HotFoot, provides the customer with 800 megabytes (Mb) of disk space. The more expensive *Very*HotFoot account provides 3200 Mb. Webbfoot has 16,000 gigabytes (Gb) of space available on the Internet. (We will use the approximation that 16,000 Gb is 16,000,000 Mb.)

Webbfoot needs your help in analyzing their options.

5.24

1. **If Webbfoot sells h HotFoot accounts, how many gigabytes of space will that take up? Write an expression in terms of h.**

2. **If Webbfoot sells v *Very*HotFoot accounts, how many gigabytes of space will that take up? Write an expression in terms of v.**

3. **Write an expression for the total space used up by both types of accounts.**

4. **Webbfoot would like to have enough customers to fill up all of its space on the Internet. Write an equation to describe a situation in which this happens.**

Your equation from question 4 above describes all the various ways Webbfoot could use up its space. For example, if it sells 10,000 HotFoot accounts and 2500 *Very*HotFoot accounts, they will use up

$$0.8 \cdot 10,000 + 3.2 \cdot 2500 + 16,000$$

which is all of its storage space.

Most of the equations we have studied so far have been linear equations of the form $y = mx + b$. The equation $0.8h + 3.2v = 16,000$ is not in that form, so it might not be a straight line. We can graph it to see if it is straight or curved. We know that $h = 10,000$ and $v = 2500$ are the coordinates of one of the points on the graph. Let's find some more points on it. How about $v = 1000$? Substituting this value into $0.8h + 3.2v = 16,000$, we have

$$0.8h + 3.2 \cdot 1000 = 0.8h + 3200 = 16,000$$

You learned how to solve equations like this earlier, so now you can find the h coordinate of this point.

Solve $0.8h + 3200 = 16,000$.

We could also pick a value of h and find v.

Find the value of v when $h = 8000$.

Now we have three points on the graph. We've put them into the table in Display 5.15. If you find a few more points, we should be able to get a pretty good picture of the graph of $0.8h + 3.2v = 16,000$.

Copy and complete Display 5.15 so that each point is on the graph of $0.8h + 3.2v = 16,000$.

h	v
10,000	2500
16,000	1000
8000	3000
	0
0	
30,000	
	2000
	4000
	6000

Display 5.15

Notice that not all of the values in your table make sense for the problem. Practically speaking, the number of accounts of each type cannot be negative, so we must have $v \le 0$ and $h \le 0$. Besides that, we cannot have a fraction of an account, so a point on the graph will only make sense if both its coordinates are whole numbers.

You now have the coordinates of several points on the graph of $0.8h + 3.2v = 16,000$. Plot these on graph paper. Just so that everyone's graph looks the same

- put the v scale on the vertical axis, from 0 to 10,000 and

- put the h scale on the horizontal axis, from 0 to 20,000.

What do you think the graph of this equation will look like? Draw it as carefully as you can.

You should notice two special points on your graph. The point with coordinates $h = 20{,}000$ and $v = 0$ is called the *h-intercept*. The point with coordinates $h = 0$ and $v = 5000$ is called the *v-intercept*.

Find these two points on the graph. Do you think they are appropriately named? Why or why not?

5.29

In the past, when we had an equation like $y = mx + b$, it was easy to find the *y*-intercept—we just had to look at *b*! When an equation is not in that form, we must work a little more. Remember that we found the *x*-intercept of $y = mx + b$ by substituting 0 for *y* and solving for *x*. We use this method to find both intercepts of $0.8h + 3.2v = 16{,}000$. The intercepts are important for a variety of reasons, and often they are the easiest two points to find on a graph.

What are the dependent and independent variables in $0.8h + 3.2v = 16{,}000$? Does *h* depend on *v*? Does *v* depend on *h*? Explain.

5.30

When an equation is in "$y = $ [something]" form and *y* is not in the [something], that's a signal that *y* is the dependent variable. If we replace all the variables in the "[something]" with numbers, we can calculate *y*. A graphing calculator or spreadsheet may require you to enter things in this "$y =$" form. Of course, the letter for the dependent variable doesn't have to be *y*; that's just the calculator's standard name for it.

If a two-variable equation is not in "$y = $" form, it may be solved for either variable. (Do you remember this from Chapter 3 in Book 1a?) This is the case with our equation involving *h* and *v*.

Here is how you can solve $0.8h + 3.2v = 16{,}000$ for *v*. No matter what the value of *h* is, $0.8h$ is some number. You can subtract that number from both sides of the equation, like this:

$$0.8h + 3.2v = 16{,}000$$
$$-\,0.8h \qquad\quad = -\,0.8h$$

The result is

$$3.2v = 16{,}000 - 0.8h$$

Now you have $3.2v$ equal to something. To find *v*, just divide by 3.2:

$$\frac{3.2v}{3.2} = \frac{16{,}000 - 0.8h}{3.2}$$

That is,

$$v = 5000 - 0.25h$$

Using Technology

5.31

1. Where did the 0.25 come from? Is a form of the Distributive Law involved here?

2. What other basic laws of algebra were used to solve for v?

3. Is the graph of this equation a straight line? If so, what is its slope? What is its v-intercept?

4. Graph this equation on your calculator. Set the **WINDOW** to match the graph you drew before and see if the calculator's picture agrees with yours.

You can think of the process of solving for v as "undoing." Why is $0.8h + 3.2v = 16{,}000$ not solved for v? Because v is multiplied by 3.2 and has $0.8h$ added to it. We undid the addition with subtraction. Then we undid the multiplication with division.

5.32

Here are some more examples of undoing for you to try:

1. To solve $y - 7 = 3x$ for y, undo the subtraction by adding 7. What do you get?

2. To solve $y - 7 = 3x$ for x, undo the multiplication by dividing by 3. What do you get?

3. To solve $5s + 3t = 35$ for s, undo the addition and then undo the multiplication. What do you get?

For equations like $0.8h + 3.2v = 16{,}000$, solving for one of the variables always works the same way:

1. Decide which variable you want to solve for.

2. Isolate that variable and its coefficient by subtracting the other term from both sides of the equation.

3. Divide both sides of the equation by the coefficient of that variable.

It works every time!

5.33

Try this three-step process again by solving

$$0.8h + 3.2v = 16{,}000 \text{ for } h.$$

Put your answer in slope-intercept form, and then use your calculator to graph what you get. How is this graph related to the previous one? Are they the same? Should they be?

Solve each of these equations for *y*. Then graph them all on your graphing calculator. (Use the Standard **WINDOW** setting.)

Using Technology

5.34

1. $3x + 2y = 6$

2. $6x - 2y = 10$

3. $7y - 4x = 28$

Which of the following points are inside the triangle formed by these three lines?

$(0, 2), (1, 3), (3, 1), (0, 3.5), (3.5, 0), (2, 4), (4, 2)$

Many formulas in science are equations in which two or more variables appear. The basic laws of algebra can be used to solve those equations for any variable that is not raised to a power. You just have to think of all the variables that you're *not* solving for as if they were numbers and apply the ideas you've just seen. For instance, you've probably heard the formula, "Distance equals rate times time," or $d = rt$. To turn that into a formula for time, just solve for *t*, instead of for distance, *d*. That is, think of *r* as a number and divide both sides by it, to get $\frac{d}{r} = t$, or, if you prefer, $t = \frac{d}{r}$. This gives you a formula for finding the time it takes to travel any distance at any (nonzero) rate of speed.

Here are a few more common formulas. Solve each one for the variable indicated. Do you recognize any of these formulas? If so, say what they represent.

5.35

1. Solve $P = 2l + 2w$ for *w*.

2. Solve $C = 2\pi r$ for *r*.

3. Solve $a = \frac{w}{v}$ for *w*.

4. Solve $a = \frac{w}{v}$ for *v*.

The Webbfoot sales staff is having a hard time selling enough accounts to use up all of its storage space. Maybe the *Very*HotFoot accounts are too expensive. If they decrease the *Very*HotFoot space and increase the HotFoot space, they can set the prices closer to each other. They are thinking about setting each HotFoot account at 1 Gb of storage space and each *Very*HotFoot account at 2.5 Gb.

5.36

1. Write an equation to describe the situations for which all 16,000 Gb of Webbfoot's space is used up.

2. Solve your equation for *v* and put it in slope-intercept form.

Using Technology

3. Graph this equation and the old Webbfoot equation (solved for v) together on your calculator.

4. Use the **ZOOM** and **TRACE** tools to find, to the nearest hundredth, how many accounts of each type will use up the total space in both plans. Check your answer by putting the numbers into both equations. (You should come close in both cases, but don't expect your answers to be exact.)

Problem Set: 5.4

For problems 1–7, use your calculator to graph the two equations and find the coordinates of the point(s) where they intersect.

1. $y = 0.5x + 1$
   $y = 1.0x + 4$

2. $y = 2x + 8$
   $y = -1x + 4$

3. $y = 2x + 8$
   $y = 2(x + 4)$

4. $y = 2x + 5$
   $y = 1.8x + 5$

5. $y = 3x^2 + 5$
   $y = 8x + 1$

6. $y = 2x^2$
   $y = 5x + 3$

7. $y = 2x^3$
   $y = 8x$

For problems 8–17, solve each equation for the indicated variable.

8. $A = \frac{1}{2}bh$; solve for h.

9. $P = a + b + c$; solve for a.

10. $L + 2 = 5m$; solve for m.

11. $LA = 2\pi rh$; solve for r. (LA is a single variable.)

12. $E = mc^2$; solve for m.

13. $V = lwh$; solve for w.

14. $P = 2l + 2w$; solve for l.

15. $SA = \frac{1}{2}pl + B$; solve for p. (SA is a single variable.)

16. $P = IE$; solve for I.

17. $I = Prt$; solve for t.

For problems 18–21, put each equation in slope-intercept form. Then use your calculator to find (approximately) the point where the two lines intersect.

18. $y = 1.49x + 11.34$

$2x + 3y = 7$

19. $x - 4y = 12$

$2x + y = 13$

20. $100a - 470b = 1600$

$50a + 15b = 500$

21. $5.2s + 1.3t = 39$

$7t - 21 = 6.3s$

22. Frank's Franks, the local hot dog stand, wants to print a full-color advertising flyer to distribute for 4th of July weekend. They got cost estimates from the two local printers. SnapPrint will print the flyers for 20 cents each plus a setup charge of $50. FinePrint will print them for 15 cents apiece plus a setup charge of $75.

(a) Write equations for each printer's total charge.

(b) What number of flyers will cost the same amount from both printers? What is that cost? How did you get your answer?

(c) Frank is willing to spend $200 for the flyers. He wants as many as he can get for that amount. Which printer should he choose? How can you see that from the graph? How many flyers will he get?

5.5 Precise Answers to Real-Life Situations

Learning Outcomes

After studying this section, you will be able to:

Solve a system of two linear equations by graphing, intercepts, and substitution of a constant for a variable

Recognize systems of equations that can be solved graphically.

Earlier in this chapter, you solved the following problem using the guessing game algorithm:

A bacterial culture is being treated with ultraviolet rays in an attempt to kill the bacteria.

Length of Treatment (*t* hours)	% Surviving (*S*)
0	100
1	91
2	82
3	73

Display 5.16

How much time it will take to kill all the bacteria?

We can also solve this problem using a graph.

5.37

Place a ruler on the data points on the graph in Display 5.17. Do they seem to fall on a straight line? Draw the best line you can. Use your graph to estimate how long it will take to kill all the bacteria. Did everyone in your class get the same result?

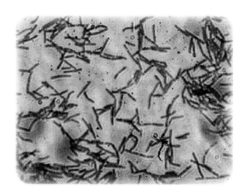

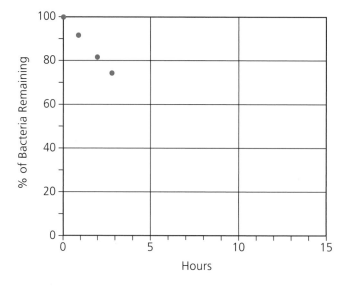

Display 5.17

Graphical methods usually give only approximate answers. Different people may get different answers, depending on how carefully they draw. There are other ways to solve problems like this that will often lead to exact answers. They are based on equation-solving skills. To use these methods, you must first translate what we know about the problem into equations. Then you can apply the algebraic tools you already know. Let's try it with our bacteria problem.

You know that the usual straight-line equation has the form $y = mx + b$, where m is the slope and b is the y-intercept. You also know that the y-intercept is the y-coordinate of the point where the line crosses the y-axis and that $x = 0$ for all points on the y-axis. In the bacteria example, x represents the amount of time and y represents the percentage of bacteria left, so the y-intercept is the percentage of bacteria at the starting time. That is, $y = 100$ when $x = 0$. (You can see the y-intercept in the upper left corner of Display 5.17.)

Knowing that the y-intercept is 100 tells us that the equation for the line we want is of the form $y = mx + 100$. Now we need to find the slope.

5.38

1. **What is the slope of a line? Can you use any two points on a line to find its slope?**

2. **Looking at Display 5.17, do you expect the slope of this line to be positive, negative, or zero? Why?**

3. **Choose two points on this line (from the data in Display 5.16) and use them to find the slope.**

4. **Write the equation for the line.**

Now that you have the equation, you can find out how long it will be until all the bacteria are dead. This is the earliest time when 0% of the bacteria are left alive. That is, when $y = 0$. The graph in Display 5.18 shows that this is the point where the line intersects the x-axis. (*All* points on the x-axis have y-coordinate 0.) This intersection point is called the **x-intercept** of the line. You can use the graph in Display 5.18 to get an approximate answer.

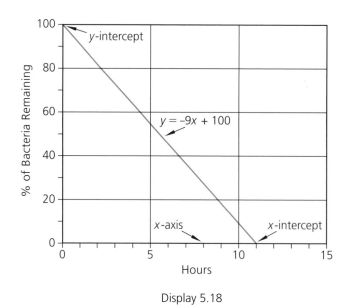

Display 5.18

It looks as though the *x*-intercept is a little more than 11. This may be close enough for our purpose, but sometimes you may need a more precise answer. You can use the equation of the line to get it. If a linear equation contains two unknowns (variables) and you know one of them, you can always find the other one. Just plug in the one you know and work out the arithmetic.

In this case, you know $y = 0$ and you want to find the corresponding value for *x*. We can think of this as solving the system of equations $y = 0$ and $y = -9x + 100$. To solve these two equations, substitute the value for *y* into the other equation:

$$0 = -9x + 100$$

Then solve this equation for *x*.

As a guide to solving this equation, keep your goal in mind. You want to end up with something that looks like "$x = ?$", where the "?" is a number. If you add $9x$ to each side of the equation, you have

$$0 = -9x + 100$$
$$\underline{9x = 9x}$$
$$9x = 100$$

Now divide by the coefficient of *x*:

$$\frac{9x}{9} = \frac{100}{9}$$
$$x = \frac{100}{9}$$

1. Check the value $x = \frac{100}{9}$ in the equation $0 = -9x + 100$. Do you get an equality?

   5.39

2. Convert your answer to a decimal, rounded to three places. Then check this answer in the original equation. Do you get an equality? Explain.

Now try solving this next real-life problem. We will help you.

How long will it take to drain a full 1250-gallon septic tank with a pump that can remove 3.6 gallons per minute?

5.40

1. Choose appropriate variables and use them to set up an equation that describes this situation.

2. Solve the equation to find out how long it will be before the tank is empty. (*Hint:* Which variable equals zero?)

3. What are the units of your answer? Change your units to hours.

So far we have been trying to solve a system of two equations in which one equation has the form $y = mx + b$ and the other is $y = 0$. However, the second equation could just as easily have y equal to some other number.

For example, you may recall that Alfredo was saving money for a trip to Central America. His Aunt Mercedes had given him $1,000 and he needed $2,400 total for the trip. Remember that if he puts his gift in a bank account paying 7% simple interest, the total amount due to him equals the principal plus the interest. That is, the total amount T (in dollars) that he would have after n years would be given by

$$T = 1000 + 1000 \cdot 0.07 \cdot n, \text{ which is}$$

$$T = 1000 + 70n.$$

Because addition is commutative, this is the same as

$$T = 70n + 1000,$$

a linear equation with T-intercept 1000 and slope 70.

What does the slope of 70 represent here?

5.41

Suppose the bank paid 4% simple interest. Find and interpret the slope and T-intercept.

5.42

Remember, Alfredo wanted to see how long it would be before $T = 2400$, so this is the second equation in our system. To solve the system, substitute $T = 2400$ into $T = 1000 + 70n$:

$$2400 = 1000 + 70n$$

This equation has only one variable. We can solve it using the tools of algebra that you already have.

5.43

Find the value of n in the equation $2400 = 1000 + 70n$. Do you think Alfredo will want to wait this long?

You solved this same problem by trial and error earlier. That took a long time and a great deal of work. You could also solve it by making a graph, but that method would also take time and might be inaccurate. Using algebra to solve an equation is quick and exact.

Originally, Aunt Mercedes was going to hold the $1,000 and eventually pay Alfredo the $1,000 and 7% compound interest. The total amount he would be due is given by

$$T = 1000 \cdot (1.07)^n$$

The compound interest curve is not a straight line. We have not studied how to use algebra to find where such a curve intersects the goal line, $T = 2400$. However, we can use the graph in Display 5.19 to make a good estimate.

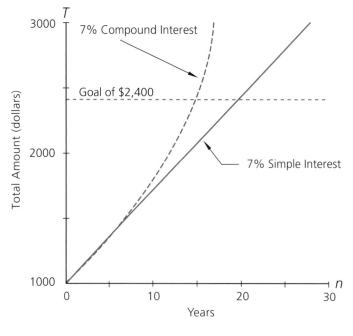

Display 5.19

Use the graph in Display 5.19 to estimate the number of years it will take Alfredo to get $2,400 if he is paid 7% compound interest. How accurate is your answer? How could you make it more accurate?

5.44

Problem Set: 5.5

1. For each pair of lines, use algebra to find the point where they intersect.

   (a) $y = 0$ and $y = 5x - 10$

   (b) $y = 5$ and $y = 3x - 1$

   (c) $y = 7$ and $y = 4x + 5$

   (d) $y = -4$ and $y = -2x + 3$

2. (a) Find the x-intercept of $y = -2x + 10$.

   (b) Find the x-intercept and the y-intercept of $y = 2.5x + 7.5$.

   (c) Find the p- and q-intercepts of $p = -3q + 15$.

3. The monthly charge for water in a small New England town is a minimum of $14 for up to 3000 gallons plus $0.003 for each extra gallon.

   (a) Let x stand for the number of extra gallons used in a month. Write an equation for the monthly water charge W in terms of x.

   (b) If the bill for a month is $20, how many extra gallons were used?

4. The outside air temperature drops by about one degree Celsius for each 100 meters an airplane flies skyward. Suppose the ground temperature is 20° Celsius.

   (a) Write an equation that can be used to determine the outside air temperature, T degrees, at a height of h meters.

   (b) What is the T-intercept of your equation? Interpret this.

   (c) Use your equation to predict how much the temperature will drop if you go to the top of the Empire State Building in New York City. (You may need to go to the library and look up the height of the Empire State Building.)

   (d) A pilot realizes that the de-icers on her airplane's wings are not working. Use your equation and the method of this section to find out how high she can fly before there is danger of ice forming on the wings.

Using Technology

5. Sonia is earning $18,000 a year. Each year, she expects to get a raise that is 5% of the previous year's salary.

   (a) Write an equation that determines her salary, *s* dollars for *y* years.

   (b) What is the *s*-intercept of your equation? Interpret this.

   (c) Sonia wants to know how long it will be before she is earning $30,000 per year. Do you think she should use the equation or make a graph to answer this question? Explain.

   (d) How many years will it be before Sonia's salary is $30,000 a year?

5.6 Using Algebra to Solve Systems of Equations

In Section 5.5 we used algebra to solve problems in which a line intersected a horizontal line. Earlier in the chapter we worked on a problem involving the Electric Company and two rate schedules. When we solved that problem graphically, we were looking for a point where two lines intersected. Neither of those lines was horizontal or vertical. Can we solve such problems with algebra? We can, and it's not very difficult.

Recall that the Electric Company's old rate schedule is described by the equation $T = 0.09u + 8.5$ and the new rate schedule is described by

$$T = 0.10u + 6$$

Since we are interested in the point where the values of T and u are the same for both rate schedules, we substitute $0.10u + 6$ for T into the equation $T = 0.09u + 8.5$. This gives us $0.10u + 6 = 0.09u + 8.5$.

Now we have an equation with the variable u on both sides. This new situation can be changed into a type of problem we already know how to solve—an equation with all the u terms on one side. One way to do this is by subtracting $0.09u$ from both sides:

$$
\begin{array}{rcl}
0.10u + 6 &=& 0.09u + 8.5 \\
-0.09u & & = -0.09u \\
\hline
0.01u + 6 &=& 8.5
\end{array}
$$

Now we have reduced our problem to solving the equation $0.01u + 6 = 8.5$. This is a form we already know how to solve.

1. **Now undo addition by subtracting 6 from both sides of the equation.**

2. **There is just one step left. What is it? Do it.**

5.45

Once you have a value for u, you can find the corresponding value of T.

Learning Outcomes

After studying this section, you will be able to:

Use algebra to solve a system of two equations of the form $y = mx + b$

Determine if a pair of values is a solution to a system of two equations in two variables.

Thinking Tip

Make a problem familiar. Sometimes when trying to solve a problem it helps to reduce it to a problem we already know how to solve.

5.46

Substitute your value of *u* into the old rate schedule equation to find the value of *T*. Then substitute your value of *u* into the equation for the new rate schedule to find the value of *T*. How do your two answers compare? Did you expect this result? Explain.

Display 5.20 is a graph of the situation.

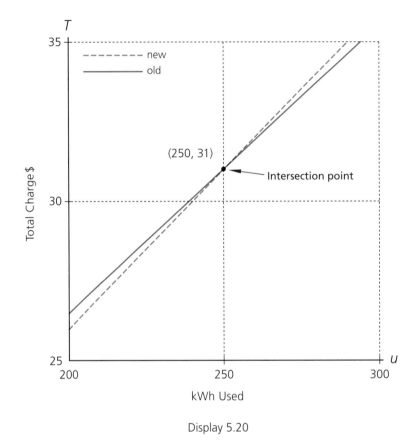

Display 5.20

In this case, *T* is the *dependent* variable because the total charge for electricity depends on the usage *u*. The dependent variable is usually graphed on the vertical axis (like *y*). The other variable here, *u*, is called the *independent* variable. It is plotted on the horizontal axis (like *x*).

When you have only two variables, such as in this Electric Company problem, solutions are often given in ordered pairs. The first value in the pair is normally for the independent variable. In the Electric Company problem, the solution is written as (250, 31). These are the coordinates of the point where the two lines intersect. They are labeled on the graph in Display 5.20.

You have just seen an example of how to solve a system of two equations involving two variables. A **solution** to such a system is a pair of values, one for each variable, that make both of the equations true. (If you have more than two equations, the solution values must make all the equations true.) To check whether a pair of values is a solution, substitute them into the equations and see if you actually get true equality statements.

Now it's your turn to solve a system of two equations on your own. Use algebra to solve the system

$$y = 3x + 14$$

$$y = 2x + 11$$

Be sure to check your answer.

Regardless of the method you use, when you solve a system of equations you should:

Always check your results in the original equations in the system to see that they are solutions. This way you will be certain that you have made no mistakes.

Check the three ordered pairs $(0, -6)$, $(1, 1)$, and $(2, -2)$ to see if they are solutions of the system

$$y = 7x - 6$$

$$y = -3x + 4$$

Do you think a system of two linear equations can have two solutions? How about three? More than three? None? Explain your answers.

A system of linear equations doesn't always come in slope-intercept form, but you can solve it in the same way. Just start by putting each equation into that form, and then follow the same steps as before. Here is a quick summary of those steps, assuming that x and y are the two variables.

- Once you have both equations in the form "$y = $ [something]" you know that the two "somethings" must equal each other (because they both equal y). Say so.
- Now you have an equation in one variable, x. Solve it for x.
- Put the x value you found back into one of the equations and solve it for y.
- Put the x and y values you found into the other equation to check that your solution is correct.

Try it. Solve this system of equations:

$$5x + 2y = 8$$

$$3x - y = 7$$

5.50

5.51

If you put the equations of a system into the form "$x = $ [something]" and then solved for y, would you get the same solution? Why or why not? Try it with the previous system.

Problem Set: 5.6

1. For the system of equations

$$y = 2x + 7$$
$$y = 3x - 5$$

decide whether each of the following ordered pairs are solutions:

(10, 27)   (11, 28)   (12, 31)

Using Technology

2. Use the method of this section to solve each system of equations or explain why this method cannot be used. If this method cannot be used, is there another method that could be used, instead?

(a) $y = 2x$

  $y = 5x + 3$

(b) $y = 0.5x + 1$

  $y = 1.0x + 4$

(c) $y = 2x + 8$

$y = 2(x + 4)$

(d) $y = 2x + 7$

$y = 2(x + 7)$

(e) $y = 3x^2 + 5$

$y = 8x + 1$

(f) $y = 8x$

$y = 2x^3$

(g) $y = \dfrac{2x + 8}{2}$

$y = 2x + 7$

(h) $y = \dfrac{2x + 8}{x}$

$y = 2x + 7$

3. Solve each of the following systems algebraically. Begin by putting each equation into slope-intercept form.

(a) $x + y = 3$

$2x - y = 4$

(b) $-2x + 6y = 5$

$x - 4y = 3$

(c) $0.4x + 1.2y = 2$

$1.5x + 3y = -1$

(d) $4x = 3y$

$6x - 2y + 10 = 0$

4. We use letters in algebra to highlight patterns. Patterns often make it easier to work with specific cases. They also help us to program computers to do some of our work for us. The following questions illustrate how this works:

(a) Think of a, b, and c as the specific numbers in the linear equation $ax + by = c$. Put this equation into slope-intercept form using these letters.

(b) Use the formula you found in part (a) to put the equations from problems 3(a) and 3(b) into slope-intercept form.

(c) Use your formula from part (a) to set up a spreadsheet so that, when the numbers a, b, and c are entered in the first three columns, the slope and y-intercept automatically appear in the fourth and fifth columns.

(d) Use your spreadsheet to find the slope and the y-intercept of all the equations in problem 3. Do your answers agree with what you got before?

5. This spreadsheet problem extends problem 4.

   (a) Suppose $y = d_1x + e_1$ and $y = d_2x + e_2$ are two equations in slope-intercept form. Write a formula for x.

   (b) Copy the slope-intercept entries from problem 4(c) so that the first two lines of your spreadsheet are the slopes and y-intercepts of two equations in columns D and E. Then use your part (a) formula to make the spreadsheet calculate x automatically in Cell F2.

   (c) Write a spreadsheet formula for Cell G2 that calculates y from your first equation.

   (d) Write a spreadsheet formula for Cell H2 that applies your x and y values to your original second equation. Which other cell should this result match?

   (e) Save your spreadsheet. Then apply it to solve all the systems of equations in problem 3. Do your answers agree with what you got before? (They should.) If not, what went wrong?

6. In Section 5.3 you used a graph to find the number of hours in which two yeast cultures would produce the same amount of insulin. We have reproduced the data here. For each strain, Display 5.21 shows the number of hours the yeast were cultured and the amount of insulin that could be harvested from each strain.

Hours	Insulin Yield (grams)	
	Strain 1	Strain 2
4	19.44	10.2
8	23.88	19.4
12	28.32	28.6
16	32.76	37.8
20	37.20	47.0
24	41.64	56.2
28	46.08	65.4
32	50.52	74.6
36	54.96	83.8
40	59.40	93.0
48	68.28	111.4

Display 5.21

   (a) Choose some variables and find an equation for each strain of yeast.

(b) Solve this system of equations to find the number of hours the yeast should be cultured so that both strains yield the same amount of insulin.

(c) Compare your solution of part (b) to the results you found graphically in Section 5.3. Which method is more accurate? Which method would you prefer to use if you had to solve problems like this every day in your job?

7. The students at White Mountain School want a soda machine in their school. The principal agrees to install one, provided that the students agree to maintain it. Rudy, the senior class president, is in charge of the project. He found an old machine that the school can buy for $120. He also found a supplier from whom he can buy soda for 45 cents a can. The student government has decided to sell the soda for 75 cents a can.

(a) Write an equation for the amount of money, A dollars, that Rudy will spend if he buys the machine and c cans of soda.

(b) Write an equation for the amount of money, M dollars, the machine will collect, if c cans of soda are sold.

(c) How much money will Rudy spend if he buys the machine and 150 cans of soda? How much money will the machine collect if all 150 cans are sold? Will the student government make a profit in this case? If so, how much?

(d) How much money will Rudy spend if he buys the machine and 500 cans of soda? How much money will the machine collect if all 500 cans are sold? Will the student government make a profit in this case? If so, how much?

(e) Solve your equations to determine the number of sodas Rudy will have to sell in order for the expenses to exactly equal the income.

(f) On one set of axes, draw a graph of your equations and mark the point on your graph that corresponds to the solution you found in part (e). This point is called the break-even point (when the expenses exactly equal the income). It helps a business to estimate the amount of a product it needs to sell before it starts to make a profit. Why is the break-even value important to everyone in business?

5.7 Pictures for Data

Learning Outcomes

After studying this section you will be able to:

Recognize some data sets that do not fit a linear model well

Make and use nonlinear graphs to compare two sets of data.

In Chapter 4 you used linear graphs to represent data. In this section you will see two sets of data that do not fit straight-line patterns very well. You will compare those data sets using graphs that are not linear.

Display 5.22 gives population figures for two states, Indiana and North Carolina, for the beginning of each decade up to the year 2000.

Year	Indiana	North Carolina
1900	2,516,462	1,893,810
1910	2,700,876	2,206,287
1920	2,930,390	2,559,123
1930	3,238,503	3,170,276
1940	3,427,796	3,571,623
1950	3,934,224	4,061,929
1960	4,662,498	4,556,155
1970	5,195,392	5,084,411
1980	5,490,214	5,880,095
1990	5,544,159	6,628,637
2000	6,080,485	8,049,313

Display 5.22

5.52

1. Why would an economist or a business owner be interested in how the populations of Indiana and North Carolina have varied over the years?

2. Why would they be interested in comparing the populations of Indiana and North Carolina? Explain.

3. Why do you think the table gives data for every 10 years?

We can see that for some decades these two states have had similar populations. The table provides accurate data but it may be difficult to see a pattern in it. A graph usually makes an overall pattern easier to see. Display 5.23 shows these populations plotted on a graph. The legend at the bottom shows the two different symbols for the two populations being compared.

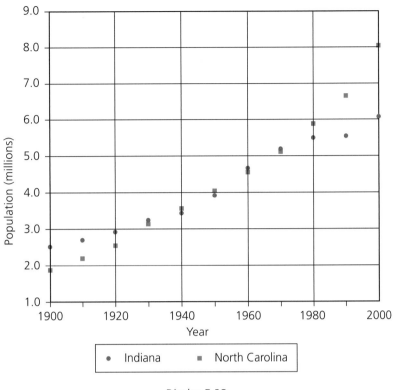

Display 5.23

In which years did Indiana have a larger population than North Carolina? In which years did Indiana have a smaller population than North Carolina? Is it easier to see this from the graph or from the table?

5.53

Find the least-squares line for each state. Do you think each line is a good fit? Why or why not? Save these equations for later use.

5.54

Using Technology

If the points are on a straight line exactly, then connecting the points gives us the line. That is not true here. We could draw the least-squares line or we could connect the points. Let's compare the two methods. In Display 5.24, we connect the points. Connecting the marks helps the eye to follow the trend in each state. It also makes it easier to interpolate from the data.

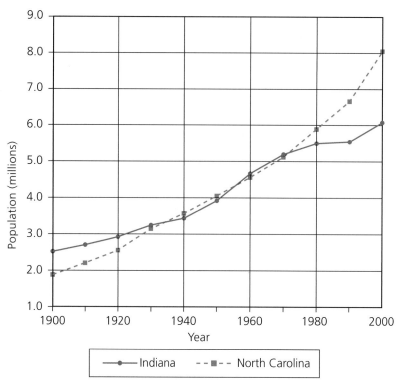

Display 5.24

5.55

Which state do you think had the larger population in 1975? In 1965? In 1955? Predict the population of each state for the year 2010. Are these questions easier to answer from the graph or from the table? Explain.

5.56

Were there any times in these years when Indiana and North Carolina had the same population? If so, state the year(s).

You may wonder when you should use a table and when you should use a graph. There is no simple rule for that. Which one you choose will depend on the situation and the question you're trying to answer.

5.57

If the least-squares lines represent these data sets well, maybe their intersection point will tell us about a year when the two states had the same population. Let's try this method and see what happens.

(a) Recall the equations for the two least-squares lines you found earlier. Round their slopes and intercepts to the nearest whole numbers. What do these slopes and intercepts mean in this situation?

(b) Solve this two-equation system algebraically. Round your *x*-value to the nearest whole number and your *y*-value to the nearest thousandth. Interpret your solution in relation to the original question.

(c) Compare your solution to what you already know about the years when Indiana and North Carolina had the same population. What do you observe? What do those observations suggest to you?

Problem Set: 5.7

1. Display 5.25 shows the populations of Hawaii and Nevada for each census of the United States up to the year 2000.

    (a) Compare the populations from 1900. What do you notice?

    (b) Compare the populations in 2000. What do you notice?

    (c) Will graphs of the populations and time for the two states intersect somewhere? Why?

    (d) Calculate the least-squares lines and correlation coefficients for these two data sets. Round the slopes and intercepts to the nearest whole number. Which set is closer to forming a straight line? How can you tell this from your calculations?

    (e) Find the intersection of these two least-squares lines algebraically. Round your *x*-value to the nearest whole number and your *y*-value to the nearest thousandth.

    (f) Make a graph to compare how the two populations grew during these years. Then write a statement expressing your comparison and its relation to the least-squares lines.

    (g) Find the year(s) in which the populations of the two states were approximately the same. Which approach is better for finding this, your equations or your graph? Why?

Using Technology

Year	Hawaii	Nevada
1900	154,001	42,335
1910	191,874	81,875
1920	255,881	77,407
1930	368,300	91,058
1940	422,770	110,247
1950	499,794	160,083
1960	632,772	285,278
1970	769,913	488,738
1980	964,691	800,508
1990	1,108,229	1,201,833
2000	1,211,537	1,998,527

Display 5.25

Using Technology

2. Display 5.26 shows some data on how homes in the United States have been heated over the years.

Percent of Homes in U.S. Heating With		
Year	Electricity	Oil
1950	0.6	22.1
1960	1.8	32.4
1970	7.7	26.0
1975	12.6	22.5
1980	17.7	18.1
1985	20.8	14.1
1991	25.5	12.3
1995	27.4	11.2
1999	30.3	9.8
2003	30.6	9.0

Display 5.26

(a) Graph both sets of data on the same pair of axes. Do the graphs of these sets appear to be linear?

(b) From your graphs, estimate when the number of U.S. homes heating with oil was equal to the number of U.S. homes heating with electricity.

(c) Enter the data into your calculator or spreadsheet and find the equations of the lines that best represent the data. Also make note of the correlation coefficients. One of them should be negative; what does that mean?

(d) Use these equations to estimate when the number of U.S. homes heating with oil was equal to the number of U.S. homes heating with electricity.

(e) Which estimate is more accurate—the one from part (b) or the one from part (d)? Explain your answer.

Looking Back

In this chapter, we looked at situations where there were two different relationships between the same two variables. For example, we looked at two different bill schedules that relate the usage of kilowatt-hours u and the total monthly electric bill T. You learned ways of comparing two such relationships using tables, graphs, and equations.

When we have more than one equation that describes different relationships between two variables we have a *system of equations*. Finding values for the variables that satisfy *all* the equations is called *solving the system*. You solved the system of two electric bill equations when you found the usage u and the total bill T that were the same for both bill schedules. The first time you did this was in Chapter 2 when you guessed. In this chapter you learned the guessing game algorithm to help you "zoom in" on answers more quickly. Tables help you display and organize your "smart" guesses. Graphing equations on the same coordinate axes is another way to solve a system of equations. A point where two graphs intersect is a pair of coordinates that satisfy both equations (a *solution to the system*). Calculators can help you "zoom in" on areas of a graph you want to see more clearly. Tables or graphs can be used to solve systems of any types of equations. These methods do not always provide an exact solution, but they can get as close as you want. Often, an approximate answer is good enough for what you need.

When both equations in a two-equation system are linear (they can be put in the form $y = mx + b$), we can use algebra to find an exact solution. We can do this by substitution. You also solved the electric bill system of equations using this method. To check whether a pair of values is a solution to a system, substitute them into each of the equations. If *both* equations are true, then the pair is a solution.

In Section 5.7, we looked at situations where the relationships between the variables were not described by equations. Instead, there was real data, as in the year-population examples. One way to compare the relationships is with regression lines. However, even when regression lines seem to represent their data well (they have a high correlation coefficient) they may not be the best models to use. Another approach is to plot the data points and connect them. This kind of graph can show more detail in the trends and give us a more accurate comparison.

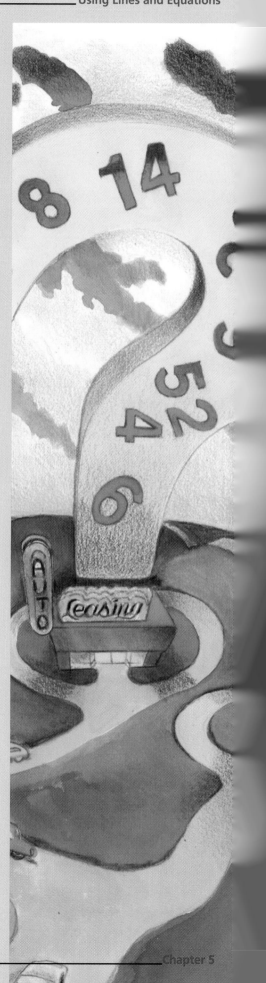

In this chapter you learned how to:

- Compare different algorithms for the same problem.
- Use the guessing game algorithm and tables to solve applied problems.
- Interpret intercepts and intersection points as solutions to a system of equations.
- Use graphs (by hand or by calculator) to solve systems of equations.
- Solve a system of linear equations algebraically by substitution.
- Determine if a pair of values is a solution to a system of two equations in two variables.
- Make and use nonlinear graphs to compare two sets of data.

Along the way, you also learned to:

- Interpret and use a tree diagram that describes an algorithm.
- Estimate roots of numbers.
- Solve an equation for one of its variables.

Review Exercises

1. Each week, Juan's grocery store buys fresh tomatoes from a local farmer. The number of pounds n that the farmer will supply to Juan depends upon the price p, in dollars per pound. The supply equation is $n = 30 + 24p$. The number of pounds of tomatoes that Juan's customers demand also depends on the price. The demand equation is given by $n = 147 - 12p$.

   (a) If Juan sets the price of tomatoes at \$3.50 per pound, will he sell out or will he have a surplus (extra tomatoes left over) at the end of the week? How many pounds extra or short will he be?

   (b) What will happen if he sets the price at \$2.75 per pound? How many pounds extra or short will he be?

   (c) At what price will the supply meet the demand? How many pounds of tomatoes will he buy (and sell) at that price?

2. Taylor is having 17 friends over for a party. She wants to make two kinds of cookies and to make enough for each person at the party (including herself) to have exactly four. She decides to make twice as many chocolate chip cookies as oatmeal cookies because more of her friends prefer them.

   (a) Write a system of two linear equations that can be used to determine how many of each type of cookie Taylor will make.

   (b) How many chocolate chip cookies will she make?
How many oatmeal cookies?

3. Kendra and Diana each began saving money w weeks ago. Kendra started with $126 and has been saving $6 a week. Diana started with $78 and has been saving $9 a week. After how many weeks do Kendra and Diana have the same amount of money saved? How much have they both saved at that time?

4. The costs for two different types of heating systems are shown in the table in Display 5.27. How many years will it take for the total spent on the solar heating to equal to the total spent on the electric heating?

System Type	Cost to Install	Yearly Operating Cost
Electric	$4,500	$1,350
Solar	$22,000	$100

Display 5.27

5. The Haul-It Co. and U-Move Trucks both rent moving trucks. The linear graphs in Display 5.28, on the next page, show the total each company charges for a truck driven a certain number of miles.

   (a) Trevor needs to rent a truck for a move totaling 40 miles. Based on cost, which company should he use? What will that company charge him?

   (b) Maria needs to rent a truck for a move totaling 100 miles. Based on cost, which company should she use? What will that company charge her?

   (c) At what mileage does each rental company charge the same? What is that cost?

   (d) Phuong needs to move from Farmington, CT, to Farmington, WA. Based on cost, which of these two companies should she use?

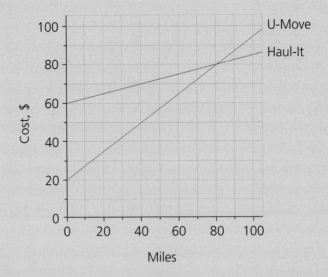

Display 5.28

6. Jordan is on vacation and wants to buy gifts for his friends and family. He has three times as many friends as he has family members and decides to buy each friend a hat and each family member a T-shirt. Hats cost $12.50, T-shirts cost $18.75, and Jordan spends a total of $281.25. How many people are in Jordan's family? How many friends does he have?

7. For each pair of equations, determine which description(s) match the system.

(a) $3y - 6x = 3$
   $6y - 12x = -36$

(b) $2y + 3 = 4x + 5$
   $y = 5x - 14$

(c) $12y + 12x = 48$
   $3y - 10 = -3x + 2$

(d) $y = 3x$
   $4y + 3 = -8x + 23$

(1) parallel lines

(2) two different equations of the same line

(3) two lines that intersect at $(1, 3)$

(4) two lines that intersect at $(3, 1)$

(5) a system with infinitely many solutions

(6) a system with one solution

(7) a system with two solutions

(8) a system with no solutions

Related Topics

Solving Systems of Equations

In this chapter, you learned what systems of equations are and how you can solve them either by graphing the equations and finding the intersection or by the method of substitution. Both of these methods depend on having the equation in the form $y = mx + b$. In this section we will explore additional methods of solving systems when they are not written in slope-intercept form.

Let's start with the following two equations:

$$2x + 3y = 1$$
$$3x - 4y = 10$$

One approach to solving this system would be to solve each equation for y and then use the substitution method that you learned in this chapter. Below you'll see how to solve each of these equations for y:

$$\begin{aligned} 2x + 3y &= 1 \\ -2x \qquad\quad -2x & \\ \hline 3y &= 1 - 2x \\ y &= \frac{1 - 2x}{3} \text{ (Equation 1)} \end{aligned} \qquad \begin{aligned} 3x - 4y &= 10 \\ -3x \qquad\quad -3x & \\ \hline -4y &= 10 - 3x \\ y &= \frac{10 - 3x}{-4} \text{ (Equation 2)} \end{aligned}$$

Now you can substitute your result for y in Equation 1 for the y-value in Equation 2 to get

$$\frac{1 - 2x}{3} = \frac{10 - 3x}{-4}$$

To solve this equation, you can treat it like a proportion and cross multiply. The result is $-4(1 - 2x) = 3(10 - 3x)$. Now distribute -4 on the left side and then distribute 3 on the right side to get $-4 + 8x = 30 - 9x$.

1. Finish solving this equation for x.

2. Plug the value that you just found for x into Equation 1 to find the y-value.

5.58

3. Now, find the value of y in the same way using Equation 2. Is this the same answer you got by using Equation 1? If not, figure out where you made a mistake.

You can verify this result by using your graphing calculator. Do you get the screens shown in Display 5.29? The first screen is the [Y=] screen, followed by the [GRAPH] screen, and then the [TABLE] screen showing that at $x = 2$, both functions yield -1 as an answer.

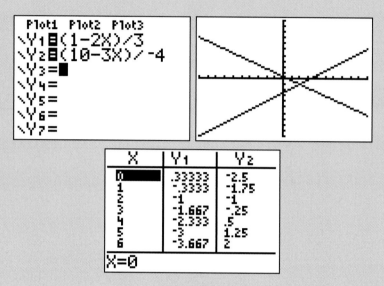

Display 5.29

That seems like a lot of work! Fortunately, there is a better way. The method of "Linear Combination" is well-suited for equations that are written in standard form (like the previous example). Let's see how this method works.

To explain the basic principle, we are going to use two simple equations from arithmetic:

$$2 + 3 = 5$$
$$5 - 3 = 2$$

Notice that these two equations are both true. Now we are going to add the equations together. Add the terms on the left hand side of the equals sign and then add the terms on the right hand side of the equals sign like this:

$$2 + 3 + 5 - 3 = 5 + 2.$$

The important question is whether or not this resulting equation is still true.

Verify that the above equation is still true.

5.59

A Fact to Know: When two true equations are added together, the new resulting equation is also true.

Let's see how you can use that principle to solve a system of equations. Consider the following system:

$$2x + y = 5$$
$$4x - y = 7$$

If you add these two equations together you will get the following:

$$2x + y + 4x - y = 5 + 7$$

Notice what happens in this case. When you combine all the like terms, you end up with $6x = 12$. This is easily solved by dividing both sides of the equation by 6, which results in $x = 2$.

Now you can take this x-value and substitute it into either of the original equations to find y. If you use the first equation, you get $2(2) + y = 5$, which equals $4 + y = 5$ or $y = 1$. If you use the second equation, you get $4(2) - y = 7$ or $8 - y = 7$, which also yields $y = 1$. In either case you get the same value for y, and so our solution to this system is the ordered pair $(2, 1)$. You only need to substitute into one of the equations to solve for the second variable. Substituting into both is a good way to verify that your work is correct.

Use the technique described above to solve the following systems:

5.60

1. $3x + y = 10$
    $x - y = 2$

2. $4x + 2y = 6$
    $3x - 2y = 1$

3. $3x + 2y = 3$
    $-3x - 4y = 3$

Notice that in all of these examples, when you added the two equations together one of the variables was eliminated. This process is called "solving a system by elimination." However, what if a variable is *not* eliminated when you add the numbers together? Let's look at the following:

$$5x + 2y = 7$$
$$3x + 2y = 5$$

In this case, when you add the equations you get $8x + 4y = 12$. This doesn't help much. It would be helpful if the "$+2y$" in the second equation was a "$-2y$". Fortunately, we can manipulate the equation to make it that way. All you need to do is multiply both sides of the equation by -1. Here are the resulting equations:

$$5x + 2y = 7$$
$$-3x - 2y = -5$$

5.61

1. **Finish solving this system.**

2. **Solve the following systems using the same techniques as above.**

   (a) $7x + 2y = 11$
   $ 3x + 2y = 7$

   (b) $3x + 2y = 12$
   $ 3x + 4y = 6$

What happens when you can't just multiply one equation by a negative sign? Let's consider the following system:

$$5x + 2y = 16$$
$$3x + y = 9$$

In this case, you are going to multiply the second equation by a particular number that will make the y-variable disappear. Look what happens when you multiply the second equation by -2:

$$5x + 2y = 16$$
$$-6x - 2y = -18$$

5.62

1. **Finish solving this system.**

2. **Solve the following systems using the same techniques as above.**

   (a) $3x + y = 3$
   $ 6x + 3y = 3$

   (b) $x + 2y = 5$
   $ 3x + 4y = 11$

What happens when you can't multiply one equation by a number and eliminate a variable? There is no reason why we can't multiply *both* equations by different numbers and then eliminate variables.

Consider this system:

$$4x - 2y = 12$$
$$3x + 5y = 35$$

In this case, we first decide which variable to eliminate, and then find the least common multiple (LCM) of the two coefficients of that variable. Because one of the coefficients of y is positive and one is negative, let's use the variable y. The LCM of the coefficients of y (2 and 5) is 10. We are going to change the equations so that the coefficients are both 10. (Actually, the coefficient in the first equation will be -10). To do this we need to multiply the top equation by 5 and the bottom equation by 2. This gives us:

$$20x - 10y = 60$$
$$6x + 10y = 70$$

1. **Finish solving this system.**

2. **Solve the following systems using the same techniques as above.**

   5.63

   (a) $-2x + 3y = -1$
   $\quad\;\; 4x + 2y = 26$

   (b) $5x + 2y = 8$
   $\quad\;\, 3x + 5y = 1$

   (c) $8x + 3y = 9$
   $\quad\;\, 3x + 4y = -11$

One last topic that we need to discuss is the possibility of getting fractions for answers. In the real world, answers do not always turn out to be integers. What happens if you solve a system and get a fraction for your first variable? Do you have to plug that fraction in to solve for the other variable? If this occurs, you can simply go back to the beginning and eliminate the other variable. For example:

$$3x + 7y = 12$$
$$4x - 3y = 13$$

1. **Eliminate the variable y in the above example and solve for x.**

   5.64

2. **Now, eliminate the variable x and solve for y.**

Problem Set

Solve the following systems.

1. $y = 2x - 2$
   $y = 4x + 5$

2. $5x + 3y = 11$
   $2x - y = 0$

3. $2x - y = 5$
   $x + y = 1$

4. $2x + 3y = 2$
   $6x - 9y = 0$

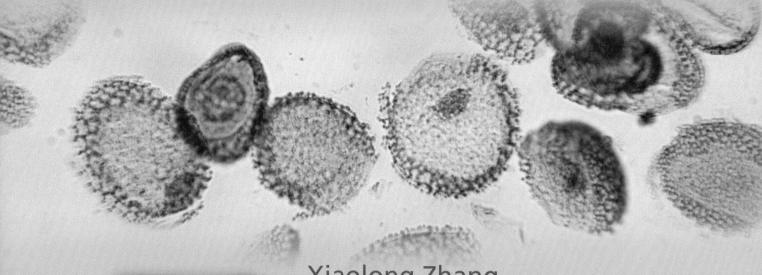

Xiaolong Zhang
Unlocking the Mysteries of Disease

Xiaolong Zhang is a researcher at the National Institutes of Health. He studies diseases such as cancer. What interests him a lot is the behavior of genes that may cause cancer.

"A gene is a 'blueprint' for all the building blocks in a cell," explains Xiaolong. "If you can manipulate a gene, you can change the blueprint.

"We don't even know when we're using math," he states, "because we use it all the time. For example, if we grow a bacterial culture, we start with a certain number of cells. Then, after a certain number of hours, we want to see how many cells have grown. What we are seeing is the exponential growth of that bacteria. From these experiments, we have developed mathematical calculations and algebraic formulas to represent those growth rates."

Xiaolong also uses math in DNA research. He explains that scientists use various techniques to make enough DNA to study. One technique Xiaolong uses is called a polymerase chain reaction.

Polymerase is an enzyme that speeds up the DNA production. "Each time you have a reaction, the number of DNA strands doubles. The growth rate is also exponential. Say you start with one double strand of DNA. If you do a reaction, you get 2 double strands. If you do two reactions, you get 4 double strands. After three reactions, you've got 8. If you do 20 reactions, you get 2 to the power of 20 double strands, and so on."

Learning which genes are linked to various diseases can lead to better treatments and cures. "It's very exciting to find something new in science," states Xiaolong. What motivates him, he adds, is 'pure curiosity.' "It's very difficult work and you just have to keep at it. Perhaps someday you'll hit something important and achieve something that in scientific terms is durable."

How Functions Function

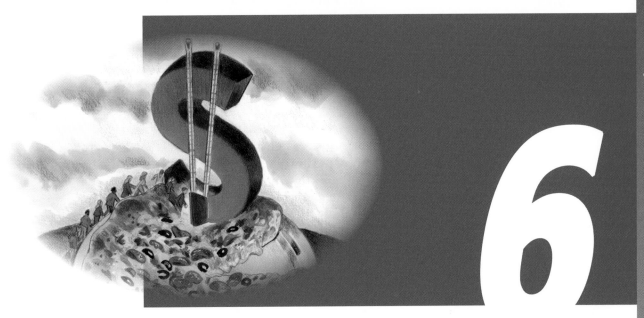

6.1 It All Depends

Learning Outcomes

After studying this section, you will be able to:

Identify and explain functions in real-world situations

Describe real-world relationships using the language of functions

Find images when given a function described in words, by a pattern, or with a table.

In Washington, D.C., the Identification Division of the FBI has a huge file of fingerprints—over 250,000,000 of them! This file has one purpose: to identify people from their fingerprints. Its use depends on the fact that no two people have the same fingerprint. Each fingerprint leads to one, and only one, person. Of course, a person may have as many as ten fingers, so several different fingerprints may belong to the same person. But no print can belong to two different people. The fingerprints in the file identify more than 81,000,000 people. When police investigators get a fingerprint from a crime scene, they can send it to the FBI for identification. If the print is in the FBI's file, then the investigators will know exactly which person was at the crime scene.

A fingerprint

Display 6.1

About Words

In the title of this chapter, *function* is used as a noun and as a verb. The verb *function* means "do something in a predictable or expected way." The noun *function*, then, means "a process that does something predictable."

The FBI's fingerprint file is an example of a **function**, a process that relates each thing in some first set to exactly one thing in a second set. The first set is called the *domain* of the function; the second set (in this case) is called the *range*. In this example, the set of fingerprints on file is the domain, and the set of people on file is the range.

In everyday English, we say that something's "function" is what it has been designed to do or is supposed to do. For instance, the function of a lawn mower is to cut grass. In some sense, the cutting of the grass depends on the proper *functioning* of the lawn mower. We say that something *functions* if it works properly.

Other uses of *function* in everyday English say that one thing depends on another.

- When your teacher says, "In this course, the amount you learn is a function of how much studying you do," you are being told that how much you learn depends on how much you study.
- If your boating partner says that the amount of water inside your leaky rowboat is a function of how fast you bail, you are being told that the faster you bail, the less water will be left in the boat.

This notion of dependence—especially of one quantity depending on another—is the basic idea of a function.

ZIP codes form another common example of a function. Each piece of mail with a ZIP code in its address is sent to exactly one post office location. The location to which the postal service delivers an item depends on its ZIP code. For instance:

- a letter marked 06417 is sent to Deep River, Connecticut
- a letter marked 37379 is sent to Soddy Daisy, Tennessee
- a letter marked 59011 is sent to Big Timber, Montana
- a letter marked 75668 is sent to Lone Star, Texas

and so on. The set of all pieces of mail with ZIP codes in their addresses is the domain of this function. The set of all post office locations is the range.

What is your ZIP code? Which post office is assigned to it? Does any other post office in the United States have the same ZIP code as yours?

6.1

Do the white pages of your local telephone directory form a function?

6.2

- **If they do, how does the function work? What is its domain? What is its range?**

- **If they don't, explain why not. What adjustments might make them form a function?**

Functions occur throughout the physical sciences, the social sciences, economics, manufacturing, business, and daily life. Here are a few examples:

- The volume of a quantity of gas is a function of the pressure put on it.
- The size of a colony of bacteria is a function of the time it has been growing.
- The amount of pressure that a steel bolt can stand before it breaks is a function of its diameter.
- The profit made by a fast-food restaurant is a function of how much food it sells.
- The pay of a cook at a fast-food restaurant is a function of the number of hours he or she works.
- The cost of a particular style of wall-to-wall carpeting is a function of the area to be covered.

We could go on for pages listing examples like this—but we won't, because you get the point: The idea of function is a fundamental building block for just about anything that can be described mathematically. It occurs so often in so many different settings that it is essential for you to have its basic meaning firmly and clearly in your mind. Here it is again:

Words to Know: A function is any process or rule that assigns to each element of a first set exactly one element from a second set. The first set is called the **domain** of the function. The thing that is assigned to a domain element is called the **image** of that domain element. The set of all the images is called the **range** of the function.

In the FBI example, the image of a fingerprint is the person whose finger made the print. In the ZIP code example, the image of a letter is the post office to which it is sent.

Each motor vehicle that travels on public roads must be registered with the Motor Vehicle Department of some state. License plates show the registration number of each vehicle.

6.3

1. **Describe this situation as a function.**

About Words

In everyday English, a *domain* is a territory ruled by a single person or government. In mathematics, it is a set ruled by a function in the sense that each of its elements is used by the function in the matching process.

6.1 It All Depends

2. What is its domain?
3. What is its range?
4. Pick out a particular domain element; what is its image?

6.4

Look up the many everyday English meanings of *range* in the dictionary. Pick the one that you think is most closely related to the mathematical meaning of *range*. Write a short paragraph explaining your choice. Do the same thing for the word *image*.

As you saw earlier, mathematical notation is used to write ideas in precise ways and to abbreviate long expressions. Here is how the language of functions is abbreviated:

The assignment of a grade to each student in a class is a function. Its domain is the set of all students in the class. If Alvin gets a grade of B, we might say:

The grading function assigns B to Alvin.

That's a long, stuffy way to express a simple idea. We can shorten it a little by using a letter to stand for the grading function; let's use g. Then we can say or write:

The image of Alvin under g is B.

Better, but not great. The phrase "The image of Alvin under g" contains two important facts:

(1) the function being used is g, and

(2) it is being applied to the domain element Alvin.

We abbreviate this information by writing the name of the function outside of parentheses and the particular domain element inside the parentheses.

$g(\text{Alvin})$ is B or $g(\text{Alvin}) = \text{B}$

which is read as "g of Alvin equals B."

Similarly, if we used F to stand for the FBI's fingerprint file function, we could represent the matching of a particular fingerprint with a person by

$F \left(\text{\raisebox{-2pt}{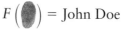}} \right) = \text{John Doe}$

We probably wouldn't write it this way, but we *could*. All the necessary information is contained in this one line.

Functions occur in many different forms. Sometimes they can be recognized from real-world situations, as in the previous examples. Sometimes they are described by a table or diagram. The diagrams in Display 6.2 define three different functions, f, g, and h. Each arrow points from a domain element to its image. All three functions match the numbers 1, 2, 3, and 4 with letters in the set {a, b, c, d}, but each function differs from the other two in some important ways.

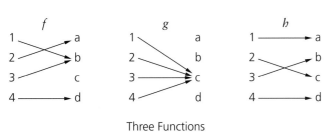

Three Functions

Display 6.2

These questions refer to the three functions shown in Display 6.2.

6.5

1. Find each of these images:

   $f(1) =$ $g(1) =$ $h(1) =$ $f(2) =$

   $g(2) =$ $h(2) =$ $f(3) =$ $g(4) =$

2. What is the range of each function?

3. For each function, describe one property that you think makes it different from the other two in some important or interesting way.

You might think that functions like the ones in Display 6.2 have nothing to do with real-world situations, but they are actually just small versions of a familiar school event: the multiple-choice test. If you were answering a four-question multiple-choice test, with possible answers a, b, c, d, you would assign exactly one of those letters to each question number, right? Of course, you wouldn't make an arrow diagram; you'd just list the choices, maybe like this:

1. b   2. a   3. b   4. d

Well, this listing is the function f of Display 6.2! The only real difference between this kind of function and answer sheets for most multiple choice tests is that the tests usually have more than four questions. That is, the domain of the function is larger.

Suppose your class takes a 10-question multiple choice quiz. Each question has four possible answers—a, b, c, or d—and only one is correct.

6.6

1. The answer sheet of one of your classmates looks like this:

   1. c   6. d

   2. a   7. c

   3. a   8. d

   4. b   9. a

   5. b   10. c

   Your teacher will give you a copy of Display 6.3. Draw in arrows to represent these answers. Is this a function?

   ```
   1           a
   2
   3
   4           b
   5
   6
   7           c
   8
   9
   10          d
   ```

   Display 6.3

2. The diagram for another person's answer sheet is shown in Display 6.4. List the 10 answers it represents. Is this a function?

   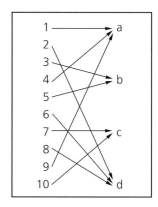

   Display 6.4

3. Make your own answer sheet by copying Display 6.5. Fill in the answers any way you want, then make an arrow diagram for it. Is it a function? Why or why not?

   ```
   1. ___     6. ___
   2. ___     7. ___
   3. ___     8. ___
   4. ___     9. ___
   5. ___    10. ___
   ```

   Display 6.5

4. When filling in your own answer sheet, what two things might you do to make sure that it's *not* a function? When you do these things on a real exam, what kind of credit do you get?

   Many of the tables in Chapter 4 of Book 1a describe functions. For instance, the table in Display 4.10—shown again here in Display 6.6—is a function from the set of Olympic years from 1904 through 2004 (the domain) to the set of winning times listed in the right column (the range). Using function notation, if we called this function t, we could write

$$t(1904) = 116.0$$

$$t(1908) = 112.8$$

$$t(1912) = 111.9$$

$$t(1920) = 113.4$$

$$\vdots$$

Years and Winning Times for Men's Olympic 800-meter Race	
Year	Winning time (seconds)
1904	116.0
1908	112.8
1912	111.9
1920	113.4
1924	112.4
1928	111.8
1932	109.8
1936	112.9
1948	109.2
1952	109.2
1956	107.7
1960	106.3
1964	105.1
1968	104.3
1972	105.9
1976	103.5
1980	105.4
1984	103.0
1988	103.45
1992	103.66
1996	102.58
2000	105.08
2004	104.45

Display 6.6

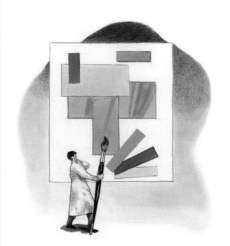

Sometimes functions are described by algebraic formulas. This method is particularly useful when the domain is a large set of numbers. For instance, the process that finds the area of a square from the length of one side is a function. Since we can make a square with a side length as large or as small as we please, the domain of this function is the set of all positive numbers. That's a very large set of numbers! As you know, the area is found by squaring the side length—that is, by multiplying it by itself. If s stands for the side length and A stands for the area, then this process is represented by the formula

$$A = s^2$$

Both A and s are *variables* here; each one can represent many, many different numbers. We are free to choose any domain element for s, so s is called an *independent variable*. However, once we have chosen a particular side length s, the value of the area A is determined. For this reason, the area A is called a *dependent variable*. We can show that its value depends on the choice of s by writing it as $A(s)$. That is, the area function A can be written as

$$A(s) = s^2$$

For instance, if we choose a side length s of 7 cm, then the area of this square is

$$A(7 \text{ cm}) = (7 \text{ cm})^2 = 49 \text{ cm}^2$$

Assume that A is the area function for squares, as just described.

1. Write in function notation: "The area of a square 5 miles on a side is 25 square miles."

2. Evaluate $A(3.2 \text{ ft.})$. Then explain what it means.

3. Choose s to be any number you want. Find $A(s)$ and explain what it means.

4. If $A(s) = 36 \text{ cm}^2$, what is s? Explain your answer in terms of a square.

When a function is defined by a formula, the symbol that stands for the domain element is the independent variable, and the symbol that stands for its image is the dependent variable. Think of a function as a tool, a process that you use to get a particular result, and think about independent and dependent variables like this:

- you control the independent variable
- the function controls the dependent variable.

Here is another example: As you may already know, the area inside a circle is found by the formula

$$A(r) = \pi r^2$$

where r is the radius of the circle and π is a specific number (about 3.14). If you want to use this formula, *you* supply the radius of the circle, so r is the independent variable. Once you have told the function the value for r, your choosing is done. The function takes control and gives you a number for $A(r)$, so $A(r)$ is the dependent variable. You, or a machine, do the arithmetic, of course, but the function tells you how to do it.

Two standard sizes of round pizza are 10-inch and 14-inch.

6.8

1. To what do these measurements refer?

2. About how much more pizza is in the 14-inch size than in the 10-inch size?

3. If a 10-inch pizza costs $5 and a 14-inch pizza costs $9, are you getting your money's worth?

4. Generalize your work on questions 1–3 to write a formula for the area inside a circle as a function of its diameter.

Explain your answers.

What formula describes the perimeter of a square in terms of its side length? Express it as a function called P. What is the independent variable in your formula? What is the dependent variable? Find $P(7 \text{ cm})$.

6.9

Problem Set: 6.1

1. For each part, decide whether or not the statement describes a function. Explain your answer. For each function, what is its range? In each case, the elements mentioned first are in the first set.

   (a) Each word in this sentence is matched with its first letter.

   (b) Each word in this sentence is matched with its last letter.

   (c) The first letter of each word in this sentence is matched with the last letter of that word.

   (d) Each word in this sentence is matched with the number of letters it contains.

   (e) Each of the numbers 1, 2, 3, 4, 5, 6, 7, 8, 9, 10 is matched with every word in this sentence having that number of letters.

2. For each of the six diagrams in Display 6.7, state whether or not it describes a function with domain {1, 2, 3, 4}. If it does, give the image of 2; then list all the elements of the range. If it does not, explain why not.

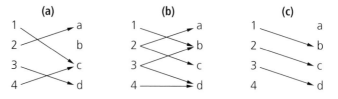

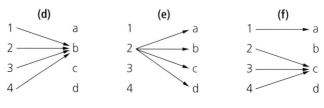

Display 6.7

3. Display 6.8 (on page 436) shows part of the 5% Sales Tax table that was used by retail stores in Maine a few years ago. It describes a function, which we'll call *T*, that matches each price from $0.01 to $40.00 with a specific tax amount. Use this table to answer these questions.

(a) Find *T*(5.00).

(b) Find *T*(0.67).

(c) Find *T*(5.67).

(d) Find *T*(0.45).

(e) Find *T*(12.45).

(f) Find *T*(36.79).

(g) Find *T*(19.98).

(h) Find *T*(20.05).

(i) What is the domain of *T*?

(j) What is the range of *T*?

(k) Suppose a customer buys an item costing $95.48. Explain how this table can be used to find the proper amount of sales tax.

4. Which of these situations can be viewed as functions? For each one that can, describe the domain and the range, and explain how the function works. For each one that cannot, explain what "goes wrong" with the idea of function.

(a) Every taxpayer has a Social Security number.

(b) Every child has a mother.

(c) Every mother has a child.

(d) Every licensed driver in a state has a numbered driver's license.

(e) A fast-food restaurant has a cash register with icons (pictures) on the keys.

(f) Every football player on the team has a number.

5. A switch that controls a 60-watt light bulb can be thought of as a function in this way: Its two positions, *on* and *off*, form the domain. The image of *on* is 60-watts, the amount of power being used by the bulb; the image of *off* is 0 watts.

(a) If the bulb burns out, is this situation still a function? Why or why not?

(b) Describe a lamp that has a 3-way bulb (50-100-150 watts) as a function. What is its domain? What is the image of each domain element?

(c) Some lights (such as stage lights) have a rheostat control, a knob or lever that can be used to vary the light intensity gradually from totally dark to very bright. Can this be viewed as a function? If you think so, describe its domain and explain how the function works. If you don't think so, explain what goes wrong with the function idea in this situation.

6. Here is a true story. As a special promotion, a pizza restaurant made 36-inch pizzas. A person who called in to order one was told that they were no longer available, but he could have two 18-inch pizzas for the same price. The customer agreed, but later wondered if this was fair. He wrote a letter to the consumer advocate column of the local newspaper asking whether or not this was a fair deal.

(a) If you were the newspaper columnist, how would you answer this letter? Explain.

(b) If f is a function, is it always true that $f(2x) = 2 \cdot f(x)$? Use part (a) to explain your answer to this question.

5% Sales Tax Schedule		
Sale		**Tax**
From	**To**	
$0.01	$0.09	$0.00
0.10	0.29	0.01
0.30	0.49	0.02
0.50	0.69	0.03
0.70	0.89	0.04
0.90	1.00	0.05

The tax to be collected is the amount indicated below for each dollar of the sale price plus the amount indicated above for any fraction of a dollar.

Sale	Tax	Sale	Tax
$1.00	$0.05	$21.00	$1.05
2.00	0.10	22.00	1.10
3.00	0.15	23.00	1.15
4.00	0.20	24.00	1.20
5.00	0.25	25.00	1.25
6.00	0.30	26.00	1.30
7.00	0.35	27.00	1.35
8.00	0.40	28.00	1.40
9.00	0.45	29.00	1.45
10.00	0.50	30.00	1.50
11.00	0.55	31.00	1.55
12.00	0.60	32.00	1.60
13.00	0.65	33.00	1.65
14.00	0.70	34.00	1.70
15.00	0.75	35.00	1.75
16.00	0.80	36.00	1.80
17.00	0.85	37.00	1.85
18.00	0.90	38.00	1.90
19.00	0.95	39.00	1.95
20.00	1.00	40.00	2.00

Display 6.8

7. The use of "DNA fingerprinting" depends on the assumption that it can be viewed as a function. Write a paragraph explaining this statement. You might start by reading about DNA fingerprinting in an encyclopedia or conducting an Internet search. Then explain why DNA fingerprinting might not be a function.

8. Describe two situations from your everyday life that can be viewed as functions. For each one, specify its domain and its range, and explain how the function works.

9. (a) How can a piano keyboard be viewed as a function?

(b) Pick any other musical instrument that you know and explain either (i) how it can be viewed as a function, or (ii) why it can't be viewed as a function.

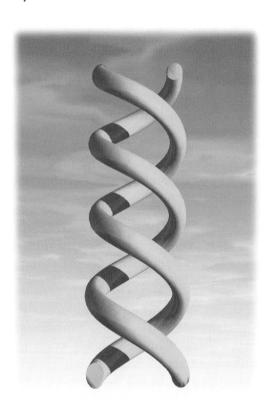

6.2 Functions Step by Step

6.10

Ms. Terius is giving a 10-question, multiple-choice quiz to her three science classes. Each question has five possible answers, labeled (a) through (e), with only one correct answer. She can label the correct answer with any of these five letters.

1. Help Ms. Terius make up an answer key to the quiz for her first class. For each question, choose a letter to label the correct answer. List your 10 choices.

2. Ms. Terius wants to give the same questions to the second class, but she wants the correct answers to be labeled differently in the two classes. (For example, if the correct answer for question 1 is (a) in the first class, it should be (b), (c), (d), or (e) in the second class.) Make up an answer key to the quiz for her second class.

3. Is your first answer key a function? If you say Yes, describe its domain, its range, and the image of 7. If you say No, explain how it doesn't fit the definition of a function.

4. Is your second answer key a function? If you say Yes, describe its domain, its range, and the image of 7. If you say No, explain how it doesn't fit the definition of a function.

5. She wants to change the quiz form for her third class. The first eight questions will be the same, but questions 9 and 10 will say "Choose as many as apply," and there will be three correct choices for each of these questions. Make up an answer key to this quiz.

6. Is your third answer key a function? If you say Yes, describe its domain, its range, and the image of 9. If you say No, explain how it doesn't fit the definition of a function.

Functions are all around us, just waiting to be recognized. For instance, every restaurant menu is a function. It assigns a price to each item the restaurant sells. In the same way, every price list or catalog describes a function. In each case, the domain is the set of all things for sale, and the range is the set of all prices. The image of each item is its price. If we wanted to treat a fast-food restaurant's menu as a function in a very formal way, we might call it m and write the prices as

$$m(\text{hamburger}) = \$1.00$$
$$m(\text{cheeseburger}) = \$1.20$$
$$\vdots$$

Of course, it's pretty silly to do that when a simple listing of items and prices gives you the same information.

| hamburger | $1.00 |
| cheeseburger | $1.20 |
$$\vdots$$

And that's the point of this paragraph.

You get exactly the same information about a function f from the ordered pair (a, b) as you do from the expression f(a) = b.

Both expressions tell you that f assigns the range element b to the domain element a.

So why bother with all this function notation? The reason is that the interesting, useful functions in mathematics, science, and business usually don't have domains as small as a restaurant menu. Most of them have domains that are too large to count, let alone list. In order to deal with these functions, we need some way to describe the matchups between domain and range elements without listing each pair.

Example 1: Secret Messages
Suppose you want to make up a simple letter-substitution code for sending secret messages, and you want to give the code to a friend who will read them. One easy way to make a code is to change each letter into the letter two places further along in the alphabet, starting over when you get to the end. This is a function, which we shall call c. What is its domain? What is its range? This verbal description is good enough to understand how the code works, but a list of the letter matchups probably would make decoding easier. We could write this listing of c in the three different ways shown in Display 6.9; they all provide exactly the same information.

A ——→ C	(A, C)	$c(A) = C$
B ——→ D	(B, D)	$c(B) = D$
C ——→ E	(C, E)	$c(C) = E$
D ——→ F	(D, F)	$c(D) = F$
E ——→ G	(E, G)	$c(E) = G$
F ——→ H	(F, H)	$c(F) = H$
G ——→ I	(G, I)	$c(G) = I$
H ——→ J	(H, J)	$c(H) = J$
I ——→ K	(I, K)	$c(I) = K$
⋮	⋮	⋮
X ——→ Z	(X, Z)	$c(X) = Z$
Y ——→ A	(Y, A)	$c(Y) = A$
Z ——→ B	(Z, B)	$c(Z) = B$

Display 6.9

6.11

1. What is the code letter for N? Write this matching in the three different ways shown in Display 6.9.

2. What is the code letter for V? Write this matching in the three different ways shown in Display 6.9.

3. Write your full name (first and last) using the code function *c*. Of the four ways in which this coding function was described (words and three different lists), which did you use?

4. Decode the message "JCXG C PKEG FCA." Of the four ways in which this coding function was described, which did you use?

Example 2: Fuzzy Friends Toy Co.

Pre-holiday business has been good at the Fuzzy Friends Toy Co. Management tells the Payroll Office to give each of the company's 150 employees a holiday bonus of $100. To print the paychecks, the Payroll Office has to add $100 to each employee's regular salary for the last week of December. Listing the new amount for each of the 150 employees would be a long, tedious job. Instead, they put into the computer a "holiday check" function, *h*, defined by

$$h(s) = s + 100$$

where *s* is an employee's regular salary for the week.

1. What is the domain of *h* (the holiday check function in Example 2)?

2. What is the independent variable for the function *h*? What is its dependent variable?

3. Calculate *h*(450). Then interpret its meaning in Example 2.

4. Business at Fuzzy Friends continues to be good, so the management decides to give every employee a 4% raise. Write a "raise function" *r* that will compute each employee's new salary from his/her old one. (Note: The old salary does not include the holiday bonus, which was a one-time gift.)

5. What is the domain of *r*? What is its range?

6. If you were earning a weekly salary of $300 before the raise, what will you be earning after the raise? Write this statement in function notation.

6.12

In Example 2, it was easier to write a formula for the function than to list all the pairings of old and new salaries, but it would have been possible to list the pairs. In the next example, listing all the pairs for the function is absolutely impossible. We *must* use a formula.

Example 3: Doubles
Let's match each natural number with its double. That's an easy enough idea, right? We list the first few pairs of this matching:

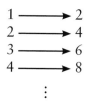

But, no matter how long a list we make, we can never list all the matchings for this function. The only way to describe all the images of all the natural numbers is by some rule, either in words or in symbols. In this case, the words describe a function, which we'll call *d*, that can be symbolized like this:

$$d(n) = 2n$$

The independent variable is *n*; it stands for any natural number. The domain of this function is the set of all natural numbers, which is abbreviated as ℕ. Its range is the set of all even natural numbers because every even number is the double of some number.

6.13

The first three questions refer to the "doubling" function of Example 3.

1. What is $d(5)$? What is $d(20)$? What is $d(351)$?

2. If $d(n) = 12$, what is n? If $d(n) = 454$, what is n?

3. Why does the statement $d(n) = 35$ not make sense?

4. Define in words another function—call it f—on the domain $\mathbb{N}$ of all natural numbers. Then write a formula for f, if possible. If you cannot write a formula for f, explain why it can't be done.

5. Use the function f you just defined to find $f(3)$, $f(25)$, and $f(100)$. If you can't find one or more of these values, what makes you believe that f is a function with domain $\mathbb{N}$? Explain.

Example 3 illustrates a very important kind of function, called a *sequence*.

A Word to Know: A sequence is a function that has the set of all natural numbers as its domain.

Does this definition surprise you? Do you think of a sequence as a list that has a first element, then a second, then a third, and so on? Do you think:

$$4, 7, 10, 13, 16, \ldots, \text{is a sequence?}$$

If you said Yes, you're right! This is just another way of writing a function that has the natural numbers as its domain. Each of the numbers listed in a sequence is called a **term**. If we call this sequence s, then:

the first term is the image of 1 (that is, $s(1) = 4$)
the second term is the image of 2 (that is, $s(2) = 7$)
the third term is the image of 3 (that is, $s(3) = 10$)
and so on.

Sometimes the "..." can be troublesome. The symbol ..., called an **ellipsis**, indicates that the pattern set up by the first few terms continues. There are two problems with this.
- The pattern of a particular sequence may not be obvious to everybody (or to anybody).
- Even if it is clear how to get from each term to the next, finding out what value corresponds to a large natural number can be a long, tedious job.

1. In the sequence 4, 7, 10, 13, 16, ..., how can you find each term (after the first) from the term just before it? Use this process to find $s(6)$ and $s(17)$.

6.14

About Words

In English, saying that something *recurs* means that it happens again.

2. Can you use this process to find $s(99)$? What about $s(567)$? (Don't actually do this.) What is the problem with defining a sequence just by saying how to get from each term to the next one?

When a sequence is described by saying how to get each term from the one before it, we say that it is **recursively defined**. Finding the first few terms of a recursively defined sequence is usually pretty easy, but finding terms farther along can get tedious. As you just saw, it's easy to find $s(6)$, but it's not so easy to find $s(17)$, and it's really annoying to find $s(99)$ or $s(567)$.

Once you recognize how to get from each term to the next, a spreadsheet program or a calculator can get you many terms in a hurry. They make finding $s(17)$ and $s(99)$ almost as easy as finding $s(6)$. But what about $s(1000)$ or $s(1,000,000)$ or $s(1,000,000,000)$? Even the best spreadsheets and calculators have their limitations, but the natural numbers go on forever. If a sequence really is a function on $\mathbb{N}$, then we must be able to find the image of any natural number, no matter how large it is. That is, we need a rule that will supply $s(n)$ for any natural number n. Finding such a rule begins with looking for a pattern.

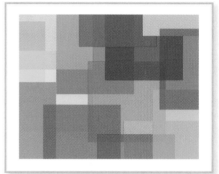

Let us use calculator power to help find a pattern for this sequence:

6.15
Using Technology

1. Enter 4, 7, 10, 13, 16, ... into your calculator as a recursively defined sequence. Then store the first 99 terms of this sequence in one of your calculator's lists. Your teacher will explain how to do this.

2. Look at the list of terms you just made. These are the images of the numbers 1 to 99. Do you see a pattern in the way each image is related to its domain element? If so, describe it in words and then in symbols. If you don't see it right away, try focusing on the images of

$$10, 20, 30, 40, 50, \ldots$$

Now do you see the relationship? Describe it.

3. Use your answer to part 2 to find $s(1000)$, $s(567)$, and $s(1,000,000)$.

4. Use the algebraic form of your answer to part 2 to define a sequence in your calculator. Then store the first 99 terms of this sequence in a different list. How is this list related to the first one? Is that surprising? Why or why not?

Did you get two copies of the same 99 terms in your two lists? Good! That's what was supposed to happen.

"So what?" we hear you say. "If I just get what I already had, why bother putting in another formula?"

We bother because the formula can do something that the recursive definition can't do. Try this: Pick your favorite four-digit number and suppose that's *n*. To find its image in this sequence using the recursive definition, you'd have to list more than a thousand terms, right? But if you put your number into the algebraic formula, the calculator will give you that term right away! Try it. That's the power of defining a function in terms of its independent variable, the variable that you control.

6.16

Look back at the two ways in which the pattern of the sequence 4, 7, 10, 13, 16, ..., was described—first as a process that goes from each term to the next, then as an algebraic formula. Do the same thing for the sequence

$$3, 8, 13, 18, 23, ...$$

Call this new sequence *s* during this discussion. Make sure you answer these questions along the way.

1. Find $s(4)$, $s(6)$, and $s(10)$.

2. Describe in words the pattern you see.

3. Use the pattern to find $s(25)$.

4. Describe how each term of the sequence is related to the one before it.

5. Describe how each term of the sequence is related to its corresponding domain element. Write this correspondence as an algebraic formula for $s(n)$.

6. Find $s(1,000,000)$.

6.17

"Skip counting" is an arithmetic exercise for children in the primary grades. Starting with some number, the students skip a particular amount each time before saying the next number. Here's a simple example: Starting at 1, skip 10 each time:

$$1, 11, 21, 31, 41, 51, ...$$

1. Explain why $s(n) = n + 10$ is NOT a correct formula for this sequence. Write the first five terms of the sequence it describes.

2. Write a formula for the sequence 1, 11, 21, 31, 41, 51.... Can you find more than one way to do this?

3. Write the first five terms of the sequence that starts at 4 and skips by 10 each time. Then write a formula for that sequence.

4. Write the first five terms of the sequence that starts at 2 and skips by 5 each time. Then write a formula for that sequence.

5. If you start at 1 and, instead of adding, you multiply each term by 10 to get the next one, what sequence do you get? Write its first five terms and a formula for it.

The work you have just done shows that you can describe a function in two different ways and get the same results. This suggests an important question:

What does it mean to say that two functions are the same?

Two functions, f and g, on the domain of natural numbers, are defined by these formulas:

6.18

$$f(n) = n + n \qquad\qquad g(n) = 2n$$

In what way(s) are these two functions the same? In what way(s) are they different?

When you look at the formulas defining the two functions f and g in the question above, you can see that any number n is matched with the same thing by both f and g. That is,

$$f(n) = g(n)$$

for every number n because adding any number to itself gives the same answer as multiplying it by 2. But f and g are not *identical*; they are defined by different operations. That might not seem very important to you, but in some situations it could be. For example, a very simple adding machine—one that can't multiply or can't store a constant number (in this case, 2)— would be able to deal with f, but not with g.

To clarify the sense of sameness we are using, we talk about functions being *equal*, rather than *the same*, like this:

A Word to Know: Two functions are **equal** if they have the same domain and if each domain element is paired with the same image by both functions. That is, two functions f and g with the same domain are equal if

$$f(x) = g(x)$$

for every element x of the domain.

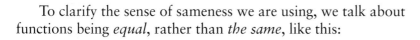

Before ending this section, we should tie up one loose end. We have been using function notation for sequences, to emphasize that they are functions on the domain of natural numbers. In function notation, the terms of a sequence s are

$$s(1), s(2), s(3), ..., s(n), ...$$

where n is the independent variable and $s(n)$ is the dependent variable. Once you know this (which you do now), there is no need to keep using such clumsy notation and language. Most books list the terms of a sequence like this:

$$s_1, s_2, s_3, ..., s_n, ...$$

The subscript numbers are the domain elements; they tell you the position of each term in the list. The general formula for finding a term is written as s_n and is called the "nth term" of the sequence. Both ways of writing sequences give you exactly the same information.

6.19

This sequence s lists the "perfect squares"

$$1, 4, 9, 16, ..., n^2, ...$$

1. Copy the following list and fill in the values.

   (a) $s_2 =$ $s(2) =$

   (b) $s_3 =$ $s(3) =$

   (c) $s_5 =$ $s(5) =$

   (d) $s_{10} =$ $s(10) =$

   (e) $s_n =$ $s(n) =$

2. In what way does s_n represent a rule? In what way does it represent a number? Explain.

Problem Set: 6.2

1. Find the Index at the back of your textbook. Is it a function? If you answer Yes, describe its domain, its range, and the image of one particular domain element. If you answer No, explain how it doesn't fit the definition of a function.

2. Make a letter substitution code by listing the letters of the alphabet in order, then listing the letters in reverse order and directly matching the two lists. For example, A is matched with Z, B with Y, C with X, and so on. This is a function; call it r.

   (a) What is the domain of r? What is its range?

(b) Find these values:

$r(D) =$ ____ $r(J) =$ ____ $r(M) =$ ____ $r(T) =$ ____

(c) Write this sentence in code.

(d) Write your answer to part (c) in code.

(e) Parts (c) and (d) suggest that this code has a peculiar property. What is it? Do you think that every letter-substitution code has this property? Check your thinking by trying an example using the code in Example 1.

3. (a) Make up a letter substitution code different from the one in Example 1 and from the one described in problem 2 above. Describe your code in words, then write it in one of the list forms shown in Display 6.9. Use it to encode the message

   THIS IS A MESSAGE.

   Which list form did you choose? Why?

   (b) Are some letter substitution codes easier to describe by a list than in words? Explain your answer briefly.

4. Sleeping Giant Mattress Co. and the union representing its 275 workers are starting contract negotiations. The current total annual payroll for these workers is $7,150,000.

   (a) The union proposed a 12% annual salary raise. By how much would this increase the company's annual payroll?

   (b) Management knows that many changes to this percent figure will be discussed during the bargaining. Members of its bargaining team want to have a function in their calculators that computes the increase in the annual payroll for any percentage of raise. Write this function for them; call it m for "management."

   (c) Use the function m to find out how much the company's annual payroll would increase if it agreed to a 10% raise, a 7% raise, a 5% raise, a 3% raise, a 1.5% raise. Write each of these payroll increases in function notation.

   (d) Management proposes a total annual payroll increase of $100,000, to be distributed equally to all the workers. How much more money would each worker earn in a year?

   (e) The union knows that many changes to this total increase amount will be discussed during the bargaining. Members of its bargaining team have a function in their calculators that computes the salary increase per worker from any total payroll increase. Write this function for them; call it *u* for "union."

(f) Use the function *u* to find out each worker's annual salary increase if the total payroll increase is $150,000, $200,000, $275,000, $350,000. Write each of these payroll increases in function notation.

(g) After several days, the bargaining teams finally agree on this salary settlement: Each worker will get a 4% raise plus an additional $350 for the year. How much will this increase the company's total payroll?

(h) The Payroll Office needs a function that will compute each worker's new annual salary from his/her old annual salary. Write one for them; call it *p* for "payroll."

(i) Use the function *p* to compute the new annual salary for a worker whose old annual salary was $19,000, $22,500, $26,150, $31,233. Write each of these salary increases in function notation.

Using Technology

5. The game of chess probably originated in India many centuries ago. It is said that when the inventor of chess presented the game to his king, the king was so pleased that he said to the inventor, "You can have anything in my kingdom! Just tell me what you want."

And the inventor said, "I only want some wheat. Give me one grain of wheat for the first square on my chessboard, two for the second, four for the third, and keep on doubling the number of grains for each square, until the last one [the 64th]. I want just that much wheat, nothing more."

Was this a foolish choice by the inventor of such a clever game, or was it smart? Let's analyze this situation. Think of the 64 chessboard squares as the numbers 1 through 64. Then the inventor is describing a function that has {1, 2, 3, ..., 64} as its domain; call this function *g* (for "grains").

(a) What are the values for $g(4)$, $g(5)$, $g(6)$, and $g(10)$?

(b) If you know a value for a square, how do you find the value for the next square? What formula can you use to list all 64 values recursively?

(c) What formula can you use to compute $g(n)$ for a particular square *n* without first finding the values for all the squares before it? Explain how you got this formula.

(d) Use your formula to find $g(10)$, $g(25)$, $g(31)$, $g(40)$, and $g(64)$. Do the computations with a calculator.

(e) How much space would be filled by $g(64)$ grains of wheat—a bushel? A barrel? A boxcar? A barn? How could you estimate the approximate number of cubic meters in this much wheat? Do it, if you can.

(f) Of course, $g(64)$ is not the total amount of wheat the inventor requested; it's only the amount for the last square. The total amount is:

$$g(1) + g(2) + g(3) + \ldots + g(64)$$

which is just about twice as much as $g(64)$. In fact, it's 1 grain less than twice as much. Can you figure out why this last statement is true?

(g) Compute the total amount of wheat the inventor requested (in grains); then estimate its volume in cubic meters. Estimate the size of this amount of wheat by relating it to the size of some well-known object (anything you choose).

(h) Was the inventor's request smart or foolish? What do you think? Explain your answer.

6. In each part, list the first five terms and the tenth term of the sequence defined by the formula:

(a) $s(n) = 3 + n$

(b) $s(n) = 3n$

(c) $s(n) = 2n + 5$

(d) $s(n) = 4(n - 1)$

(e) $s(n) = n^2 + 1$

(f) $s(n) = 2^n + 1$

(g) $s(n) = n^2 - 3n + 2$

(h) $s(n) = \frac{1}{n}$

(i) $s(n) = \frac{n}{2}$

(j) $s(n) = \frac{n}{n + 1}$

7. A sequence s begins 13, 23, 33, 43, 53, ...

(a) What are the next two terms of this sequence? How did you find them?

(b) Define this sequence recursively.

(c) Write a formula for $s(n)$.

(d) Use your formula to find $s(200)$.

8. A sequence t begins 4, 11, 18, 25, 32, ...

(a) What are the next two terms of this sequence? How did you find them?

(b) Define this sequence recursively.

(c) Write a formula for $t(n)$.

(d) Use your formula to find $t(200)$.

9. A Certificate of Deposit that pays interest only at the end of each year can be thought of as a recursively defined function. (Remember Alfredo's bank account?) If you make an initial deposit of $5000, say, and the bank is paying 4% interest at the end of each year, then your total amount is a function of the number of years you keep the money in the bank.

(a) How much money would you have after 1 year? After 3 years?

(b) Describe the recursive step. That is, how do you get from one yearly amount to the next?

(c) Write an algebraic formula for this function. Then use it to find your total amount after 12 years. Round your answer to the nearest penny.

10. Which of these pairs of functions are equal on the domain of natural numbers? For those that are not, find at least one number n for which $f(n) \neq g(n)$:

(a) $f(n) = 3(n - 2)$ $g(n) = 3n - 2$

(b) $f(n) = 3(n - 2)$ $g(n) = 3n - 6$

(c) $f(n) = 3n - 2$ $g(n) = 2 - 3n$

(d) $f(n) = 3n - 2$ $g(n) = -2 + 3n$

(e) $f(n) = n^2$ $g(n) = 2^n$

(f) $f(n) = n^2$ $g(n) = n + n$

(g) $f(n) = n^2$ $g(n) = n \cdot n$

(h) $f(n) = n^2 + n$ $g(n) = n(n + 1)$

6.3 Between the Dots

In Sections 6.1 and 6.2 we saw that a function can be represented in different ways—in a table, by a diagram, as a set of ordered pairs, and sometimes by a formula. If a function matches numbers with numbers, it can also be pictured on a coordinate plane.

Here's an example. Suppose that we want to match each even digit in the set

$$\{0, 1, 2, 3, 4, 5, 6, 7, 8, 9\}$$

with the odd digit that comes right after it, like this:

$$0 \longrightarrow 1$$
$$2 \longrightarrow 3$$
$$4 \longrightarrow 5$$
$$6 \longrightarrow 7$$
$$8 \longrightarrow 9$$

We could represent this function by marking the digit points on a horizontal axis and on a vertical axis, then draw a point for each ordered pair of digits in the matching, as shown in Display 6.10. This is called making a **graph** of the function.

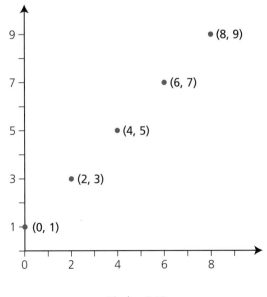

Display 6.10

Learning Outcomes

After studying this section you will be able to:

Identify and describe real-world examples of step functions

Explain some common-sense restrictions on the domains of functions

Use graphs to represent functions and to find images of domain elements

Interpret graphs of step functions in real-world situations.

6.20

What is the domain of the function pictured in Display 6.10? What is its range?

Of course, not all functions have such a nice, simple pattern or such a small domain. Here is an example of a function f on the domain $\mathbb{N}$ of all natural numbers that has a more scattered graph. (What is a function with domain $\mathbb{N}$ called?)

Match 1 with itself and match any natural number greater than 1 with its smallest positive factor other than 1. (A *factor* of a number divides that number without leaving any remainder.)

For instance, $f(2) = 2$, $f(6) = 2$, $f(9) = 3$, and so on. The graph of the first 25 ordered pairs of this function is shown in Display 6.11.

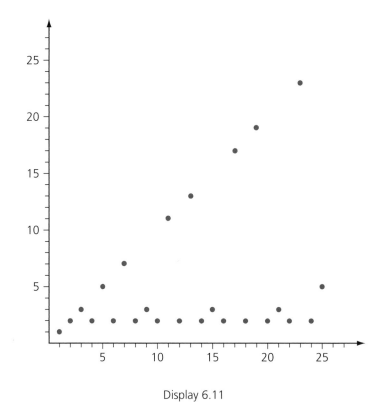

Display 6.11

6.21

These questions refer to the function f in Display 6.11.

1. Find $f(26)$ and $f(27)$. What ordered pairs do you get from these images? Where are these points in Display 6.11?

2. Find $f(77)$ and explain why your answer is correct.

3. Find a number n larger than 25 such that $f(n) = 11$. What is the smallest such number? Explain.

4. Give an example of a natural number that is not the image of any number. Explain your answer.

5. What is the range of *f*?

6. How would the graph of the function look if we dropped the phrase "other than 1" from the end of its definition? Why?

Near the bottom of Display 6.11, there seems to be a regular pattern, starting with the point (2, 2).

6.22

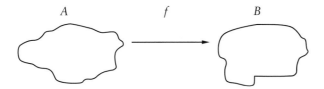

Do you think that this pattern continues forever? Explain your answer. (*Hint:* What are the domain elements for the points in this pattern?)

Often the graph of a function can help you to see patterns that are not obvious from a list or a table. But coordinate axes usually represent the entire number line, so a graph may not show clearly the domain and range of the function. Look again at Display 6.11, for example. The numbers listed below the horizontal axis are only a very small part of the domain; the range of this function contains only some of the numbers listed next to the vertical axis, but many others, too.

For a function to be clearly defined, it is not enough just to know its rule for assigning images. We must also know its domain and what kinds of things can be images. That is, since every function matches the things from some domain with images in some set, we need to know what these sets are, too. You might picture a function *f* as "going from" a domain set A and "going to" a set B that contains all the images (and maybe other things), as in Display 6.12.

![Diagram showing set A with arrow labeled f pointing to set B]

Display 6.12

The function in Display 6.11 goes from and goes to the same set, the counting numbers. Another example like this is the "doubling" function *d*, defined by the rule $d(n) = 2n$. Its graph is shown in Display 6.13.

6.3 Between the Dots

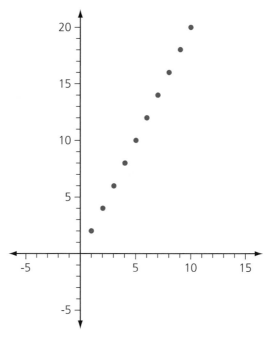

Display 6.13

"Wait a minute!" you say. "A coordinate axis has a number for every point on it, not just for the counting-number points. What about them?"

You're right, of course. A coordinate axis does have a number for each point on it, and these numbers form a much bigger set than the counting numbers. That set is called the **real numbers**; its symbol is $\mathbb{R}$.

"What happens to those other numbers? The dots don't tell us that. What happens between the dots?"

It depends.

"On what?"

On the domain of the function and on the rule for finding images. If the function only makes sense on the set of counting numbers, then nothing at all happens between the dots—only the counting numbers have images. The smallest-factor function f of Display 6.11 is like that. The idea of *factor* applies only to integers; it doesn't make sense to try to apply it to numbers like $\frac{2}{3}$ or 23.856 or any of the other numbers between the counting numbers.

On the other hand, the rule that defines the doubling function d of Display 6.13 makes sense for all numbers. Any number can be doubled. The function d was defined only on the natural numbers. However, the rule makes sense for every real number, so we can extend its domain to include all real numbers. Formally, we define a "new" function D that applies to every real number x using the same rule: $D(x) = 2x$. This new function D agrees with the old function d on every natural number, but it fills in the picture between the dots, as Display 6.14 shows. Compare Displays 6.13 and 6.14 to see how D connects the dots of d.

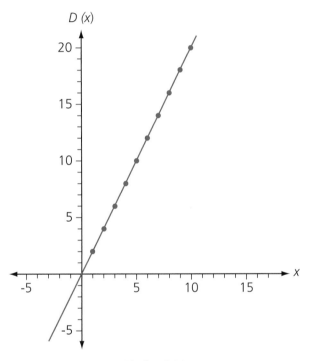

Display 6.14

Display 6.6 (on page 431) describes a function t that matches the set of Olympic years 1904 through 2004 with the set of winning times for the men's 800-meter race in that year's Olympic Games. Its graph is shown in Display 6.15 (on the next page). Does it make sense to extend this function to the domain of all years between 1904 and 2004?

6.23

- If you answer Yes, then explain what $t(1911)$ and $t(1953.47)$ mean.

- If you answer No, explain why it doesn't make sense.

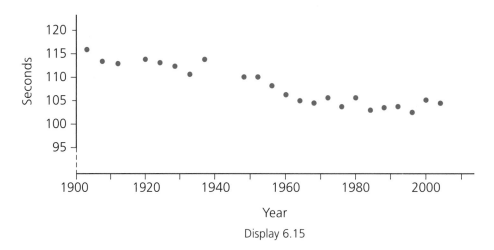

Display 6.15

6.24

The table in Display 6.16 and the graph in Display 6.17 describe a population function p. The points on the graph represent the population of the United States in each of the census years 1820 through 2000. Does it make sense to extend this function to the domain of all years between 1820 and 2000?

- If you answer Yes, then explain what $p(1911)$ and $p(1953.47)$ mean.

- If you answer No, explain why it doesn't make sense.

Year	Population (millions)
1820	9.638
1830	12.866
1840	17.069
1850	23.192
1860	31.443
1870	38.558
1880	50.156
1890	62.948
1900	75.995
1910	91.972
1920	105.711
1930	122.775
1940	131.669
1950	150.697
1960	179.323
1970	203.185
1980	227.757
1990	248.710
2000	281.422

Display 6.16

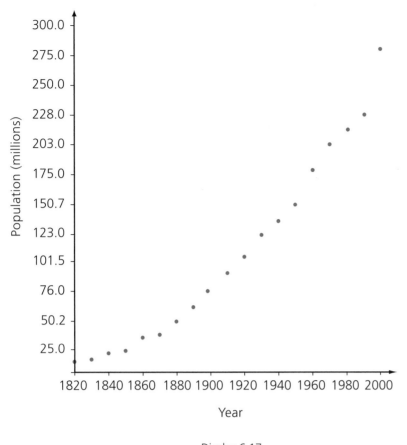

Display 6.17

Even when it makes sense to extend the graph of a function from a few known points to a much larger domain, there may be more than one sensible way to do it. Here is an example, based on a function used in everyday life.

The state of Maine has a 5% sales tax; that is, the tax is 1 cent for every 20 cents. Every taxable item sold has a certain amount of tax added to its price. This means that the 5% sales tax process is a function that assigns a tax amount to each price. If we think in pennies, this tax function sets up the pairings shown in Display 6.18 (on the next page). Thus, the graph of this function, which we'll call f, contains the points

$$(20, 1)\ (40, 2)\ (60, 3)\ (80, 4)\ (100, 5)$$

These five points are shown in Display 6.19.

How can we extend the graph in Display 6.19 to show how this tax function f works on all possible prices; that is, on all positive real numbers?

Price (¢)	Tax (¢)
20	1
40	2
60	3
80	4
100	5
·	·
·	·
·	·

Display 6.18

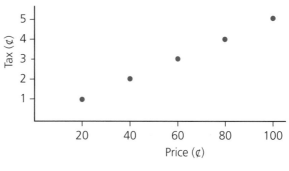

Display 6.19

Finding 5% of a number is simple enough—just multiply the number by 0.05. So the 5% tax function can be described by the formula

$$f(x) = 0.05x$$

Now, when we graph a function, the y-axis is the $f(x)$-axis. In other words, the images of the domain numbers are found on the vertical axis. Therefore, the graph of this function is the graph of

$$y = 0.05x$$

This is a straight line with slope 0.05 and y-intercept 0. It is shown in Display 6.20.

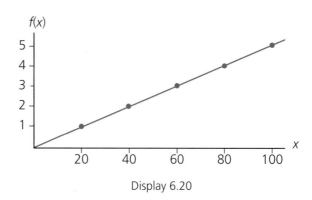

Display 6.20

The graph in Display 6.20 shows how this tax function can be extended in a neat, simple way from the five points we know to a function defined on the set of all positive real numbers. Saying that a function is **defined on** a particular set means that this set is within the domain of the function.

Unfortunately, real life is not always so neat and simple. Display 6.20 is not an accurate picture of how this tax function really works in Maine! Display 6.21 (on the next page) shows part of the table used to describe the actual tax function, which we'll call t. As you can see from this table, t agrees with f on the five points we have been using as examples, but behaves differently between them. Both functions assign exactly one tax amount to each purchase amount, but they don't always agree.

1. Find $f(0.25)$ and $t(0.25)$.

2. Find $f(4.62)$ and $t(4.62)$.

6.25

3. Find two prices higher than $5.00 for which these two tax functions agree. Use them to copy and complete parts (a) and (b).

(a) $f(\quad) = $ _____ $\qquad$ $t(\quad) = $ _____

(b) $f(\quad) = $ _____ $\qquad$ $t(\quad) = $ _____

4. Find two prices higher than $5.00 for which these two tax functions disagree. Use them to copy and complete parts (a) and (b).

(a) $f(\quad) = $ _____ $\qquad$ $t(\quad) = $ _____

(b) $f(\quad) = $ _____ $\qquad$ $t(\quad) = $ _____

5% SALES TAX SCHEDULE
ALL SALES EXCEPT
AUTO AND LODGING RENTALS

For sales of $1.00 or less, the tax shall be added as indicated below:

Sale		Tax (cents)
From	To	
$0.01	$0.10	0
0.11	0.20	1
0.21	0.40	2
0.41	0.60	3
0.61	0.80	4
0.81	1.00	5

This table shows tax to $100 by units of $1.00. For fractional parts of one dollar, add amount appearing above. For example, tax on a sale of $59.50 would be $2.95 from table below plus $0.03 from table above or a total tax of $2.98.

Sale	Tax	Sale	Tax
$1.00	$0.05	$51.00	$2.55
2.00	0.10	52.00	2.60
3.00	0.15	53.00	2.65
4.00	0.20	54.00	2.70
5.00	0.25	55.00	2.75
6.00	0.30	56.00	2.80
7.00	0.35	57.00	2.85
8.00	0.40	58.00	2.90
9.00	0.45	59.00	2.95
10.00	0.50	60.00	3.00
⋮	⋮	⋮	⋮

Display 6.21

The graph of the function t appears in Display 6.22. It shows that the tax doesn't increase gradually as the price increases, but moves up in steps, 1 cent at a time (as you would expect). Each time it takes a step, it stays at that level for a while before moving up again. A function that changes in this way—jumping from one value to another in a fairly regular pattern and staying at each value level for a span of domain numbers—is called a **step function**.

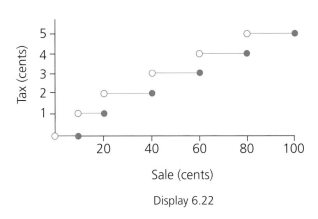

Display 6.22

Display 6.22 illustrates a common custom used in drawing graphs. The left end of each segment is an open dot, while the right end is a solid dot. The graph "jumps" at each of these places, and it is important to know which level shows the image of the jump point. The solid dot signals the image of that point; the new level applies right *after* the open dot. For instance, the image of 20 is 1, but the image of 21 (or of 20.5 or of 20.001) is 2. An open dot at the end of a line segment means that the segment includes all the points up to the endpoint, but not the endpoint itself. A solid dot at the end means that the segment includes the endpoint, as well.

The new U.S. Postal Service rates for packages appears in Display 6.23 (on the next page). This table defines a function, which we shall call p.

6.26

1. What is the domain of p?

2. Find $p(4)$, $p(4.2)$, $p(4.9)$, and $p(8.75)$.

3. Make a graph of the function p.

4. Draw the straight line determined by the pattern of the whole ounce rates, then answer these questions about it.

   (a) Write an equation for this line, treating it as a function called s. That is, write an equation in the form "$s(x) = \ldots$"

   (b) If s were the postage function, what would it cost to send something that weighed absolutely nothing (if such a thing existed)?

FIRST-CLASS MAIL	
Weight not over (oz.)	**Packages**
1	$1.13
2	1.30
3	1.47
4	1.64
5	1.81
6	1.98
7	2.15
8	2.32
9	2.49
10	2.66
11	2.83
12	3.00
13	3.17

Display 6.23

6.27

Display 6.24 shows a bank advertisement for a Certificate of Deposit (CD), exactly as it appeared in the bank's flyer. The outside of the flyer says:

Our 5-year CD is only good for one year.
Then it gets better.

Is the graph they have drawn an accurate representation of the interest rate arrangement they are offering? Discuss.

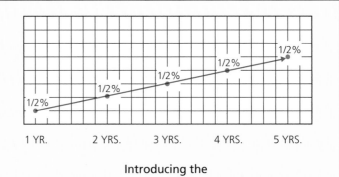

Introducing the
Peoples Heritage Rising Rate CD

With a Rising Rate CD from Peoples Heritage Bank, you know you're getting ahead. Your interest rate increases 1/2% every year until maturity, guaranteed. And we allow you to withdraw all or part of the certificate at the end of any 12-month period, without penalty. When you want a good interest rate now, and a guaranteed better interest rate later, ask about Rising Rate.

From "Rising CD Rates" advertising flyer by Peoples Heritage Bank. Copyright © by Peoples Heritage Bank. Reprinted by permission.

Display 6.24

A particular step function is built into many calculators. It is called the **greatest integer function**, which is shortened to "**int**" in the calculator's language. This function matches each real number with the largest (greatest) integer that is less than or equal to that real number. For instance:

int(4.9) = 4   **int(6) = 6**   **int(–2.1) = –3**

1. Use your graphing calculator to find **int(3.2)**, **int(7.0338)**, **int(5)**, and **int(–3.2)**.

Using Technology

6.28

2. On a piece of graph paper, draw the graph of **int** over the domain of all real numbers between –4 and 4, inclusive. Mark each endpoint of each segment in your graph with a filled-in or an open circle, depending on whether or not that point represents a pair of numbers matched by the function.

3. Use your graphing calculator to draw the graph of **int** over the domain of all real numbers between –4 and 4, inclusive. Once you have the graph, use **TRACE** to find **int(2.7)**, **int(0.685)**, **int(–0.685)**, and **int(–2.7)**.

4. Compare the calculator graph of part 3 with the graph you drew in part 2. How are they alike? How are they different? Which do you think is easier to make? Which do you think is easier to use? Give reasons for your answers.

Problem Set: 6.3

1. A function on the set {0, 1, 2, 3, 4, 5, 6, 7, 8, 9} matches each digit with the next one in the list, up to 9, and it matches 9 with 5. Make a graph of this function.

2. A function f on the set {0, 1, 2, 3, 4, 5, 6, 7, 8, 9} is defined by

$$f(d) = 4 \text{ if } d \text{ is even}$$

$$f(d) = 7 \text{ if } d \text{ is odd}$$

Find $f(1)$, $f(2)$, and $f(3)$. Then make a graph of this function.

3. An airport parking lot has these rates posted for short-term parking:

$2.00 for first hour or fraction thereof

$1.00 for each additional hour or fraction thereof, up to a maximum of $10.00 for any 24-hour period.

(a) Make a table that the parking lot attendants can use to find the total charge from the number of hours shown on a customer's time ticket, up to 24 hours.

(b) Draw a graph of this parking fee function for a 24-hour period.

4. Draw a graph of the tax function t that extends Display 6.22 (on page 461) to the domain of all sale prices up to $2.00.

5. Suppose the State of Maine had decided to set up its 5% sales tax table by rounding the tax amount to the nearest cent, with halves always rounded up. Then the top part of the table in Display 6.21 (on page 460) would have to be changed.

(a) Your teacher will give you a copy of Display 6.25. Complete the table to show how this tax applies to sales up to $1.00. Assume that the rest of Display 6.21 applies to this new tax function, which we shall call r.

Sale		Tax (cents)
From	To	
$0.01		0
		1
		2
		3
		4
	1.00	5

Display 6.25

(b) Find $r(0.25)$, $r(0.98)$, $r(2.87)$, and $r(3.99)$. Then compute the tax on these same amounts by using the function t.

(i) Which sale amounts have the same tax amounts under r and t? Which have different tax amounts?

(ii) Are r and t equal functions? Why or why not?

(c) Does the function t ever result in a smaller tax amount than the function r? If so, in what case(s)? If not, explain how you know this.

6. The Fuzzy Friends Toy Co. marketed a new product in Maine right at the start of football season—plush, brown, potato-shaped pillows, which they advertised as "Couch Potatoes." They sold 8000 pillows in the first two weeks, at a special introductory price of $3.89 each.

   (a) How much tax did the State of Maine collect on these sales, assuming that the tax function *t* of Display 6.21 was being used at the time? How much less tax would they have collected using the rounding-off tax function *r* of Display 6.25?

   (b) Draw a graph of *r*, similar to the one in Display 6.22 (on page 461). Then, on the same coordinate system, draw the straight line $y = 0.05x$ that represents the "pure" 5% function.

7. Telephone numbers beginning with the area codes 900, 976, 940, or 550 connect to information or entertainment services that charge at a fairly high rate per minute of connection time. One such service recently advertised on TV said, at the end of its commercial, "Calls cost $2.95 per minute or fraction thereof."

Using Technology

   (a) What is the cost of a 2 minute call?

   (b) What is the cost of a 2 minute, 10 second (2:10) call?

   (c) What is the cost of a 2 minute, 55 second (2:55) call?

   (d) Make a graph of the cost function for calls of up to 10 minutes in length. Call your function *c* (for "cost").

   (e) Mark your graph to show your answers to parts (a), (b), and (c).

   (f) Use the function **int** to define a new function by
   $$f(x) = 2.95 \cdot \textbf{int}(x)$$

   For which times do *c* and *f* give you the same value?

   (g) Use the function **int** to define a new function by

   $$g(x) = 2.95 \cdot \textbf{int}(x + 1)$$

   For which times do *c* and *g* give you the same value? Are *c* and *g* equal over this domain? Why or why not?

6.4 Describing Functions With Algebra

Learning Outcomes

After studying this section, you will be able to:

Use any linear equation of the form $y = ax + b$ as a function

Find images of real numbers using linear functions and some other functions

Use a graphing calculator to find images for linear functions and some other functions

Use a graphing calculator to draw graphs of linear functions and some other functions.

Sometimes people describe a function as a "machine" or a "mystery box" like the one in Display 6.26—you put a thing in, something happens to it, and some (related) thing comes out.

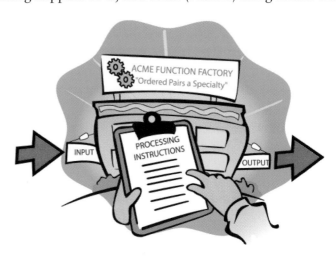

Display 6.26

The point of this picture is not that a function is magic or mysterious, but that *it's an "automatic" routine.* When you put a domain element into a function, the process automatically gives you one, and only one, image. It might take some (brain) power to run the machine, but there is no puzzle or uncertainty about it. Once something is put in, exactly one result can come out.

Viewed in this way, functions show you the power of using symbols for numbers. We work through a process once, mapping out what happens to a "typical" input (domain element) that is represented by a symbol. Then we can plug any number we want into the place of the input symbol, and we get the corresponding output without any further hard work. It becomes a routine, something that can be done over and over again in exactly the same way, without having to think much about it.

The following example illustrates the power and efficiency of using algebra to describe a process in function form.

You are an assistant to the weather forecaster for a large TV network in the U.S. During each broadcast, the forecaster presents the latest temperatures from around the world. Your job is to get the latest temperatures as they come into the studio from 25 different foreign cities and put them onto a list to be read during the show.

The difficulty is that most countries measure and report temperature in degrees Celsius, but the U.S. measures it in degrees Fahrenheit. Ten minutes before the start of each broadcast, you have to prepare the list for the U.S. audience by converting each temperature from Celsius to Fahrenheit.

As soon as you get this job, you look up the Celsius and Fahrenheit scales of temperature measurement. The first thing you find out is that 9 Fahrenheit degrees measures the same change in temperature as 5 Celsius degrees. This means that each Fahrenheit degree equals only $\frac{5}{9}$ of a Celsius degree. (Do you see why?) That is, a Fahrenheit degree is a little larger than half of a Celsius degree.

You also know that water freezes at 32°F and 0°C, and it boils at 212°F and 100°C. That is,

$$32°F = 0°C \text{ and } 212°F = 100°C$$

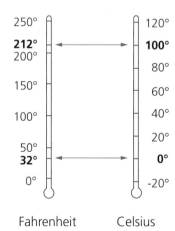

Fahrenheit   Celsius

Display 6.27

1. Since 1 Fahrenheit degree equals $\frac{5}{9}$ of a Celsius degree, do we convert Celsius temperatures to Fahrenheit just by multiplying the Celsius temperature by $\frac{5}{9}$? In particular, if the temperature outside is 18° Celsius, is it 10° Fahrenheit? Why or why not?

6.29

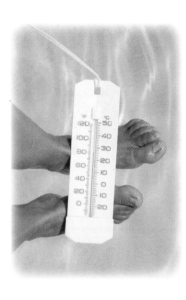

2. How many Fahrenheit degrees equal one Celsius degree?

3. Do we convert Celsius temperatures to Fahrenheit just by multiplying the Celsius temperature by your answer to question 2? Why or why not?

Now pull together the ideas from these three questions. Suppose the report from Buenos Aires says that their current temperature is 30°C. This means that their temperature is 30° Celsius degrees above the freezing point of water. Now, each Celsius degree is "worth" $\frac{9}{5}$ Fahrenheit degrees, so this temperature is $\frac{9}{5} \cdot 30$ Fahrenheit degrees above the freezing point of water. But water freezes at 32°F, so the Fahrenheit temperature must be

$$\frac{9}{5} \cdot 30 + 32$$

That is, the current temperature in Buenos Aires must be 86°F.

6.30

A report from Calgary says that their current temperature is 5°C. Rewrite the preceding paragraph, substituting Calgary for Buenos Aires and 5°C for 30°C and finding the current temperature in Calgary.

6.31

1. Where is Buenos Aires? Do you think that 30°C is a likely temperature for that city? At what time of year?

2. Where is Calgary? Do you think that the temperature could be 5°C in Calgary at the same time that it is 30°C in Buenos Aires? Explain.

By doing the exercise about Calgary you can see that the process of converting temperatures from Celsius to Fahrenheit is the same, no matter what Celsius temperature you are given. If we let x represent any given Celsius temperature, we can summarize this process by the formula

$$\text{Fahrenheit temperature} = \frac{9}{5}x + 32$$

This formula gives us exactly one Fahrenheit temperature for each Celsius temperature, so it is a function. (What is its domain?) If we call this function F, we can write the formula as

$$F(x) = \frac{9}{5}x + 32$$

Now that you have a formula, converting Celsius temperatures to Fahrenheit becomes automatic, a routine that you can do without thinking about anything except the arithmetic.

Complete the chart in Display 6.28 for your boss. Your teacher will give you a copy. Round your entries to the nearest Fahrenheit degree. Can you name the country for each of these major cities?

6.32

City	°C	°F
Berlin	2	
Buenos Aires	30	86
Calgary	5	
London	10	
Moscow	−5	
Nairobi	32	
Rome	19	
Sydney	18	
Tokyo	14	

Display 6.28

Unfortunately, the table you just completed is only part of the 25-city list that your boss needs. Worse yet, the entire list has to be updated three times a day! Doing all that arithmetic can get pretty boring. Let's get a calculator to do it. We have already done the difficult part—writing the conversion function as an algebraic formula. The algebra tells the calculator exactly what it needs to do its work.

The calculator ought to do three things:

1. It ought to ask you for the Celsius temperatures that you want to convert. (These are the domain elements you want to use.)

2. It ought to compute the corresponding Fahrenheit temperature. (This is the function step.)

3. It ought to tell you its answers. (These are the images in the range of the function.)

A graphing calculator can do this chore in several different ways. Perhaps the simplest way uses its built-in spreadsheet style lists. Make one of those lists—call it **L1**—the "input" (the domain of the function) and another—call it **L2**—the "output" (the range). You'll have to fill in the domain list by hand, but the list of images (the range) can be calculated automatically. Just treat **L2** as the dependent variable and define it by the formula we found, using **L1** as the independent variable. That is, define

$$L2 + (9/5) * L1 + 32$$

This is usually done at the top of the range column. Try it. Enter the Celsius temperatures of Display 6.28 into the **L1** column.

Then define **L2** by the formula and enter it. You should get all the Fahrenheit temperatures automatically!

6.33

The latest Celsius temperatures for the other sixteen cities your boss needs are listed in Display 6.29. Your teacher will give you a copy of the chart. Use your calculator to find the corresponding Fahrenheit temperatures. Round your entries to the nearest Fahrenheit degree. Can you name the country for each of these major cities?

City	°C	°F
Athens	21	
Bangkok	28	
Barcelona	13	
Beijing	7	
Cairo	19	
Calcutta	27	
Havana	25	
Istanbul	12	
Melbourne	7	
Mexico City	20	
Paris	9	
Quebec	−8	
Reykjavik	−15	
Rio de Janeiro	23	
Singapore	33	
Stockholm	1	

Display 6.29

The algebraic form of the Celsius to Fahrenheit conversion function,

$$F(x) = \frac{9}{5}x + 32,$$

says something important about the way the Celsius temperatures are related to their Fahrenheit images. Recall your work with linear equations earlier in **MATH** *Connections* and think of $F(x)$ as the dependent variable. If you graph this equation using the *y*-axis for the $F(x)$ values, you get a straight line.

1. What is the slope of the straight line $F(x) = \frac{9}{5}x + 32$? What is its y-intercept? What does the y-intercept represent?

6.34

2. Your teacher will give you a copy of Display 6.30; draw the graph of this function F on your coordinate axes. What part of this picture represents the range of F?

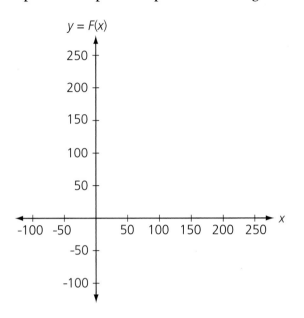

Display 6.30

The graph of F illustrates an important idea. Earlier we saw that any straight line graph, except for the vertical ones, has an equation of the form

$$y = ax + b$$

where a is its slope and b is its y-intercept. Each point on the line corresponds to an ordered pair (x, y) of numbers for which the equation becomes a true statement. For instance, $(5, 4)$ is on the line

$$y = 0.6x + 1$$

because $4 = 0.6(5) + 1$ is true.

How would you find another point on this line? One way is to pick a number for x and then compute the y that makes the equation true. If $x = 2$, then

$$y = 0.6 \cdot 2 + 1 = 2.2,$$

which means that $(2, 2.2)$ is on the line. Each time you pick a value for x, the equation gives you exactly one correct value for y.

In other words, the equation

$$y = 0.6x + 1$$

describes a *function* on the domain of all real numbers. For each number x you choose, the y value for that equation is the image of x. The equation

$$f(x) = 0.6x + 1$$

is the rule that describes this function.

Of course, there's nothing special about this particular slope or y-intercept. The equation of any nonvertical straight line, in the form

$$f(x) = ax + b$$

describes a function that assigns real numbers to real numbers.

These functions are particularly nice because it is easy to draw a picture of how they work. The function $f(x) = 0.6x + 1$, for instance, is shown in Display 6.31. To find the image of a number on the x-axis, just move vertically (up or down) until you hit the line. Then move horizontally (left or right) until you hit the y-axis; that y-axis number is the image you want.

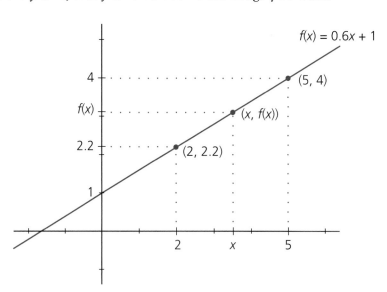

Display 6.31

1. Why don't vertical lines represent functions?

2. Are the functions represented by horizontal lines special in any way? Explain.

6.35

The linear functions are only one kind of function that can be described with algebra. Many other kinds can be written algebraically, too. You have seen some already, and you will see many others soon. Various kinds of functions occur throughout mathematics and science, as well as in economics, business, psychology, and many other fields. But you do not need to see all these different kinds now to understand the basic message of this section.

A function that can be expressed as an algebraic equation usually can be handled much more easily than a function expressed only in words.

Algebra is the key that unlocks the toolbox of coordinate systems, graphing calculators, and many mathematical techniques that turn difficult questions into routine exercises. For example, here is a function that is not linear, but that can be handled with many of the same tools.

The area enclosed by a circle is equal to pi (π) times the square of the radius (r^2).

If we call this statement function A and the radius of the circle r, then we have a familiar formula:

$$A(r) = \pi r^2$$

Of course, we can use either this formula or the description in words to compute the area inside a circle "by hand." For instance, if the circle has a radius of 5 meters, then the area inside is $\pi \cdot 5^2$, which is $\pi \cdot 5^2$ square meters. Since π is approximately 3.14, this area is approximately 78.5 square meters.

However, if we need to compute the area for many circles, or if the answer has to be precise, a calculator comes in handy. And the calculator's language is algebra. Using algebra, we can just enter the formula in the calculator's function list and let the machine do the rest of the work.

Try it. Enter the formula into your calculator as a function. To speak the calculator's language, you'll probably have to treat the image symbol, $A(x)$, as **Y** and use **X** (the variable key) in place of r in the formula. That is, you should enter

Y = π * X^2

in some **Y=** line. Now your work is pretty much done.

To find the areas, you can use **TRACE** with the graph of this function. You may have to change the **WINDOW** settings to get close enough to the answer you want, but the calculator will do all the computations for you.

Using Technology

6.36

1. Set your calculator's **WINDOW** to **Integer** coordinates. This is done by pressing **ZOOM, 8**, then **ENTER**. Use **TRACE** to check the area for a circle of radius 5. Then find the areas inside circles of radius 3, 4, and 7. Round your answers to two decimal places.

2. Use **TRACE** and whatever **WINDOW** settings you prefer to find the areas inside circles of radius 1.7, 3.2, and 24.

Problem Set: 6.4

Round your answers to two decimal places.

1. In a *Rand McNally Road Atlas*, a map of Arizona is drawn to the scale of 38 miles per inch.

   (a) On this map, the (straight line) distance between Yuma and Tucson measures $5\frac{1}{2}$ inches. How far is the real distance between these two cities? Round your answer to the nearest mile.

   (b) Write a function that will compute the distance between any two points in Arizona from its measurement in inches on this map. Call this function d for "distance."

   (c) Your teacher will give you a copy of the table in Display 6.32. (Yes, these are all real places in Arizona.) Enter the function d into your graphing calculator and use it to fill in the distances in this table. Round your answers to the nearest mile.

   (d) The longest north-south distance in Arizona is about 380 miles. How long is the state, top to bottom, on this map? Explain how you found your answer.

   (e) Draw a graph of d on a piece of paper. You may use your calculator to help you. What maximum and minimum values should you choose for the x-axis? For the y-axis? Why? On your graph, mark the points that represent each distance of Display 6.32.

	Places	Distance	
		Map (in.)	Real (mi.)
(1)	Phoenix — Oracle	$2\frac{1}{2}$	
(2)	Bullhead City — Friendly Corners	$6\frac{1}{4}$	
(3)	Cottonwood — Snowflake	$2\frac{7}{8}$	
(4)	Flagstaff — Sentinel	$4\frac{5}{8}$	
(5)	Casa Grande — Sierra Vista	$3\frac{1}{4}$	
(6)	Skull Valley — Tombstone	$6\frac{5}{16}$	
(7)	Tuba City — Steamboat Canyon	$2\frac{1}{8}$	
(8)	Moccasin — Geronimo	$7\frac{13}{16}$	
(9)	Rough Rock — Round Rock	$\frac{9}{16}$	
(10)	Red Rock — San Luis	11	

Display 6.32

2. Find an atlas of the United States in your library. Look up the map of your state. If you are in Arizona, choose some other state. Then write a problem just like problem 1, choosing towns and cities in your state for the locations in your problem. Even if the map you find may not say exactly what its scale is in miles per inch, it will have some scale notation on it. In this case, explain how you figure out what the scale is. Test how good a question writer you are by having a classmate work out the answers to your questions.

3. Betsy and Oliver are sister and brother model railroaders. They have an HO scale railroad layout, called the "B & O Road," in their basement. The word *scale* here refers to a ratio of lengths; HO scale is $\frac{1}{8}$ inch to the foot. In order for their layout to look realistic, Betsy and Oliver must make sure that all the measurements of their models are in proportion with this ratio.

(a) Betsy and Oliver want to make a model of their own house for the layout. After they measure the parts of their house, they need to convert the measurements to HO scale so that they can build the model accurately. Write a function h that will convert their measurements (in feet) to HO scale measurements (in inches).

(b) Copy the table in Display 6.33 (on the next page). Then enter the function h into your graphing calculator and use it to fill in the measurements in this table. Round your answers to the nearest $\frac{1}{16}$ inch.

House Parts		Real (ft.)	Scale (in.)
(1)	outside length	30	
(2)	outside width	24	
(3)	height to eaves	18	
(4)	front door height	$6\frac{1}{2}$	
(5)	front door width	3	

Display 6.33

(c) Draw a graph of h on a piece of paper. You may use your calculator to help you. What maximum and minimum values will you choose for the x-axis? For the y-axis? Why? On your graph, mark the points that represent each measurement of Display 6.32.

(d) What railroad is the real B & O Road? Where is it? Why is it important in American history?

4. This problem continues the story, begun in problem 3, of the B & O model railroad. Betsy and Oliver have just found the plans for a small town station in a British railroad magazine. They want to build it in HO scale, but all the measurements are in meters!

(a) Write a function m that will convert their measurements (in meters) to HO scale measurements (in inches). (1 inch = 2.54 cm)

(b) Copy the table in Display 6.34. Then enter the function m into your graphing calculator and use it to fill in the measurements in this table. Round your answers to the nearest $\frac{1}{10}$ inch.

(c) The graph of the function m is a straight line. What is its slope? What is its y-intercept?

Station Parts		Real (m)	Scale (in.)
(1)	building length	10	
(2)	building width	7	
(3)	platform length	45	
(4)	platform width	4.3	
(5)	freight door height	2.6	
(6)	front door width	1.25	

Display 6.34

5. Estimate (in feet or meters) the real measurement of each of the following objects. Then use either the function h from problem 3 or the function m from problem 4 to help you find the corresponding measurement in HO scale. Round your answer to the nearest $\frac{1}{10}$ inch.

   (a) the dimensions of your classroom (length, width, height)

   (b) your own height

   (c) 4 feet $8\frac{1}{2}$ inches, the distance between the rails of a standard gauge railroad track

   (d) the length of a boxcar

   (e) the length of a pickup truck

   (f) the height of a cat

   (g) the length of a football field

   (h) the height of your school building

   (i) the height of the Empire State Building

   (j) the length of an ocean-going supertanker

6. Converting temperatures from Fahrenheit to Celsius works like the Celsius to Fahrenheit function F that you studied in this section. This problem asks you to write a similar description of the Fahrenheit to Celsius function, which we'll call C.

   Using Technology

   (a) Write C as an algebraic formula in the form

   $$C(x) = \underline{\hspace{2cm}}$$

   where x stands for a given Fahrenheit temperature. Explain how you got your algebraic expression.

   (b) Your assignment as assistant weather forecaster has changed. Now you have to translate the Fahrenheit temperature of 24 major U.S. cities into Celsius for Canadian listeners. The list of cities and their latest Fahrenheit temperatures appears in Display 6.35 on the next page. Enter these temperatures into one of your calculator's lists. Then use your function to have your calculator find and list the corresponding Celsius temperatures automatically.

City	°F	°C
Anchorage, AK	18	
Atlanta, GA	59	
Bismarck, ND	28	
Boston, MA	48	
Cincinnati, OH	51	
Dallas, TX	56	
Denver, CO	49	
Detroit, MI	44	
Hartford, CT	45	
Honolulu, HI	86	
Los Angeles, CA	76	
Memphis, TN	57	
Miami, FL	78	
Minneapolis, MN	30	
New Orleans, LA	60	
New York, NY	50	
Phoenix, AZ	82	
Pittsburgh, PA	47	
Portland, ME	42	
Reno, NV	58	
Richmond, VA	54	
St. Louis, MO	55	
Seattle, WA	49	
Washington, D.C.	53	

Display 6.35

(c) The function C can be represented as a straight line. What are its slope and its y-intercept?

(d) Your teacher will give you a copy of the coordinate axes and the dotted line shown in Display 6.36.

   (i) Draw the graph of C on these axes. Think of the y-axis as the range of C.

   (ii) Draw the graph of F on the same coordinate axes. This time think of the y-axis as the range of F.

   (iii) What is the equation for the dotted line? Do you see any interesting relationships among these three lines? If so, describe what you see.

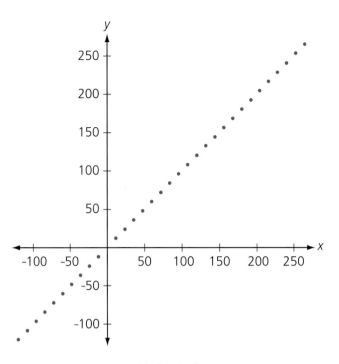

Display 6.36

7. Internet connection services allow you to connect with the World Wide Web. One such service, InfoMatic, has a $10 monthly service fee plus a connect-time charge of $15 per hour. The hourly charge is billed for actual connection time, which its computer tracks automatically and exactly.

(a) Write the formula for a function f that computes the total monthly bill for InfoMatic based on the time used. Then use f to compute the March bill for a subscriber who used 2 hours and 40 minutes of connect time that month and also for a second subscriber who used 4 hours and 6 minutes of connect time.

(b) The function f can be represented as a straight line. What are its slope and its y-intercept? Copy the coordinate axes shown in Display 6.37 and draw the graph of f on these axes. Think of the y-axis as the range of f.

(c) Another online service, DataLine, has a monthly service fee of $25 which includes 2 free hours of connect time. Additional connect time is charged at $20 per hour. Describe a function g that computes the total monthly bill for DataLine based on the time used. Then use g to compute the March bill for a subscriber who used 1 hour and 37 minutes of connect time that month and also for a second subscriber who used 4 hours and 15 minutes of connect time.

(d) Draw the graph of *g* on the same coordinate axes you used for part (b). Think of the *y*-axis as the range of *g*.

(e) The graph of *g* that you drew in part (d) should have two straight line pieces. Write an algebraic formula for each piece, and specify the domain values for each formula.

(f) For which amounts of connect time is InfoMatic the better deal? For which amounts is DataLine the better deal? When are they exactly the same?

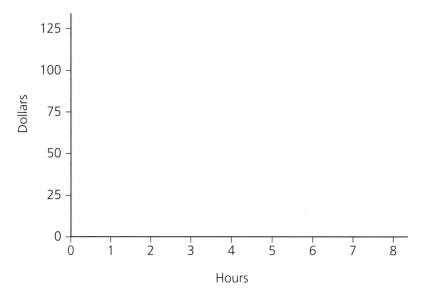

Display 6.37

6.5 Growth Functions

A rich uncle has died and left you $100,000 on the condition that you put it in a bank account and leave it untouched for at least 5 years. You want to get the most for your money, so you talk with the managers of the three local banks. All three banks need more money to lend out, so each one offers you a special deal.

- "Put your money with us!" says Bank 1. "We'll give you 10% of your initial deposit each year it stays with us. You'll make another $50,000 in 5 years!"

- "Put your money with us!" says Bank 2. "We'll pay you 9% annual interest, and we'll compound it every year." "What does 'compound it every year' mean?" you ask. "At the end of each year, we'll add to your account the interest earned and we'll base the next year's interest on that new, larger amount. That way you'll earn interest on your interest!"

- "Put your money with us!" says Bank 3. "We'll pay you 8% annual interest, and we'll compound it every quarter." "What does 'compound it every quarter' mean?" you ask. "We won't wait until the end of a year to add on the interest you've earned; we'll do it every quarter-year— every 3 months. That way your interest goes to work for you faster!"

All three banks advertise that "interest is paid from day of deposit to day of withdrawal."

In your opinion, which of these three banks is offering you the best deal? Which offer is the worst? Explain your thinking.

6.37

How can you figure out which bank is offering you the most interest for your money? One way is to make a table showing the total amount of money you would have in each account at the end of each year. For Bank 1, that's easy. They will pay you 10% of your initial deposit each year. (Recall that interest paid only on the original deposit is called *simple interest*.) That's an additional $10,000 a year. The amounts for Bank 2 are a little more difficult to compute, but they're not so bad if you take them one at a time. At the end of Year 1 you'll have 9% more than you started with. The amount at the end of Year 2 will be 9% more than the amount at the end of Year 1; and so on.

Learning Outcomes

After studying this section, you will be able to:

Explain why an exponential function is a good model for growth

Compare the effects of different growth rates

Use exponential functions to describe compounding

Evaluate exponential functions and draw their graphs with a graphing calculator.

Thinking Tip

Make a table. Making a table of values sometimes can help you see patterns that show you how a process works.

6.38

Fill in the columns for Banks 1 and 2 in the copy of the table in Display 6.38 that your teacher will give you.

Year	Bank 1	Bank 2	Bank 3
0	$100,000.00	$100,000.00	$100,000.00
1	$110,000.00		
2			
3			
4			
5	$150,000.00		

Display 6.38

Did you fill in the Bank 2 column by hand, or did you use your calculator? Either way is OK. Do you see how to compute each entry by a single multiplication step? You don't have to do it this way, but it's easier. In case you missed it, here's how that works.

To fill in the amount for the end of Year 1, add 9% of $100,000 to the original $100,000. That's

$$\$100,000 + 0.09 \cdot \$100,000$$

By the Distributive Law, this is the same as

$$(1 + 0.09) \cdot \$100,000$$

which is

$$(1.09) \cdot \$100,000$$

That is, increasing a number by 9% is the same as multiplying it by 1.09. This means that you can find each entry of the Bank 2 column by multiplying the one above it by 1.09.

Thinking Tip

Look for a pattern.
Sometimes thinking about different ways to fill in a chart or table uncovers useful hidden patterns.

Besides being easy to find the amounts this way, the pattern here will make it easier to fill in the next column. It tells us that the yearly amounts for Bank 2 can be found as in Display 6.38.

Year	Bank 2
0	$100,000.00
1	1.09 · $100,000
2	1.09 · (1.09 · $100,000)
3	1.09 · (1.09 · (1.09 · $100,000))
4	
5	

Display 6.39

What are the missing entries for 4 years and 5 years in Display 6.39?

6.39

Because multiplication is associative, this clumsy pattern can be abbreviated by using exponents. Display 6.40 shows how.

Year	Bank 2
0	$100,000.00
1	$1.09 \cdot \$100,000$
2	$1.09^2 \cdot \$100,000$
3	$1.09^3 \cdot \$100,000$
4	
5	

Display 6.40

6.40

1. **What are the missing entries for year 4 and year 5 in Display 6.40?**

2. **Explain what associativity has to do with the change from Display 6.39 to Display 6.40.**

Now let's summarize this pattern. Notice that the only thing that changes as we move down the list in Display 6.40 is the number of years. The amount of money is *a function of* how many years it has been in the account. This function—we'll call it B_2, for Bank 2—depends on the number t of years according to the formula

$$B_2(t) = 1.09^t \cdot \$100,000$$

This kind of function is called an **exponential function** because the independent variable (in this case t, for time in years) is used as an exponent.

Writing this process as an exponential function makes it much easier to find how much money would be in the account after any number of years. Instead of having to build up to the answer one year at a time, we can just put the number of years in for t and let the calculator compute it. For instance, the amount of money in the account after 10 years is

$$B_2(10) = 1.09^{10} \cdot \$100,000$$

How much is that?

This exponential pattern can be used to fill in the Bank 3 column, too, but we have to be a little careful. The following questions show you why.

Using Technology

6.41

1. If the bank's annual interest rate is 8%, what do you think their quarterly interest rate is?

2. If you deposit $100,000, how much money should you have at the end of the first quarter? At the end of 6 months? At the end of the first year?

3. How many quarter-years are in 2 years? In 3 years? In t years?

4. The Bank 3 amount function can be written as

    $$B_3(t) = 1.02^? \cdot \$100,000$$

    Where does the number 1.02 come from? What is the exponent in this case? Explain. (*Hint*: Look back at your answers to parts 1 and 3.)

5. Use this formula for $B_3(t)$ to fill in the Bank 3 column of Display 6.38.

6. Write a formula to describe the way Bank 1 computes the amount you would have at the end of each year. Call this function B_1. Explain how it works.

Now that you have formulas for the way your money would grow in each bank, you can use them to decide which bank gives you the best deal for *any* time period.

6.42

1. Which bank gives you the most money for the 5-year period? Which gives you the least? Do these results agree with your answers at the beginning of this section?

2. If you only had to keep the money in the bank for 3 years, which bank would give you the most money? Which would give you the least? Justify your answer.

3. Suppose you decide to leave your money in the bank for an extra year. Which bank pays the most for the 6-year period? Which pays the least? Justify your answer.

Which (if any) of the functions B_1, B_2, and B_3 have graphs that are straight lines? Which do not? Defend your answers.

6.43

Earning interest is a way to make your money grow. Compounding is a way to make it grow faster. Compound interest functions are examples of **growth functions**, which express the amount of something at a particular time based on how much there was just before that time. Compounding shows how the growth of an amount of anything (people, rabbits, rats, bacteria) fuels the growth "engine" as it runs along. Let's take a more careful look at the compound interest effect.

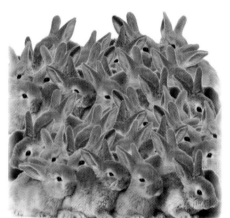

The more often interest is compounded, the faster the total amount grows. Is there any limit to how much faster you can make the money increase just by compounding more frequently? Think about that as we work through the following situation together.

You have $10,000 to invest for one year. Two investment companies are competing for your money. One offers you $12\frac{3}{4}\%$ simple interest. The other company offers you 12% interest, but says that you can decide how often you want it to be compounded. Which is the better deal?

One way to approach this problem is to try different compounding periods for the 12% rate for a single year. Then you can compare those results with what you would have at $12\frac{3}{4}\%$ simple interest, which is

$$1.1275 \cdot \$10,000 = \$11,275.$$

Display 6.41 provides a way to keep track of what you find. As you work through it, here are some things to keep in mind.

*   Choosing the length of the compounding period changes the rate you'll use.
*   Each different rate gives you a different "Amount" function. We have labeled them with subscripts to tell them apart: y for yearly, q for quarterly, and so on.

- The independent variable for each of these functions is t, which is the time in years. Since you want to know the results for one year, $t = 1$ in each case.

Total Amount After 1 Year at 12%				
Compounded...	Periods per year	Rate for one period	Function for 1 year	Amount
yearly	1	0.12	$A_y(1) = 1.12^1 \cdot \$10{,}000$	$11,200.00
quarterly	4	0.03	$A_q(1) = 1.03^4 \cdot \$10{,}000$	
monthly	12		$A_m(1) =$	
weekly			$A_w(1) =$	
daily			$A_d(1) =$	
other	n		$A_n(1) =$	

Display 6.41

Using Technology

6.44

Your teacher will give you a copy of Display 6.41 to fill in as you answer these questions. Parts of the first two lines are already done for you. Use your calculator to do the computations.

1. A_q is the function for 12% interest compounded quarterly. Explain why 1.03 instead of 1.12 appears in this formula, and why the exponent is 4. Then compute and fill in the total amount you would have at the end of the year.

2. What is the interest rate for one month? Fill in the formula for $A_m(1)$. Then compute and fill in the total amount you would have at the end of the year.

3. What do A_w and A_d stand for? Complete these two rows of the table.

4. Explain how to find the total amount at the end of the year if the 12% interest were compounded every hour. Don't compute the exact amount, but estimate about how much it would be. Do you think finding the exact answer to this question would be worth the effort? Why or why not?

5. Describe in words the method for finding the total amount at the end of one year for $10,000 at 12% interest if the length of the compounding interval is not yet known to you. Then fill in the last row of the table. Display 6.41 focuses on how different compounding functions work for a single year. But what about more

than one year? After all, the domain variable for each function is the number of years t that the money is left in the bank.

1. These questions are about the quarterly compounding function, A_q, from Display 6.41.

   6.45

   (a) If you applied this process for 2 years, how many compounding periods would there be? What would be the interest rate for each period?

   (b) If you applied this process for 3 years, how many compounding periods would there be? What would be the interest rate for each period?

   (c) If you applied this process for t years, how many compounding periods would there be? What would be the interest rate for each period?

   (d) Use your answer to part (c) to write a formula for $A_q(t)$.

2. Your answer to 1(d) is a formula for a $10,000 starting deposit that earns 12% annual interest, compounded quarterly, for t years. Now let's generalize this idea in a few different ways.

   (a) If you start with $20,000 at 12% annual interest, compounded quarterly, for t years, you have a new total-amount function. Write a formula for it. What if you start with $30,000? Write a formula for that, too.

   (b) The starting amount is sometimes called the "principal." Write a formula for the total-amount function for a principal P at 12% annual interest, compounded quarterly, for t years.

3. (a) How would you modify your answer to 2(b) to get a formula for a principal P at 8% annual interest? How about at 5% annual interest?

   (b) Suppose that the interest rate, in decimal form, is r. Modify your answer to 2(b) to handle that rate.

4. Your answer to 3(b) is a formula that lets you write a function for any principal amount and any interest rate compounded quarterly (that is, 4 times a year). What about other compounding periods? Let's see.

   (a) What part of that formula tells you that the compounding is done quarterly?

   (b) How would you rewrite the formula for monthly compounding? For weekly compounding?

Thinking Tip

Choose good notation.
Symbols can help to clarify patterns in your thinking.

(c) Compounding can be done any number of times a year, just by dividing the year into that number of equal pieces. How can you change the formula to handle n compounding periods in a year?

Your answer to part 4(c) above is a very general, very useful formula for calculating compound interest. Once you decide how much money to begin with (that's P, the principal) and the bank tells you the annual interest rate r and the number n of compounding periods per year, you have a function that shows how much money you will have at the end of t years. It should look like this:

$$A(t) = (1 + \tfrac{r}{n})^{nt} \cdot P$$

As you filled in Display 6.41, did you notice how the differences between the total amounts in the last column kept shrinking as the compounding periods got shorter? Look again at your figures for that column. Notice that, at the end of 1 year:

$A_q(1)$ is about \$55.00 larger than $A_y(1)$

$A_m(1)$ is about \$13.00 larger than $A_q(1)$

$A_w(1)$ is about \$5.00 larger than $A_m(1)$

$A_d(1)$ is about \$1.35 larger than $A_w(1)$

 Use the compound interest function $A(t)$ and your calculator to check these differences after 3 years. That is, using the same principal and interest rate, calculate $A(3)$ for annual, quarterly, monthly, and weekly compounding. Then calculate it for hourly compounding. List the differences from each result to the next.

6.46

As you might guess, even if we compounded every minute or every second, the total amount at the end wouldn't get much bigger than your hourly compounding answer. In fact, this compounding process is limited by an exponential function that describes something called "continuous compounding." Continuous compounding is a lot like compounding every second of every minute of every day.

This limiting function depends on a very special number called e. Exponential functions involving e are so useful that many calculators have a special key for them, labeled e^x. The story of where this number e comes from and why it works the way it does will have to wait until you have learned some more mathematics. However, your graphing calculator makes it easy to see how it works for growth functions. Here's how to use this function key to settle the simple vs. compound interest question we've been working on.

For \$10,000 and an annual interest rate of 12%, the amount resulting from continuous compounding is given by

$$A_c(t) = e^{0.12t} \cdot \$10{,}000$$

where t is the number of years. To see what happens at the end of 1 year, just substitute 1 for t. Press the e^x key on your calculator and fill out the rest of the formula like this.

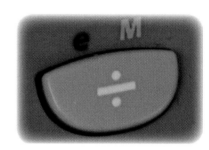

e^(0.12)*10000

This is the largest amount you can possibly get from a 12% rate in 1 year, no matter how often the interest is compounded. The $12\frac{3}{4}$% simple interest offer was better by about 3 cents!

What would you have at the end of 3 years by continuous compounding? How much better than hourly compounding is that?

6.47

1. **What if you invest your \$10,000 for two years? Which is better—$12\frac{3}{4}$ % simple interest or 12% compounded continuously? How much better?**

6.48

2. **How can you get your calculator to approximate the value of e?**

The example we just did illustrates the general form of continuous compounding functions. If you know the interest rate r and the principal P, then the amount of money you end up with depends on the number of years t you let it grow. The formula for such a function is

$$A_c(t) = e^{rt} \cdot P$$

Continuous compounding applies to many things besides money. It is the key to describing the growth of large groups of people, mice, bacteria, or anything that reproduces itself. As an example of this, let us look at world population.

Statistical surveys say that the growth rate of the world's population in recent years is about 1.2% per year. There were about 6.1 billion (6,100,000,000) people living on this planet in 2000. At this rate, about how many people will be living on it in the year 2010? In the year 2020? In the year 2035?

Unlike bank accounts, the compounding of population growth does not take place annually or quarterly on some special day. It's going on all the time. Every second of every hour, many people are being born and many others are dying. This means that the growth rate, the overall effect of these births and deaths, can be viewed as a continuous process. To answer these questions, then, we can use a continuous compounding function. In this case, r stands for the growth rate and P stands for the original population.

$$A_c(t) = e^{rt} \cdot P$$

$$A_c(t) = e^{0.012t} \cdot 6{,}100{,}000{,}000$$

Now the questions are easy to answer. To find the approximate world population in the year 2010, which is 10 years after 2000, just compute $A_c(10)$.

Using Technology

6.49

1. Do it. Use your calculator to compute $A_c(10)$.

2. If you want to find the population in the year 2020, what t should you use? Write the formula for that case, then use it to compute the approximate world population in 2020.

3. Compute the approximate world population in the year 2035.

4. Enter the function $A_c(t)$ into your graphing calculator. Then graph it for the years 2000 to 2060. As you do this, answer these questions.

    (a) What key must you use for t when you enter the formula?

    (b) Use 6.1 for P. What unit of measure will your answer be in?

    (c) Proper **WINDOW** settings are important for getting a useful picture. Why is setting **X** from 0 to 60 reasonable? What does it mean?

    (d) Why is 5 a reasonable minimum for **Y**? What does this 5 represent? What is a reasonable maximum for **Y**?

5. Now evaluate your function for the years 2010, 2020, 2040, and 2060. The first two of these should agree with answers you got before.

Not all countries have the same population growth rate. In recent years, the rate in the United States has been about 0.97% per year. The 2000 census said that the U.S. population at that time was about 284 million.

Using Technology

6.50

1. Write a formula for a function U that gives the U.S. population t years after 2000, assuming the same annual growth rate.

2. Use the function U to compute the approximate U.S. population in the years 2010, 2035, and 2060.

3. At this rate of growth, how many years will it take the U.S. population to double? In what year will that occur? Explain how you found your answers.

Problem Set: 6.5

1. You just received a brand new Prestige Platinum credit card. You are allowed to charge up to $10,000, and you don't have to make any payments for an entire year. However, the annual interest rate on the unpaid amount is 24%, compounded monthly. You buy a new motorcycle for $8,000 and charge it to your Prestige Platinum card.

   (a) If you don't charge anything else and don't make any payments for a year, how much do you owe at the end of that time? Explain how you found your answer.

   (b) If you were charged simple interest at the rate of 24%, how much would you owe? Which amount is more, this one or your answer to part (a)? How much more? Explain why you think your answer is reasonable.

2. Make a table just like Display 6.41, except that the time period is 2 years. Use the same interest rate, 12%. What is the least simple interest rate (rounded up to the nearest quarter-percent) that would be a better deal than any of these compounding arrangements for the two-year period? Justify your answer.

3. Your teacher will give you a table just like Display 6.41 (with a time period of 1 year), except that the annual interest rate is 16%. There is a new a row at the bottom for the continuous compounding function that limits all the compounding functions above it. Compute the total amount you get using this continuous compounding function.

4. A local bank recently advertised a CD (Certificate of Deposit) at an annual interest rate of 6%, compounded monthly. They claim that it has an effective annual yield of 6.17%.

(a) A CD of this type was purchased for $1,000. Compute its value at the end of 1 year and at the end of 5 years.

(b) What do you think "effective annual yield" means? Explain.

(c) This same bank advertises that its Access Account has an interest rate of 3.20%, compounded daily. What is the effective annual yield of this account? Explain how you found your answer.

(d) Find a bank in your neighborhood (or a bank ad in your local paper) that advertises the interest rate and the effective annual yield of an account. Write down the name of the bank and the description of the account. Then check the bank's claim by computing the effective annual yield of the account. Write a short explanation of your work.

Using Technology

5. Andy and Zoe are both 25 years old. They decide to deposit $5,000 into an account that earns 6% annual interest and leave it there until they retire, sometime between 65 and 70 years old. These questions are about how much money they will have then, depending on the compounding deal they get.

(a) Write the formulas for the total amount functions for simple interest and for quarterly, monthly, weekly, daily, and continuous compounding.

(b) Write a few sentences about how you think it would look to graph all six of these functions at the same time. What patterns would you expect to see?

(c) Now use your calculator to graph them all at the same time. Set your **WINDOW** for the time span between when they are 65 and when they are 70. What minimum and maximum amount values will give you a good picture?

(d) Does your picture for part (c) match what you expected? Are there any differences between what you predicted in part (b) and what you got? Write a few sentences describing what things were the same and what were different.

Using Technology

6. In recent years, the annual population growth rate in China has been about 0.6%. The *United Nations Population Division* says that there were about 1.313 billion people in China in 2005.

(a) Write a formula for a function C that gives the population of China t years after 2005, assuming the same growth rate. Design your function to give the answer in millions of people.

(b) Use the function C to compute the approximate population of China in the years 2015, 2040, and 2065.

(c) Put the formula for C into your graphing calculator.

Then graph it, setting the **WINDOW** values like this:

X from 0 to 60 with a scale of 10; **Y** from 1000 to 2800 with a scale of 500.

(d) At this rate of growth, how many years will it take the population of China to double? In what year will that occur? Explain how you found your answers.

Keep this function C in your calculator. You will need it for problem 8.

7. In recent years, the annual population growth rate in India has been about 1.5%. The *United Nations Population Division* says that there were about 1.134 billion people in India in 2005.

Using Technology

(a) Write a formula for a function I that gives the population of India t years after 2005, assuming the same growth rate. Design your function to give the answer in millions of people.

(b) Use the function I to compute the approximate population of India in the years 2015, 2040, and 2065.

(c) Put the formula for I into your graphing calculator. Then graph it, setting the **WINDOW** values like this:

X from 0 to 60 with a scale of 10; **Y** from 1000 to 3000 with a scale of 500.

(d) At this rate of growth, how many years will it take the population of India to double? In what year will that occur? Explain how you found your answers.

Keep this function I in your calculator. You will need it for problem 8.

8. If you did problems 6 and 7 above, display the graphs of both the functions C and I on the same set of axes. Where (approximately) do these two curves intersect? What do the coordinates of the intersection point tell us about the populations of these two countries?

9. In recent years, the annual population growth rate in Kenya has been about 2.7%. At that rate of growth, how many years will it take for the population of Kenya to double? Explain your answer.

6.6 Links in a Chain: Composition of Functions

Learning Outcomes

After studying this section, you will be able to:

Describe function composition as a "followed-by" process

Identify function composition in real-world situations

Construct the composite of two functions, and describe it in words and by an algebraic formula.

Thinking Tip

Break things into simpler parts. You get better understanding and control of a concept if you see how it can be built up from simpler ideas.

Two commonsense ideas make functions a powerful mathematical tool.

1. What "comes out" of a function is completely controlled by what "goes in."
2. Complicated processes often can be broken down into very simple functions.

The second of these ideas is the topic of this section. It is an example of *analysis*, the process of separating something into simpler parts to understand it better. Chemical analysis, for example, examines a thing by trying to discover the elements it is made of and how much of each it contains. *Compounds* are chemicals that are put together from the elements. When you study chemistry, one of the first things you come across is the "periodic table." This table organizes the chemical elements into groupings and patterns so that they can be better understood when they appear in compounds.

In many uses of mathematics we do a similar kind of analysis. If there is a process in which output depends on input, we try to describe it as a function. This is the abstraction step. Then we try to break this function into simpler functions so that, by applying each simpler function in turn, we end up with the same result as from the original function.

Here's an example of how a function can be broken into simpler functions. This one doesn't come from mathematics; it's from a newspaper cartoon of many years ago. Display 6.42 shows the input and output of cartoonist Rube Goldberg's bottle opener. It begins by feeding an elephant a bag of peanuts and ends by pulling the cork from the bottle. If we believe Rube Goldberg, this is a function. Pulling the cork from a bottle depends on feeding the elephant a bag of peanuts. Each time you put a bag of peanuts in, a cork comes out. But how does it work?

Display 6.42

The steps that go from the elephant to the bottle are shown in Display 6.43, along with the inventor's explanation of how they work. The output of the first step is the falling spike, which becomes the input of the second step. The output of the second step is the exploding balloon, which becomes the input of the third step. And so on.

"Elephant (A) eats peanuts (B) — as bag gets lighter weight (C) drops and spike (D) punctures balloon (E) — explosion scares monkey (F) — his hat (G) flies off and releases hook (H), causing spring (I) to pull string (J) which tilts tennis racket (K) — racket hits ball (L), making it spin around on attached string, thereby screwing corkscrew into cork (M) — ball hits sleeping dog (N) who jumps and pulls cork out of bottle with string (O) — my, how simple!"

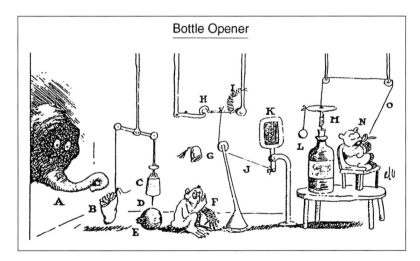

Display 6.43

6.51

1. What is the output of the third step of the Rube Goldberg bottle opener?

2. What are the input and the output of the fourth step?

3. Describe the input and the output of each step from the fifth one to the end of the process when the cork is pulled.

About Words

In English, to *compose* something means "to put it together or make it up (from pieces)." A composer of a song or a symphony doesn't make up the sounds, but puts them together in a creative, artistic way. *Function composition* means "putting together two or more functions to create a single function."

The process of following one function by another, so that the images from the first function are in the domain of the second, is called **function composition**. The function that results from this putting together process is called the **composite** of the original functions.

The composite of a function *f* followed by a function *g* is usually denoted by the symbol *g* ∘ *f*. That seems backward, doesn't it? It's not, if you remember how images of functions are symbolized. If we start with some *x* and apply *f* first, we get *f*(*x*). Now, if we apply *g* to that, we get *g*(*f*(*x*)). That is,

$$(g \circ f)(x) = g(f(x))$$

Display 6.44 shows an example of this process. It starts with a function *f* from {a, b, c, d} to {1, 2, 3, 4} and continues with a function *g* from {1, 2, 3, 4} to {*, \$, #}. The composite function *g* ∘ *f* goes from {a, b, c, d} to {*, \$, #}.

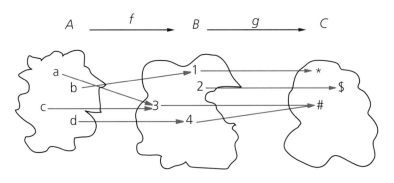

Display 6.44

The composite function $g \circ f$ of Display 6.44 goes from set A to set C. Complete the listing of values for $g \circ f$ on the copy of the table your teacher will give you. The first row is done for you.

6.52

$(g \circ f)(a) = g(f(a)) = g(3) = $ #

$(g \circ f)(b) = g(f(b)) = g(\_\_) = \_\_\_\_$

$(g \circ f)(c) = \_\_\_\_\_ = \_\_\_\_\_ = \_\_\_\_$

$(g \circ f)(d) = \_\_\_\_\_ = \_\_\_\_\_ = \_\_\_\_$

When functions are written as formulas, their composite doesn't have to be described one element at a time. You can use algebra to do it all at once. Here is an example. Suppose you want the composite of the "add 3" function, $f(x) = x + 3$, and the "squaring" function, $g(x) = x^2$. If you want to use f first, then g, you're saying "add 3 to the number, then square the result." Of course, "the number" can be any number in the domain of f. We say all of this very easily with algebra.

$(g \circ f)(x) = g(f(x))$ Do f first, then do g to get the result.

    $= g(x + 3)$ f adds 3 to any number.

    $= (x + 3)^2$ g squares any number.

Thus, $(g \circ f)(x) = (x + 3)^2$. For instance,

$$(g \circ f)(5) = g(5 + 3) = 8^2 = 64.$$

Let f and g be the two functions just described.

6.53

1. Calculate $(g \circ f)(4)$ and $(g \circ f)(-4)$.

2. Write an algebraic formula for $(f \circ g)(x)$. Are the functions $g \circ f$ and $f \circ g$ equal? Why or why not?

Now think of two other functions, h and j, defined by the formulas

$$h(x) = 2x \quad \text{and} \quad j(x) = 5 - x$$

3. Describe in words what h and j do to a number.

4. Write formulas to describe the composite functions $h \circ j$ and $j \circ h$.

5. Calculate $(h \circ j)(7)$ and $(j \circ h)(7)$.

6. Are the two composite functions $h \circ j$ and $j \circ h$ equal? Why or why not?

Here is an example that shows how composition of functions occurs in business. Imagine yourself in this situation: Your band has just recorded a great album! By careful planning and hard work, you were able to make a master for $20,000 of your own money. A record company has offered you a contract for producing and marketing your album as a CD. There's a lot of legal language, but the offer boils down to the following:

1. The company will market the CD at a list price of $15.

2. Your band will be paid 10% of the net amount that the company receives for your album, after retailer and distributor discounts. (Your 10% is called a *royalty*.)

3. Each month you will receive a statement showing the number of CDs sold and your total royalty amount for that month.

It sure is exciting to be offered a contract! You don't understand all the technical words in this offer, but the company assures you that it is "a standard recording contract." You sign it right away and wait for the money to start rolling in.

While you're waiting, you dream about the "big bucks" your band will get in royalties. Let's see...

1000 CDs at $15 each is $15,000

2000 CDs at $15 each is $30,000

How about making a table to get a better idea of the money involved?

 **Using Technology**

6.54

Clear the lists on your graphing calculator. We're going to use several lists in this example. We'll call the first one **L1**, the second one **L2**, and so on, which is probably what your calculator calls them, too. We'll use n to represent the number of CDs sold.

1. In **L1**, list some possible values for n, from 500 to 10,000 in steps of 500: that is, list 500, 1000, 1500, ..., 10,000. (Do you know how to do this automatically, without putting in each amount by hand? If not, find out.)

2. In **L2**, list the amount of money (in dollars) collected by the stores for these sales (without sales tax). This amount is usually called *gross sales*. What formula will make **L2** list the gross sales amount for each number of CDs in **L1**? Enter it. At this point, your calculator lists should look something like Display 6.45.

3. Can you compute from these sales figures how much you should be paid in royalties? If you can, do it in **L3**; then explain your thinking. If you can't, explain what extra information you need.

L1	L2	L3
500	7500	
1000	15,000	
1500	22,500	
.	.	
.	.	
.	.	
9500	142,500	
10,000	150,000	

Display 6.45

Display 6.45 represents a function. The amount of gross sales depends entirely on the number of CDs sold. In the language of this chapter, "gross sales" is the dependent variable and "number of CDs sold" is the independent variable. This technical language can be shortened by saying that the gross sales amount *is a function of* the number of CDs sold. We'll call this function g.

The formula for **L2** suggests an easy way to write this function algebraically. If n is a particular number of CDs sold, then $g(n)$ is the gross sales amount for that number of CDs, so

$$g(n) = 15n$$

1. Compute $g(800)$.

2. Compute $g(5114)$.

6.55

3. Suppose you knew that gross sales amounted to $127,365. How would you find the number of CDs sold? What is that number?

Six months later, the album is on the market and your band gets its first royalty check. In the first month, 5114 CDs have been sold, but the check amount is only $3,451.95. There must be some mistake! You call the record company.

"There's no mistake," they say. "Your royalty is 10% of net sales, not of gross sales. It's all explained in the contract you signed." Back to the fine print in the contract.

• The retail stores get a 40% discount off the list price. That is, the wholesale price of the CD is 60% of its list price.

- The distributor gets a 25% discount off the wholesale price. The remaining 75% of the wholesale price is the net sales price.

- Your band's royalty is 10% of the net sales price.

Remembering what you learned in math class, you see that each of these three steps is a function.

- The wholesale amount is 60% of the gross sales amount. That is, if the gross sales amount is x, then the wholesale amount, $w(x)$, is

$$w(x) = 0.6x$$

The function w turns gross sales amounts into wholesale amounts.

- The net sales amount is 75% of the wholesale amount. If the wholesale amount is x, then the net sales amount, $s(x)$, is

$$s(x) = 0.75x$$

The function s turns wholesale amounts into net sales amounts.

- The royalty is 10% of the net sales amount. If the net sales amount is x, then the royalty, $r(x)$, is

$$r(x) = 0.1x$$

The function r turns net sales amounts into royalty amounts.

Each royalty amount, then, is an image of an image of an image of an image of n (the number of CDs sold). Each amount depends on the amount from the step before. The lists of your calculator can illustrate this chain of functions. To see how, work through the questions on the next page.

Using Technology

6.56

Recall that **L1** in your calculator contains some sample numbers of CDs sold and **L2** contains their gross sales amounts.

1. In **L3**, enter a formula to compute the wholesale amounts from the gross sales amounts in **L2**. Which function is this?

2. The correspondence between **L1** and **L2** is the gross sales function g. What function describes the correspondence between **L1** and **L3**? Write it as a formula, if you can.

3. In **L4**, enter a formula to compute the net sales amounts from the wholesale amounts in **L3**. Which function is this?

4. What function describes the correspondence between **L1** and **L4**? Write it as a formula, as simply as you can.

5. In **L5**, enter a formula to compute the royalty amounts from the net sales amounts in **L4**. Which function is this?

6. What function describes the correspondence between **L1** and **L5**? Write it as a formula, as simply as you can.

7. If 3500 CDs are sold, how much royalty money does your band get? What if 9000 CDs are sold? Explain how to read the answers from the calculator lists.

8. If 37,458 CDs are sold, how much royalty money does your band get? Explain how to get the answer without entering new data into your lists. (*Hint:* Look at your answer to part 6.)

Question 8 above shows that you don't really need the calculator lists to compute your band's royalty on the sale of a particular number of CDs. You only need the effect of the chain of functions that describe the lists. The four simple functions—g, w, s, and r—are put together, one after another, to form the composite "royalty function"

$$r \circ (s \circ (w \circ g))$$

Function composition is what makes electronic spreadsheets such powerful tools for handling numbers. Entire bookkeeping systems can be built step by step from simple functions in this way.

Making spreadsheets is only one of many applications of function composition. Following one function by another to form a new function is one of the most useful, basic ideas in all of mathematics. It is useful in two ways:

- It lets us break down a complicated process into simpler steps. Each step is easier to understand, so the entire process becomes easier to use.

- It lets us combine a series of steps into a single function that can be used more efficiently than going through each step separately.

The royalty function is an example of combining steps into a single, more efficient function. The following questions ask you to break down a familiar process into simpler pieces.

6.6 Links in a Chain: Composition of Functions

6.57

The Celsius-to-Fahrenheit function F of Section 6.4 was defined by $F(x) = \frac{9}{5}x + 32$

1. Write F as the composite of two simpler functions. Try out your answer by converting 20°C to Fahrenheit using your two-step process. Compare your answer with what you get by using the original function F. (You should get the same thing.)

2. Does it matter which of your two functions is used first in forming the composite? Why or why not?

Algebra can help you handle function composition quickly and easily. For example, suppose you want to see if there is any interesting pattern in the list of squares of odd numbers. (Some people do that sort of thing just for fun.) You can get a formula for all the numbers in that list by composing two simple functions on the set of counting numbers. Here they are:

$f(n) = 2n - 1$ gives you the list of consecutive odd numbers. (Try it on the first few numbers to see how it works.)

$$g(n) = n^2$$

The composite function $g \circ f$ ("f followed by g") makes each counting number into an odd number and then squares it. Now you can combine these two steps into a single formula, like this:

$$(g \circ f)(n) = g(f(n)) = (f(n))^2 = (2n - 1)^2$$

Notice that g, the squaring function, works on whatever number is "handed to it" by f. That's what $g(f(n))$ means.

6.58

The first two of these parts refer to the functions f and g just described.

1. For each counting number n, the composite function $g \circ f$ should give you the square of the nth odd number. To see how it works, calculate $(g \circ f)(n)$ for $n = 1, 2, 3, 4, 5,$ and 6. Then find the square of the 48th odd number.

2. What does the composite function $f \circ g$ do? Describe it in words; then write it algebraically. To check your thinking, calculate $(f \circ g)(n)$ for $n = 1, 2, 3, 4, 5,$ and 6. Do you get the same six answers as in part 1?

3. Now extend the squaring function g to the set of all integers, and let h stand for the function that reverses the sign of any number. That is, $h(x) = -x$. Describe the two composite functions "g followed by h" and "h followed by g" in words; then write them algebraically. Are these two composite functions equal? Why or why not?

4. Let a denote the absolute value function on the integers; that is $a(x) = |x|$ for every integer x. Describe the two composite functions "g followed by a" and "a followed by g" in words; then write them algebraically. Are these two composite functions equal? Why or why not?

Problem Set: 6.6

1. Determining the correct postage for a piece of mail is actually a composite of two functions:

   (i) finding the weight of the letter or package by using a scale, and

   (ii) matching the weight with a postage amount by using a chart or table of postage rates.

   Describe two other processes from everyday life that can be thought of as composite functions.

2. In each of these parts there are formulas for two functions, f and g, on the set of rational numbers. In each case,

   • Find formulas for the functions $g \circ f$ and $f \circ g$.

   • Use your formulas to compute $(g \circ f)(10)$ and $(f \circ g)(10)$.

   (a) $f(x) = 4x$ and $g(x) = x + 6$

   (b) $f(x) = x - 2$ and $g(x) = \frac{x}{4}$

   (c) $f(x) = -3x$ and $g(x) = x + 5$

   (d) $f(x) = x^2$ and $g(x) = x - 1$

   (e) $f(x) = 0.5x$ and $g(x) = 2x$

   (f) $f(x) = x^2$ and $g(x) = x^3$

3. (a) A function f on the rational numbers is defined by the formula

   $$f(x) = 7x - 3$$

   Define two functions, g and h, such that $f = h \circ g$.

   (b) A function p on the rational numbers is defined by the formula

   $$p(x) = 5x^2 + 8$$

   Define three functions, q, r, and s, such that $p = s \circ (r \circ q)$.

4. A function p matches each integer with its opposite (the integer with the same absolute value, but the opposite sign). A function d matches each integer with its double.

   (a) Write formulas for the functions p and d.

   (b) Write a formula for the composite function $d \circ p$; then compute $(d \circ p)(15)$ and $(d \circ p)(-12)$.

   (c) Write a formula for the composite function $p \circ d$; then compute $(p \circ d)(15)$ and $(p \circ d)(-12)$.

   (d) Are these two composite functions equal? Why or why not?

5. A function p matches each integer with its opposite (the integer with the same absolute value, but the opposite sign). A function t matches each integer with the integer that is two greater than the integer.

   (a) Write formulas for the functions p and t.

   (b) Write a formula for the composite function $t \circ p$, then compute $(t \circ p)(15)$ and $(t \circ p)(-12)$.

   (c) Write a formula for the composite function $p \circ t$, then compute $(p \circ t)(15)$ and $(p \circ t)(-12)$.

   (d) Are these two composite functions equal? Why or why not?

6. Earlier in **MATH** *Connections*, you saw that equations for straight lines can be written in the form $y = mx + b$, where m is the slope and b is the y-intercept. These equations are actually functions of x. That is,

$$f(x) = mx + b$$

   The letters m and b are constants here. That is, they stand for particular numbers.

   (a) Describe f as the composite of two functions—a slope function and an intercept function.

   (b) These two functions tell you two different things about the picture of the function. What does the slope function tell you about the picture? What does the intercept function tell you?

   (c) Does the order in which you compose these two functions matter? Why or why not?

7. Display 6.8 (from Section 6.1) describes a 5% sales tax function. This is actually a composite $r \circ p$ of two functions, a percentage function p and a rounding function r.

   (a) Explain in your own words how p and r work on the sales amounts from $0.01 to $1.00.

(b) Using the upper part of Display 6.8 , shown below, as a model, define a 7% sales tax function for all sales amounts from $0.01 to $1.00. Describe this tax function first as a composite of a percentage function and a rounding function; then make a table for it.

5% Sales Tax Schedule		
Sale		**Tax**
From	**To**	
$0.01	$0.09	$0.00
0.10	0.29	0.01
0.30	0.49	0.02
0.50	0.69	0.03
0.70	0.89	0.04
0.90	1.00	0.05

The tax to be collected is the amount indicated for each dollar of the sale price plus the amount indicated above for any fraction of a dollar.

Top part of Display 6.8

Display 6.46

8. (a) Is function composition commutative? How would you convince someone that your answer is correct?

   (b) Is function composition associative? How would you convince someone that your answer is correct?

Looking Back

Function is one of the most basic and important ideas in all of mathematics. A function is a process or rule that assigns exactly one image or output (range element) to every input (domain element). They exist all around us in the real world. For example, a price list assigns a price to each item and the FBI fingerprinting file assigns a person to each fingerprint.

There are many ways to describe a function. We can use words, diagrams, tables, or ordered pairs. These ways can be used for functions with any type of domain or range. When functions match numbers to numbers, algebraic formulas and graphs can also be used. They are especially useful for describing functions with large domains. They also allow us to use tools of algebra, graphing, and calculators to work with them. Functions with different descriptions may still be equal. This happens when both functions have the same domain and match each domain element to the same image.

In this chapter you have seen many different kinds of functions, including sequences, step functions, linear functions, and exponential functions. You saw how a step function assigns postage to the weight of a letter, how a linear function converts Celsius degrees to Fahrenheit degrees, and how exponential functions model compounding and population growth. Function composition lets you build more complex functions by applying simpler functions one after another. This can help you understand a complicated process by breaking it down into a string of simpler steps.

The idea of function, an unambiguous way to assign items from one set to those in another, is at the heart of many complex theories and applications. Such relationships occur surprisingly often—in science, in business, in everyday life, almost everywhere. Recognizing them as functions lets us link the power of mathematics to the real world. Then we can use the toolbox of mathematical techniques, coordinate systems, and calculators that make difficult questions easier to answer.

In this chapter you learned how to:

- Identify and explain functions in real-world situations.
- Construct and describe functions using words, a diagram, a table, or ordered pairs, and find images using these descriptions.
- Use function notation to abbreviate statements about functions.
- Determine whether or not two functions are equal (in some cases).
- Identify and describe real-world examples of step functions.

- Use graphs to represent functions and find images of domain elements.
- Use algebraic formulas for functions and find images of domain elements.
- Use a graphing calculator to draw graphs and find images for linear and some other functions.
- Explain why an exponential function is a good model for growth.
- Use exponential functions to describe compounding.
- Describe function composition as a "followed-by" process and identify function composition in real-world situations.
- Construct the composite of two functions and describe it in words and sometimes by an algebraic formula.

Along the way, you also learned to:

- Describe sequences recursively and algebraically and use those descriptions to find specific terms.
- Apply slope and linear equations to a variety of real-world situations.
- Use exponents, decimals, and percents to analyze competing claims.

Review Exercises

1. The functions f, g, h, and w are defined on real numbers as follows:

$$f(x) = 2x - 1 \qquad g(x) = -5x \qquad h(x) = 3x^2 \qquad w(x) = 2x$$

Calculate each of the following values.

(a) $h(-12)$

(b) $w(5)$

(c) $f(x)$ when $x = -3$

(d) $w(x)$ when $x = -3$

(e) x when $f(x) = 77$

(f) x when $g(x) = 65$

(g) $(g \circ h)(-2)$

(h) $(f \circ w)(4)$

(i) $g(f(3))$

(j) $w(g(-1))$

(k) $g(h(x))$ when $x = -6$

(l) $h(g(x))$ when $x = 5$

Write a formula for each of the following composite functions.

(m) $(f \circ g)(x)$

(n) $(g \circ h)(x)$

(o) $(w \circ f)(x)$

(p) $g(f(x))$

(q) $h(g(x))$

(r) $w(g(x))$

2. Write the first five terms of each of the sequences defined below.

(a) $s_n = n^2 + 7$

(b) $s(n) = 6 + 10n$

(c) $a_1 = 2$ and $a_n = 3a_{n-1} + 5$

(d) $a(n) = 1000 + 1.5n$

(e) $s(n) = 1000(3^{n-1})$

(f) $a(1) = 6$ and $a(n) = a(n - 1) + 10$

3. Each term s_n of the sequence s is the sum of the first n counting numbers. The formula for the sequence s is $s_n = \dfrac{n(n + 1)}{2}$.

(a) What is the value of s_{21}?

(b) What is the sum of the first 130 counting numbers?

4. The Short-Stop Parking Garage opens at 9 a.m. each morning and closes at 11 p.m. Cars are not allowed to remain overnight. The graph in Display 6.47 shows the amount drivers are charged to park their cars for a given period of time. Use it to answer the following questions:

(a) What is the cost of parking for exactly 3 hours?

(b) What is the cost of parking for exactly 4 hours?

(c) Riley parks at 9:05 a.m. and leaves at 5:10 p.m. How much did she pay?

(d) Steven parks at 10:45 a.m. and leaves at 6:40 p.m. How much did he pay?

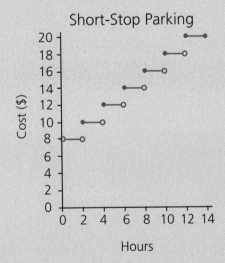

Display 6.47

5. A certain strain of bacteria has a population growth rate of 60% every hour, and a lab culture begins with 100 bacteria.

    (a) Write a formula for the function $N(h)$ that gives the number of bacteria N after h hours.

    (b) How many bacteria are there after 2 hours? After 6 hours?

6. Trey plans to invest $10,000. One Certificate of Deposit (CD) pays an annual interest rate of 5% compounded each year.

    (a) The table in Display 6.48 shows the value of the CD, v_1, t years after it is opened. Complete the copy your teacher will give you.

    (b) Write an equation that gives the value of the CD, v_1, after t years.

    (c) What will this CD be worth after 15 years? After 50 years?

t (years)	v_1 (dollars)
0	10,000
1	
2	
3	

Display 6.48

    (d) A second CD offers to pay 4.8% annual interest compounded *continuously*. If Trey invests his $10,000 in this one, the value, v_2, of the CD after t years is given by the equation $v_2(t) = 10{,}000e^{0.048t}$. How much will this CD be worth after 1 year? After 15 years? After 50 years?

    (e) These CDs can be cashed in anytime after the first year. If Trey wants to invest his money for 18 months, which CD should he choose? What if he wants to invest it for two years? For $2\frac{1}{2}$ years? For 3 years? Justify your answers.

7. Determine which graph(s), if any, in Display 6.49 on the next page match each of the following descriptions. (Some statements may match more than one graph.) The tick marks on the axes are the integer points.

    (a) an exponential growth function

    (b) a function with domain $\{x \mid 0 < x \leq 4\}$

    (c) a function with range $\{y \mid 2 \leq y < \infty\}$

    (d) a graph that does not represent a function of x

    (e) a function f such that $f(0) = 2$

(f) a function f such that $f(2) = 0$

(g) a function f such that $f(1) = 2$

(h) a function with y-intercept 2

(i) a constant function

(j) a function with domain $\{x \mid -3 \le x \le 4\}$

(k) a step function

(l) a function with x-intercept 2

(m) a linear function

(n) a function with apparent range $\{y \mid -\infty < y < \infty\}$

(o) a function with range $\{y \mid 0 < y < \infty\}$

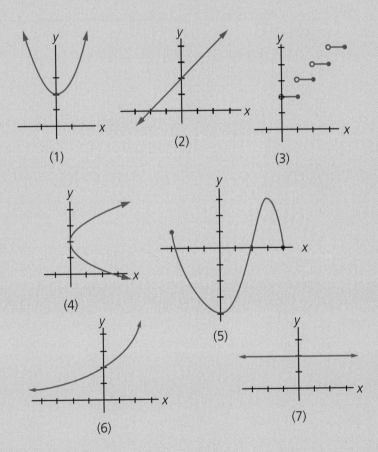

Display 6.49

Related Topics

Algebraic Proportions

In this chapter, you revisited unit conversions that you first learned about in earlier mathematics and science classes. As you progress in your mathematics and science classes throughout high school, you will find many more applications for unit conversions. In this section, we are going to look at this topic a little differently. Rather than a numerical approach, we are going to look at proportion and percentage problems more algebraically.

Let's start by looking at some percentage problems. Nancy is a smart shopper who carefully researches everything that she would like to purchase and only buys an item when it is on sale. Recently, she researched high definition televisions and found a TV that she wanted. It normally sells for $1,800, but it was on sale at an online site for 30% off the regular price. How much was the discount and what did she pay before taxes?

In earlier math classes, you were presented with a method to solve problems like these that involve using proportions. As you may remember, a percent is a fractional part of 100 units. So, 30% can be written as $\frac{30}{100}$. You would use this to set up the proportion $30 : 100 =$ discount $: 1800$ or $\frac{30}{100} = \frac{discount}{1800}$. You would then solve the problem by using *cross multiplication*. This method results in the following equation: $30 * 1800 =$ discount $* 100$. Next, divide both sides by 100 to get $540 for the discount. To finish the problem, you need to subtract this value from $1,800 to find out what Nancy paid for the television ($1,260).

This leaves us with a question. What is "cross multiplication" and why does it work? In order to understand how cross multiplication works, let's look at the words. The term "cross multiply" comes from the fact that when you *multiply* each of the pairs of terms diagonally *across* from each other, the products are equal to each other. You can think of cross multiplication as a set of steps you can use to rewrite a proportion. The process can be simplified to the following statement: If $\frac{a}{b} = \frac{c}{d}$ then $ad = bc$. The terms a, b, c and d can be numbers, other variables, or expressions. For example, in the proportion $\frac{2x + 1}{x} = \frac{5}{2}$ a equals the expression $2x + 1$, b equals x, c equals 5, and d equals 2.

6.59

Which of the following are proportions?

1. $\dfrac{3}{5} = \dfrac{x}{x+1}$

2. $\dfrac{x}{8} = \dfrac{2}{x}$

3. $\dfrac{x}{8} = \dfrac{2}{3} + 4$

4. $\dfrac{30}{100} = \dfrac{x}{1800}$

Going back to the proportion $\dfrac{a}{b} = \dfrac{c}{d}$, how can we rewrite this proportion without fractions while following algebraic principles and properties? First, let's find the common denominator of the two fractions (bd). Next, we want to multiply both sides by this common denominator to eliminate the fractions.

$$(bd)\dfrac{a}{b} = (bd)\dfrac{c}{d} \qquad \text{[Multiplication Law of Equality]}$$
$$ad = bc \qquad \text{[Simplify]}$$

As you can see, we are left with the product a and d on the left-hand side and the product b and c on the right. Notice that these are the products of the two pairs of terms diagonally across from each other.

$$\dfrac{a}{b} \diagup\!\!\!\!\!\diagdown \dfrac{c}{d} \;\Rightarrow\; ad = bc$$

If you are given the following proportion, what would you multiply each side by so that you no longer had a fraction in the equation?

$$\dfrac{2x+1}{x} = \dfrac{5}{2}$$

You should end up with $2(2x + 1) = 5x$ and you are now able to solve for x. You should see that you are left with the product of the diagonal terms (or the expressions diagonally across from each other on either side of the equation). But remember, this only works when you have the equation set up as a proportion.

6.60

Try a few on your own. Solve for x in each of the following.

1. $\dfrac{3x-1}{2x} = \dfrac{5}{4}$

2. $\dfrac{2x-1}{x+2} = \dfrac{7}{6}$

3. $\dfrac{2x+1}{3} = \dfrac{x+4}{5}$

Let's go back to Nancy and her shopping expertise. If she received 30% off of her $1,800 purchase, that would mean her cost was 70% of the original price of the item. Setting up the proportion, you have: $\frac{70}{100} = \frac{Cost}{1800}$. Solve for the cost. Does it agree with what you worked out before?

Let's look at this problem another way. Nancy paid 70% of the $1,800. We can translate this into an algebraic equation. Her cost is (=) 70% of (*) $1,800. Simplified, this is Cost = 70% * $1,800. Convert 70% to a decimal (0.70) and multiply to get the result. This process allows us to look at other percent problems algebraically. If Nancy paid $1,350 for the $1,800 TV, what percent discount did she receive? In earlier mathematics classes, you may have approached this as a proportion, setting it up as follows: $\frac{x}{100} = \frac{1350}{1800}$. Using cross multiplication, you would rewrite this equation as $1800x = 100 * 1350$. Divide by 1800, and you will get $x = 75$, which means her cost was 75% of the original cost. This translates to a 25% discount. Using our new approach and looking back at the translation of the last problem, we can say that the $1,350 is (=) what percent (x) of (*) $1,800. Simplified, this is $1350 = x * 1800$. In order to solve for x, you would divide both sides by 1800. This also gives us $x = 0.75$ or 75%, meaning that Nancy received a 25% discount.

The final type of question that you may be asked is if you know that Nancy received $600 off an item, and it had been discounted by 30%, what was the original price? Using the proportion method, you have: $\frac{30}{100} = \frac{600}{x}$, which simplifies to $x = \$2,000$. Translating this directly into an equation, you have $600 is (=) 30% (0.30) off of (*) the original price (x) or $600 = 0.30 * x$. Dividing both sides by 0.30, you get $x = \$2,000$ for the original price.

You now know multiple approaches for solving these percentage problems.

Answer each of the following using both proportions and algebraic equations.

6.61

1. You received a 40% discount on a $1,500 entertainment system. How much of a discount is this and how much will you pay?

2. You paid $1,200 for a $1,500 entertainment system. How much of a discount did you receive?

3. If you paid $1,000 for a new entertainment system after receiving a 40% discount, what was the original price of the system?

Let's look at another type of algebra problem involving fractions. What if you had two rational functions of the form $y = \frac{a}{x}$ and wanted to find out what point that they had in common? Let's look at $y = \frac{3}{x+1}$ and $y = \frac{2}{x-1}$. What point do they have in common?

You know that you can use the substitution method and rewrite this as:

$$\frac{3}{x+1} = \frac{2}{x-1}$$

If you cross multiply and then solve, you get the following value for x.

$$3(x-1) = 2(x+1)$$
$$3x - 3 = 2x + 2$$
$$x = 5$$

Substituting the x-value into either of the equations, you get $y = \frac{1}{2}$. Thus, the point of intersection is $\left(5, \frac{1}{2}\right)$.

Again, you can use your graphing calculator to verify your algebraic results. Enter both equations into the $\boxed{Y=}$ menu and then go to the $\boxed{CALC}$ menu ($\boxed{2ND}\boxed{TRACE}$) and use the intersection function. You should see the screens in Display 6.50 as you work through the problem.

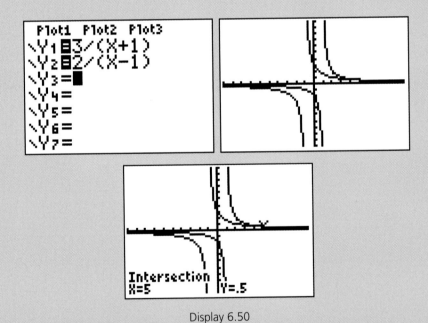

Display 6.50

6.62

Now it is your turn to practice solving these systems of rational functions. Use both an algebraic and a graphical approach on your calculator to find the point of intersection.

1. $y = \dfrac{1}{x - 3}$

   $y = \dfrac{2}{x + 4}$

2. $y = \dfrac{3}{x - 2}$

   $y = \dfrac{4}{x + 3}$

As you noticed again in solving the above problems, you end up creating a proportion that needs to be solved. You will find that this situation will continue to occur. As you were introduced to shapes in geometry, you may recall that some figures are said to be similar if the ratio of their sides are proportional. In other words, suppose you were given the two rectangles in Display 6.51 with the given lengths and widths, and were told that they were similar rectangles.

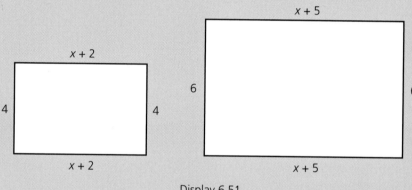

Display 6.51

Then, you could solve for x by setting up the proportion $\dfrac{4}{x + 2} = \dfrac{6}{x + 5}$ or $\dfrac{x + 2}{x + 5} = \dfrac{4}{6}$. Either solution produces the following equation when you cross multiply: $4(x + 5) = 6(x + 2)$. Solve for x and determine the missing lengths. Check your solutions by setting up the proportions with the lengths you determined. Are they proportional?

1. Solve for x given that the two rectangles in Display 6.52 are similar.

6.63

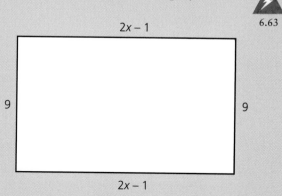

Display 6.52

2. **Solve for x given that the two triangles in Display 6.53 are similar.**

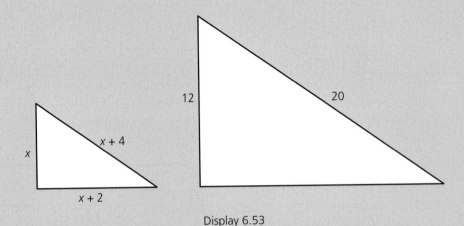

Display 6.53

Finally, we are going to return to unit conversions. If you want to convert 4 feet to inches, then you need to know the basic conversion of feet to inches—1 foot is equivalent to 12 inches. This gives us the proportion:

$$\frac{1 \text{ foot}}{12 \text{ inches}} = \frac{4 \text{ feet}}{x \text{ inches}}$$

After cross multiplying, you have $x = 48$. But what if there were a number of conversions that you wanted to make between feet and inches? Could you use what you have learned to develop a formula for this conversion? Let's take a closer look at what we just did. If you want to convert from feet to inches, you would look at the ratio 12 inches : 1 foot. If you let y represent the number of inches and x represent the number of feet, then you would have the proportion:

$$\frac{y \text{ inches}}{x \text{ feet}} = \frac{12 \text{ inches}}{1 \text{ foot}}$$

If you multiply both sides by x feet, you end up with the equation y inches $= \frac{12 \text{ inches}}{1 \text{ foot}} * x$ feet. After simplifying, you have y inches $= 12$ inches $* x$. You may be more comfortable simplifying this to $y = 12x$. In words, this represents that y inches is 12 times the number of x feet. Let's reverse this. What if you are being given the number of inches and want to convert to feet. The independent variable is now inches (x) and the dependent variable is feet (y). If you have $\frac{x \text{ inches}}{y \text{ feet}} = \frac{12 \text{ inches}}{1 \text{ foot}}$, and solve for y, you end up with $y = \frac{1}{12} * x$. In words, this means that the number of feet is $\frac{1}{12}$ the number of inches. We can rewrite these formulas so that they make more sense. If you let I represent inches and F represent feet, then you have $F = \frac{1}{12}I$ and $I = 12F$. Using x and y would work very well with your graphing calculator but you need to be careful to remember what the variables represent when you are doing these conversions.

1. How many inches is 3.5 feet? 5 feet?

2. How many feet is 120 inches? 600 inches?

3. Given that there are 5280 feet in a mile, determine the two formulas that can be used to convert from miles to feet and from feet to inches.

6.64

Problem Set

1. Translate the following into both a proportion and an algebraic equation then solve for the missing value.

    (a) Mary is purchasing a gift for a friend that costs $50. If the item is on sale for 30% off, how much will she pay?

    (b) John purchased a new baseball glove for $80 after receiving a 40% discount. What was the list price of the glove?

    (c) Evan bought a new pair of track shoes that usually cost $120. He has a $30 discount coupon. What percent will he save using the discount coupon?

2. Matt is looking at purchasing a video game system. Two stores offer the system. One store has a 30% off discount and the system costs $350. The other store has a 40% off discount and the system costs $425. Which is the better deal?

3. For each of the following proportions, solve for x.

    (a) $\frac{4}{x} = \frac{12}{15}$

    (b) $\frac{12}{50} = \frac{36}{x}$

    (c) $\frac{x-3}{2} = \frac{2x+5}{3}$

    (d) $\frac{x}{3} = \frac{12}{x}$

4. Find the point of intersection for the graphs of $y = \frac{3}{x+2}$ and $y = \frac{2}{x-5}$.

5. Determine the two formulas that are needed to convert from yards to miles.

Sequences

Earlier in this chapter you studied sequences. You learned to define these sequences both recursively and explicitly. What was not included earlier was a discussion on the types of sequences. There are two major sequence types that you will study in high school: arithmetic and geometric.

An **arithmetic sequence** is a sequence where the difference between any two successive terms of the sequence is constant. The following is an example of an arithmetic sequence.

$$2, 5, 8, 11, 14, \ldots$$

From earlier in the chapter, you learned that you could write the terms as $a_1 = 2$, $a_2 = 5$, $a_3 = 8$, $a_4 = 11$, $a_5 = 14$, and so on. If you find the difference between any two consecutive terms, you will find the constant difference. In this case, $a_4 - a_3 = 3$ and $a_3 - a_2 = 3$. This shows that 3 is being added to each term to get the next term in the sequence. You also learned earlier that you could define this in recursive form as follows.

$$a_1 = 2$$
$$a_n = a_{n-1} + 3$$

This formula does not always help. Let's say that we want to find the 100th term, a_{100}. You would need to do a lot of calculating. Actually, you would need to add 3 to the first term 99 times. This sort of gives us a hint toward a different type of formula to use. In the above sequence, you start with the first term and then you add 99 threes to get to the 100th term. Generalizing this, we get the formula:

$$a_n = a_1 + (n - 1)d$$

Where n is the term that you are looking for, a_1 is the first term and $(n - 1)$ is telling us how many of the common differences d that we need to add to a_1. This formula is called the **explicit form** of an arithmetic sequence.

Thus, using this formula for the previous problem, we get $a_{100} = 2 + (100 - 1)3 = 299$.

6.65

Now it's your turn to try one! Given the sequence 3, 8, 13, 18, 23, ..., answer the following questions.

1. What are the next two terms?

2. What is the recursive formula for this?

3. **Is the sequence an arithmetic sequence?**

4. **Write the explicit formula for this sequence.**

What if you were given the 3rd, 4th and 5th terms of an arithmetic sequence, could you find the 100th term from this information? Let's go back to the first sequence that we looked at. These terms would be 8, 11, and 14. You know the common difference is still 3, but how many times do we need to add 3 to the first term that we know (a_3)? Well, we need terms 4 up to 100, so it would be $100 - 3$ more times. Can we generalize this? If we know the mth term of an arithmetic sequence, we can find the nth term by using the formula, $a_n = a_m + (n - m)d$.

You are given $a_4 = 10$ and $d = 6$, find the 100th term.

6.66

Another way to look at sequence problems is to address them through the use of technology. A sequence links a term number with the value of the term. As you may recall, if you have the sequence 3, 7, 11, 15, ..., you can replicate this sequence on the main screen of your calculator by entering the first term and pressing the ENTER key. This is followed by pressing the + key followed by 4 and ENTER again. Your screen should look like Display 6.54.

Display 6.54

Now if you continue to press enter, then you will see the subsequent members of the sequence. All you need to do is count carefully in order to find the term that you are looking for. But this method does not give you a formula for the sequence. Back in Chapter 4, you found lines of best fit. You can use the same method to determine the equation for an arithmetic sequence. In **L1**, you will enter the term number and in **L2** you will enter the value of that term. Then go to the **STAT** menu and find the linear regression equation for **L1** and **L2**. You should end up with the two screens in Display 6.55.

```
L1      L2      L3     1
1       3       ------
2       7
3       11
4       15
5       19
                ------
L1(6)=
```

```
LinReg
y=ax+b
a=4
b=-1
```

Display 6.55

This would give you the equation $a_n = 4n - 1$. In an algebraic solution to this problem, you would get $a_n = 3 + (n - 1)4$. If you simplify this, you will end up with the same solution as the calculator. Both forms are correct.

A **geometric sequence** is a sequence where each term is found by multiplying the previous term by a non-zero number which is called the **common ratio**. An example of a geometric sequence is 3, 6, 12, 24, 48, ... You can see that the second term is twice the first, the third is twice the second, and so on. You can calculate the common ratio by dividing a term by the previous term. If all of the common ratios are the same, then the sequence is geometric. The common ratio, denoted r, is equal to $\frac{a_n}{a_{n-1}}$.

We could define this sequence recursively as:

$$a_1 = 3$$
$$a_n = a_{n-1} * 2$$

This is similar to the arithmetic sequence with the difference being multiplication rather than addition. If we want the 10th term, we would need to multiply the previous term by 2 nine times. From this, we can generalize the formula to the explicit form as:

$$a_n = a_1 r^{n-1}$$

Where a_1 is the first term and r is the common ratio.

Now let's take a look at another geometric sequence 2, 6, 18, 54, ...

1. How would you define this sequence recursively?

2. How would you define this sequence explicitly?

As with the arithmetic sequences, we can use a technology approach in working with geometric sequences. If we are only using the main screen, then we can find missing terms of the last sequence by repeated multiplication. Do this on your own. Do you get the screen shown in Display 6.56?

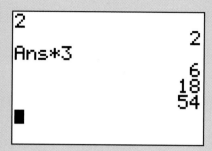

Display 6.56

Again, this helps with finding specific term values but will not give us an algebraic formula to use. Enter the sequence in two lists on your graphing calculator, as before, and take a look at the scatterplot of this sequence.

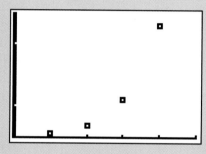

Display 6.57

From what you studied in Chapter 4, you can tell that this is not a linear function. So, using linear regression on our calculator will not help us. This type of function is called exponential. The calculator can determine the exponential function that fits the data. The command for this is called **ExpReg** and you will find it under the **STAT CALC** menu.

Try it for the last sequence you were working with (2, 6, 18, 54, ...) and you should get the screen in Display 6.58.

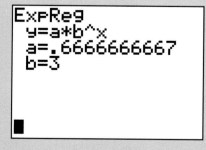

Display 6.58

This looks very different from what the explicit formula gives us. Re-writing this, you have $a_n = \frac{2}{3}(3)^n$. An algebraic trick, turns this into $a_n = \frac{2}{3}(3)(3)^{n-1} = 2(3)^{n-1}$. Now it looks just like the explicit form.

There are sequences that do not fit the profiles of either arithmetic or geometric sequences. Let's look at the sequence 2, 0, 2, 0, 2, ... You can see a pattern but the next term is not determined by the same operation on the previous term throughout the sequence. What you have here is an alternating pattern, but it is not arithmetic or geometric.

Can you create an alternating pattern that is arithmetic or geometric? Let's look at 2, −2, 2, −2, ... Does it fit the profile that we are looking for in either an arithmetic or geometric sequence? Let's look closely. Find the ratio of $a_2 : a_1$ and $a_3 : a_2$. Are they equal? Continue this process for $a_4 : a_3$. Still work? This is a geometric sequence and the common ratio is −1.

Another famous sequence is the Fibonacci sequence. This sequence is 1, 1, 2, 3, 5, 8, ... Can you determine the pattern? Can you write it recursively? How about explicitly?

6.68

Determine if the following sequences are arithmetic, geometric, or neither. Write the next two terms of the sequence. If possible, write a formula for a_n given a_1 through a_5.

1. −1, 3, 7, 11, 15, ...

2. 2, 3, 4, 5, 6, ...

3. −3, 6, −12, 24, −48, ...

4. 24, 12, 6, 3, 1.5, ...

5. 1, 1, 2, 3, 5, ...

6. 2, 3, 5, 8, 12, ...

Can we determine the missing terms of an arithmetic sequence given two of its terms? What if you knew $a_1 = 4$ and $a_5 = 16$. Can you find the common difference between terms? Given the formula $a_n = a_1 + (n − 1)d$, we know that $a_5 = a_1 + (5 − 1)d$. Plug in the two term values we know and solve for d.

$$16 = 4 + 4d$$
$$d = 3$$

Thus, the sequence is 4, 7, 10, 13, 16, ...

What if the given terms did not include the first term? What if we were given $a_2 = 5$ and $a_5 = 17$, and were asked to find the first six terms and determine the explicit formula for a_n? Well, one way we could look at this would be to consider a_2 as our first term and then a_5 would be considered the fourth term. Plugging these into the explicit form, we would get:

$$17 = 5 + (4 - 1)d$$
$$17 = 5 + 3d$$
$$12 = 3d$$
$$d = 4$$

Now we know that 4 is added to the previous term. So, the first term must be 1 and the sequence is:

$$1, 5, 9, 13, 17, 21, \dots$$

The formula would be $a_n = 1 + (n - 1)4$.

Determine the first six terms of these arithmetic sequences and the explicit formula for a_n given the following information.

6.69

1. $a_1 = 4$ and $a_4 = 19$

2. $a_3 = -4$ and $a_6 = -10$

What if you were told that a sequence was geometric and you knew the 3rd and 5th terms. Let's say that these terms were 4 and 16 respectively. We can again look at the problem like the previous one. Let's say that 4 is the first term and thus 16 is the third term. From the geometric sequence formula, we have $16 = 4r^{(3-1)}$. This simplifies to $r^2 = 4$ and $r = 2$ or -2. So, we have two sequences that meet the requirements.

$$1, 2, 4, 8, 16, 32, \dots \text{ or } 1, -2, 4, -8, 16, -32, \dots$$

Determine the first six terms of these geometric sequences and the explicit formula for a_n given the following information.

6.70

1. $a_1 = 3$ and $a_4 = 24$

2. $a_2 = 2$ and $a_4 = 18$

Problem Set

For each of the following problems, solve algebraically and verify your solutions using a graphing calculator.

1. For the following problems find the next two terms of the sequence and find a formula for a_n. Also, determine whether it is arithmetic, geometric, or neither.

   (a) $4, 6, 8, 10, 12, \ldots$

   (b) $-3, -6, -9, -12, -15, \ldots$

   (c) $-3, -6, -12, -24, -48, \ldots$

   (d) $1, 3, 6, 10, 15, \ldots$

2. Given the following information, find a_{10}.

   (a) $a_1 = 4$ and $d = 5$

   (b) $a_1 = 3$ and $d = -2$

   (c) $a_1 = 1$ and $r = 2$

   (d) $a_1 = -4$ and $r = \dfrac{1}{2}$

3. Given the following information, find the first six terms and the explicit formula for a_n.

   (a) An arithmetic sequence and $a_1 = 8$ and $a_5 = -4$.

   (b) A geometric sequence and $a_3 = 5$ and $a_5 = 20$.

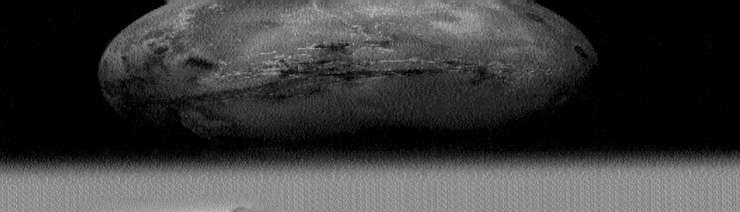

Michael Garcia
Sharing NASA's Explorations

Exploration of our solar system has reached a whole new level of activity. NASA has launched several new spacecrafts to explore planets. Every day, discoveries and data flow back to Earth.

Michael Garcia is an educator who specializes in math, physics and chemistry. He works for the Jet Propulsion Laboratory in Pasadena, California. His job is to translate the new images and data returning to Earth into programs for schools. One program Michael's team has built is a simulation using actual images from the Mars Pathfinder. Students can "launch" their own robotic spacecraft to Mars and virtually explore it for themselves.

Michael explains how coding systems, data sets, and their corresponding visualizations and diagrams are basic to the creation of interactive products. "All computers use a binary coding system, 'machine language,' to operate or compute," he explains. "To complete a task, a computer must run an algorithm. This is a sequence of steps where it translates data, or a series of data sets, into logical notation.

"Likewise, all data returned by spacecraft is binary, meaning ones and zeros," continues Michael. "Computers use binary words to make pictures. Viewing a picture, we often need to adjust the contrast or 'stretch' the image to see hidden details. Here's where we need to apply mathematical equations.

"Also, in our simulations, we often need to create images of the data and data sets. So we might use Venn diagrams. This is an easy way to see how two or more really complex data sets merge together or relate to each other. We might, for example, want to see what's happening between a planet's magnetic field and the Sun's solar wind."

Michael truly enjoys his work. "Every day I get to explore data that is being seen for the first time. Then I put it into a format that can be understood and used by many other people, everywhere."

Counting and Probability

7.1 Counting Sets of Things

A type of puzzle found in many newspapers and magazines involves taking several letters and rearranging them to form meaningful words. Usually three, four, or five letters are given. For example, one puzzle gave the letters *mslie*. By rearranging them you can form the words *miles*, *limes*, and *slime*.

Carmen, a student at Newton School, enjoys these puzzles. One day Carmen's newspaper had one that gave the letters *iter*. She found the words

rite (What does this word mean?)

and

tier (What does this word mean?)

1. Can you find any words that Carmen missed? If you can, write them.

7.1

2. Carmen's next puzzle gave the letters *opst*. She formed three meaningful words. Do you think Carmen missed any words? How many meaningful words can you form from the letters *opst*? Write as many as you can.

Carmen decides that from now on she will write out *all* arrangements of the given letters, whether they make sense or not. Then she will decide which ones are meaningful. The next puzzle gives Carmen the letters *pto*. She writes the list

pto opt top pot otp

1. Did Carmen miss any arrangements? If so, what are they? How many different arrangements of these 3 letters are there?

2. Which arrangements in the list are meaningful words?

3. Another puzzle gives Carmen four different letters. She writes a list of 20 arrangements and says that she has listed all possible arrangements of the four letters. Do you agree with Carmen? That is, are there exactly 20 different arrangements of four different letters? If you agree, justify your answer. If you disagree, how many arrangements do you think there are? Explain.

4. How many arrangements do you think can be made from 5 different letters? (*Hint:* How many arrangements can be formed from two different letters? From three different letters? From four different letters?)

Thinking Tip
Look for a pattern.

How many? This question arises everywhere—in business, in science, and in everyday life. To answer it, we need skills and strategies for counting. Computers have made it more important than ever for people to know about counting. For example, in the early 1960s a group of scientists programmed a computer to solve an arithmetic problem. The computer could perform 100,000 operations (additions, subtractions, multiplications, and divisions) per second so the scientists believed it could solve any arithmetic problem quickly. After two weeks the computer had still not solved their problem. Then the scientists analyzed the problem and found it would take more than 10^{18} operations to solve it. Next they figured out the time it would take the computer to solve the problem. They were surprised! See if you are.

A computer performs 100,000 operations per second.

1. How many operations can this computer perform in an hour?

2. How many operations can this computer perform in a day?

3. How many operations can this computer perform in a year?

4. Approximately how long will it take this computer to perform 10^{18} operations?

Counting is also important for making codes such as bar codes on supermarket items or ZIP codes on mail.

1. **What is a code?**

2. **What are some other common codes that people use?**

7.4

Why is counting important for making codes? That's a good question. Let's look at an example. A certain school has 720 students. Each student needs a computer password (or code) made up of one or more letters of the alphabet. To use a school computer, students must first enter their code. The table in Display 7.1 shows the codes for four of the students.

Name	Code
Richard	A
Mary	V
Sook	D
William	F

Display 7.1

If all of the codes had only one letter, there would only be enough for 26 students. Therefore, some students have codes with more than one letter. The table in Display 7.2 shows the codes for four other students.

Name	Code
Alice	CA
Martin	BD
Mineo	WW
Kim	DB

Display 7.2

Do you think some students will need to have more than two letters in their code? Explain your answer. This is an example of a counting problem.

7.5

The password example shows why counting is important for making codes. First we count the number of codes needed (720 different passwords, for example). Then we use counting to determine the number of symbols that must be used for each code.

Codes are used every time you listen to music on your computer or MP3 player. The codes that computers use to store information (including music) use only the digits 0 and 1. These are called **binary digits** and each digit is called a **bit**.

To get an idea of how bits are used to represent musical information let's look at how this could be done for volume. Music can have different levels of volume from very soft to very loud. These differences must be represented using 0s and 1s. Let's start with only two levels of volume, loud and soft. In this case we could code each level with one bit as shown in the table in Display 7.3.

Level	Code
soft	0
loud	1

Display 7.3

So if the code reads 0010111, then when the music is played it would be

soft - soft - loud - soft - loud - loud - loud

7.6

Use the code in Display 7.3 to write the binary code for the volume of the music if it is

soft - loud - loud - soft - loud - soft - soft

Music with only two volume levels would be very dull. Let's try four levels—very soft, soft, loud, and very loud. Now each code will need to have more than one bit. The table in Display 7.4 shows how we could code each level with two bits.

Level	Code
very soft	00
soft	01
loud	10
very loud	11

Display 7.4

So if the code reads 0111000001, then the music would be

soft - very loud - very soft - very soft - soft

Use the code in Display 7.4 to write the binary code for the volume of the music if it is

7.7

loud - very loud - soft - soft - very soft - loud

The code you just used (in Display 7.4) uses two bits for each coded item. The first volume code (shown in Display 7.3) uses one bit for each item. Can we use a mixture of one-bit and two-bit item codes? Let's try an example to see.

Level	Code
very soft	0
soft	1
loud	10
very loud	11

7.8

Display 7.5

1. Use the code in Display 7.5 to write the binary code for the volume of the music if it is

   loud - very loud - soft - soft - very soft - loud

   Compare your answers to those of your classmates. Are your codes the same? Why or why not?

2. Use the code in Display 7.5 to translate the code

   1001011010110110

   into volume levels. Compare your answers to those of your classmates. Are they the same? Why or why not?

As you can see, there are problems when codes use different numbers of bits. From now on we will only use codes that use the same number of bits for each item—no mixtures.

1. If a volume code uses three bits (for example, 101) for each level, how many different sound levels could be represented?

7.9

2. If we want to represent 1000 sound levels, how many bits do you think would have to be used for each one? Explain your answer. (*Hint:* Try an organized list. Look for patterns.) This is another example of a counting problem.

You have seen examples where counting is useful (or necessary) for puzzles, solving problems with computers, and codes. There are many other situations and jobs where counting is important. A census taker counts people, a record executive counts albums sold, and a deli owner counts the different

sandwiches he can make. In all of these cases, it is the number of objects (people, albums, sandwiches) in a collection that is being counted. In mathematics we call a collection of objects a **set**. The objects in a set are called **elements**. Sets can be collections of almost anything.

You first worked with sets in Chapter 2 when you learned to write the solution set for an equation. One way to write a set is to list all of its elements inside braces: {}. This works best if the list is fairly short. For example, to write the set of all natural numbers less than 8 we could write

$$\{1, 2, 3, 4, 5, 6, 7\}$$

7.10

Check the numbers 1, 2, 3, 4, and 5 to see if they are solutions to the equation

$$(x - 2) \cdot (x - 4) = 0$$

Then write the solution set for this equation.

In Chapter 3 you learned about sets of points on a plane. You used another way to describe sets, called *set-builder notation*. It describes how to build a set from the conditions that its elements must satisfy. Do you remember that notation? It looks like this:

{[element form] | ... [conditions] ... }

- The braces, { }, tell you that a set is being described.
- The dividing line, |, stands for "such that."
- The symbols in front of the dividing line represent a typical element of the set. For points in the plane, the form would be an ordered pair, such as (x, y).
- The conditions can be equations, inequalities, or any other statements that the elements of the set must satisfy.

7.11

1. The following sentence describes a set of points on a plane.

   "The set of all ordered pairs (x, y) such that $x = 2$ and y is between 3 and 7, inclusive."

   Write this set in set-builder notation. Then describe what you think the picture looks like.

2. Write the set $B = \{1, 2, 3, 4, 5, 6, 7\}$ using set-builder notation.

Capital letters, such as *A*, *B*, and *C* are often used as names for sets. Using a one-letter name for a set is usually easier than writing out the set notation every time we talk about it. For example, we could say, "Let *A* be the set of students in this class." In this case, *A* is the name of the set and "students in this class" is a description of the elements. Using set-builder notation, we can write

$$A = \{x \mid x \text{ is a student in this class}\}$$

Here are some practice questions about sets and set notation:

7.12

1. Consider the set of even integers between 2 and 12, inclusive. Give this set a name. Then:

    (a) Write this set by listing the elements.

    (b) Write this set using set-builder notation.

2. Write each of the following sets by listing the elements:

    (a) The set *A* of all natural numbers greater than 5 but less than 10.

    (b) The set *B* of all natural numbers less than 20 that are multiples of 3.

    (c) The set *C* of all natural numbers less than 23 that are multiples of 4 or multiples of 5.

    (d) The set *D* of all natural numbers less than 27 that are multiples of 3 and also multiples of 4.

    (e) The set *E* of all states in the U.S. bordered by the Pacific Ocean.

3. You are going to toss a coin and *A* is the set of all possible outcomes. Write the set *A* by listing the elements.

4. You are going to toss a standard six-sided die and *B* is the set of possible outcomes. Write the set *B* by listing the elements.

5. You are going to toss a pair of standard six-sided dice and *C* is the set of possible sums you can get. Write the set *C* by listing the elements.

6. You are going to toss two coins and *D* is the set of possible outcomes. Write the set *D* by listing the elements.

Whenever we count things, we are counting the elements of a set. For example, to count the girls Joan, Kim, Mary, Elena, and Maria on a basketball team, you are just counting the set B = {Joan, Kim, Mary, Elena, Maria}. We abbreviate the statement that there are 5 elements in this set by writing $\#(B) = 5$.

You probably noticed that the abbreviation $\#(\ )$ looks like the notation we use for functions, $f(\ )$. That's right! You can think of # as a function that assigns a whole number to certain sets.

7.13

1. If C is the set of students in your class, what is $\#(C)$?

2. A mathematics teacher asked students to do problems 7 through 12 for homework. If H is the set of problems assigned, what is $\#(H)$?

3. You are going to toss a coin and A is the set of possible outcomes. What is $\#(A)$?

A set may actually have no elements in it. That may seem strange at first, but it's really a very ordinary idea. A store may have no customers in it; a bag of potato chips may have no more chips in it; and so on. A set with no elements is called an **empty set**. One way to write the empty set is { }; another, more common way is to write the symbol $\varnothing$. You have already seen examples of empty sets. In Chapter 2, you saw equations such as

$$0 \cdot k = 37$$

No matter what number you replace k with, you get $0 \cdot k = 0$, not 37. So there is no solution to this equation; that is, its solution set is the empty set, $\varnothing$. To say that the empty set contains no elements, we can write

$$\#(\varnothing) = 0$$

7.14

1. Let T (for tall) be the set of all students in your class who are over 9 feet tall. What is $\#(T)$?

2. Describe three different empty sets. Be able to explain why your sets are empty.

Some sets have too many elements to be counted. That is, no matter how fast or how long anyone or any machine counted, there would always be more uncounted elements in the set. Such sets are not in the domain of the function #. We say that they have **infinitely** many elements. You have seen examples of these kinds of sets, too. Earlier in this section you looked at the set of all points with *x*-coordinate 2 and *y*-coordinates between 3 and 7 inclusive. There are infinitely many such points, so you could not describe this set by listing them all.

> **A Word to Know:** Something is **finite** if it has a limit or an end. A set is *finite* if there is an end to the number of elements it contains. In other words, the number of elements it contains is a whole number.

One of the main ideas in this chapter is counting, so for the rest of this chapter we will only work with finite sets.

About Words

In English, the prefix *in-* means "not," as in *inedible* (not fit for eating) or *inexpensive* (not expensive). A set is *infinite* if it is not finite; that is, there is "no end" to the number of elements it contains.

Problem Set: 7.1

1. (a) If we want to sort patients in a hospital into age groups: 0–9, 10–19, 20–29, 30–39, ... (years), by coding with bits, how many bits are needed in each code?
    (b) If we want a "finer" sorting by age: 0–4, 5–9, 10–14, 15–19, ... (years), how many bits are needed in each code?

2. In 1977, two Voyager spacecrafts were launched from Earth toward the giant planets in the solar system—Jupiter, Saturn, Uranus, and Neptune, the last of which was visited in August, 1989. The Voyagers had five cameras and six scientific measuring instruments. All of the pictures and the scientific information were sent back to Earth using codes formed by bits (0s and 1s). More than four trillion bits were sent back to Earth by the Voyagers, at the rate of 21,000 bits per second. (Four trillion bits is enough to represent 5000 copies of the Encyclopedia Britannica.)
    (a) How much time in hours did it take the Voyagers to send four trillion bits to Earth? How much time in days? in years?
    (b) Why would engineers want to know the answer to the question in part (a)?

3. (a) Use set-builder notation to write the set *G* of all positive integers that are less than 98.
    (b) Is *G* a finite set or an infinite set?
    (c) If *G* is finite, then find #(*G*).

4. (a) Use set-builder notation to write the set H of all positive integers that are greater than or equal to 38.
   (b) Is H a finite set or an infinite set?
   (c) If H is finite, then find #(H).

5. (a) Write the set C of all U.S. states that border Canada by listing the elements.
   (b) Find #(C).

6. (a) Write the set M of all U.S. states that border Mexico by listing the elements.
   (b) Find #(M).

7. (a) Let T be the set of all U.S. states that are in the Southern Hemisphere. Describe T using any notation you choose.
   (b) Find #(T).

8. (a) Write the set A of integers less than 25 that are multiples of 3.
   (b) Find #(A).

9. (a) Write the set D of integers less than 27 that are multiples of 4 or multiples of 5.
   (b) Find #(D).

10. (a) Write the set B of possible outcomes if you are going to toss a standard six-sided die.
    (b) Find #(B).

11. (a) You are going to toss a pair of standard six-sided dice and S is the set of possible sums that can be obtained. Write the set S.
    (b) Find #(S).

12. If C is the set of cards in a standard deck of cards, find #(C).

13. Check the numbers -2, -1, 0, 1, 2, and $\frac{1}{2}$ to see if they are solutions to the equation

$$6x - 5 = -10x + 3$$

Do you think there could be any other solutions to this equation? Why or why not?

Let A be the solution set for the equation. Write A using any notation you choose. Find #(A).

14. Check the numbers -2, -1, 0, 1, 2, and $\frac{1}{2}$ to see if they are solutions to the equation

$$(x)^2 = -4$$

Do you think there could be any other solutions to this equation? Why or why not?

Let S be the solution set for the equation. Write S using any notation you choose. Find $\#(S)$.

15. Check the numbers -2, -1, 0, 1, 2, and $\frac{1}{2}$ to see if they are solutions to the equation

$$0 \cdot w = 0$$

Do you think there could be any other solutions to this equation? Why or why not?

Let Z be the solution set for the equation. Write Z using any notation you choose. Find $\#(Z)$.

7.2 Venn Diagrams: Counting With Pictures

Learning Outcomes

After studying this section, you will be able to:

Describe the intersection, union, difference, and complement of sets

Draw and interpret a Venn diagram to solve some counting problems

Explain the idea of disjoint sets

Solve some counting problems about disjoint sets.

In the previous section you saw that counting problems can be looked at as problems about counting elements in a set. In this section we look at counting problems that involve more than one set. Solving them becomes easier when we use pictures to help us. Here is an example of such a problem.

In one class of high school students, 17 watch MTV and 12 play video games. Five students watch MTV and also play video games. Now use this information to answer these questions:

7.15

1. **How many students watch MTV but do not play video games?**

2. **How many students play video games but do not watch MTV?**

3. **How many students watch MTV or play video games (or both)?**

4. **How many students neither watch MTV nor play video games?**

If you answered all four questions correctly, give yourself a pat on the back! If you had trouble, don't worry. In this section you will see how pictures can help you answer these questions and others like them.

It is useful to have a way to picture the relationships among sets. That can help us solve counting problems about them. One common way to do this is to draw overlapping circles to represent sets that (might) have some elements in common. This type of picture is called a **Venn diagram**. It is named after John Venn, a British mathematician who introduced it in 1881. For the MTV-video game questions, we can draw one circle, *M*, for the set of students who watch MTV and another circle, *G*, for the set of students who play video games, as in Display 7.6.

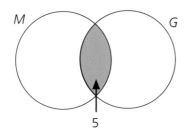

Display 7.6

Think of the 17 students who watch MTV as points inside the circle *M*. Inside the circle *G* are the 12 students who play video games. The 5 students who watch MTV *and* play video games are in the region inside *both* circles that is colored green in Display 7.6. In mathematics, whenever we say an element belongs to one set *and* another, it means that element *must* belong to both.

The green region in Display 7.6 represents a subset of *M* and of *G* called the **intersection** of the sets *M* and *G*. It contains only the elements that belong to both sets and we write it as *M* ∩ *G*. This set can also be called "*M intersect G*."

To use Venn diagrams for counting problems we label each region with the number of elements it contains. For example, we know that #(*M* ∩ *G*) = 5, so the green region in Display 7.6 is labeled with a 5. Now be careful. Think carefully about which subset of students each region represents before you label it.

You know that 17 students watch MTV (so #(*M*) = 17). That means there are 17 students inside the *entire* circle *M*. Since 5 of them are in the intersection, there must be 12 that are inside *M* but not in *M* ∩ *G*. The region that represents this set is colored blue in Display 7.7.

About Words

An *intersection* is an overlap of things. The intersection of two streets is where they overlap—a part that both streets have in common. The intersection of sets contains only the elements the sets have in common. It is shown as the region where the circles overlap.

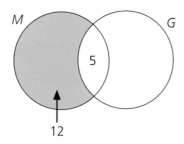

Display 7.7

The blue region in Display 7.7 represents students that watch MTV but do not play video games. In other words, it is the set of elements in M that are not in G. This is called the **difference** of M minus G and is written $M - G$. So #$(M - G) = 12$, which answers the first question from the beginning of the section.

7.16

1. Describe the set of students represented by the yellow region in Display 7.8.

2. Write the name of this set as a difference of two sets.

3. How many elements are in the set represented by that yellow region?

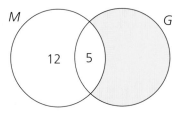

Display 7.8

The number for the yellow region in Display 7.8 answers the second question from the beginning of this section. Now let's go to the third one.

7.17

How many students watch MTV *or* play video games (or both)?

1. Describe the region(s) on the Venn diagram in Display 7.9 that represent(s) this subset of students.

2. How many elements are in this set?

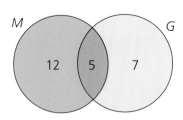

Display 7.9

In mathematics (and often in everyday speech), whenever we say an element belongs to one set *or* another it always means that element *could* belong to both. The set of all elements that are in *M* or in *G* is called the **union** of *M* and *G*. This set is written $M \cup G$. For our MTV-video game example, $\#(M \cup G)$ is the answer you just found.

1. Jason says "If *A* and *B* are sets, then $\#(A \cup B) = \#(A) + \#(B)$." Is Jason correct? Explain.

    7.18

2. How many natural numbers less than or equal to 100 are multiples of 2 or 5? How is this question related to question 1?

About Words

You have a *union* when you join or combine several things into one. A labor union joins many people into one group for a common cause. A union of sets combines all of the elements from each set into one new set.

Let's get back to our MTV-video game example and its Venn diagram. All three regions inside the two circles *M* and *G* have been labeled with the number of elements inside them. Question 4 asks how many students are not in either set. Think about this question for a minute. What do you need to know in order to answer it? What do you already know?

You already know that the sets *M* and *G* are contained in a larger set, all students in that class. So this question really depends on knowing how big that class is. In just about any question involving sets, there is an "overall" set that contains all the things you care about. This is called the **universal set,** and it is usually labeled *U*. This idea is important enough to deserve a more careful definition.

A Word to Know: When every element of one set *B* is contained in another set *A* we say that *B* is a **subset** of *A*, and we write $B \subseteq A$.

In our MTV-video game example, if *U* is the set of all students in the class, then $M \subseteq U$ and $G \subseteq U$. Also, $(M \cap G) \subseteq M$ and $(M \cap G) \subseteq G$.

Venn diagrams usually are drawn inside a box that represents the universal set. For instance, Display 7.10 (on the next page) shows *M* and *G* inside a box that represents *U*, the set of all students in the class. In this case, the set of all students not in either *M* or *G* is represented by the pink region.

7.19

1. Describe the subset represented by the blue region in Display 7.10 as a difference of two sets.

2. If there are 30 students in the class, how many students are in that subset? Explain.

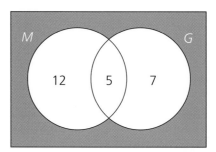

Display 7.10

Another way to describe the subset represented by the blue region is "the set of all elements in U that are not in $M \cup G$." This is a special case of a general idea that is important enough to have its own name.

A Word to Know: When you have a set A in a universe U, then the set of all elements in U that are not in A is called the **complement** of A and is written A' (read "A prime").

That is, $(U - A) = A'$. In a Venn diagram, A' is represented by the region inside the box but outside of the region A, the shaded area in Display 7.11.

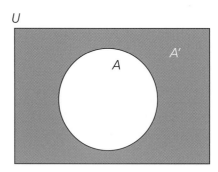

Display 7.11

Answer the following questions about *M* and *G* from the MTV-video game example. Assume that #(*U*) = 30.

7.20

1. Describe the elements in the set *M*′. Find #(*M*′).

2. Describe the elements in the set *G*′. Find #(*G*′).

3. Describe the elements in the set (*M* ∩ *G*)′. Find #((*M* ∩ *G*)′)

You have seen how Venn diagrams can be used to help solve counting problems. To use one, you must decide on the universe for the situation, choose and name the main subsets, and then draw and label the diagram. Then you figure out which region(s) represent the set of things you are counting and add up the elements.

Draw and label a Venn diagram to help you solve each of the following problems. Be sure to identify the universe and the subsets.

7.21

1. An advertising agency interviewed 1000 people. They found 786 people read *Newsweek*, 664 read *Time*, and 461 read both magazines.

    (a) Of the 1000 people interviewed, how many people read at least one of the two magazines, *Newsweek* or *Time*? Justify your answer.

    (b) Of the 1000 people interviewed, how many people read one of the two magazines but not both? Justify your answer.

2. A survey is taken at an ice cream parlor. People are asked to list their two favorite flavors. 74 list vanilla and 37 list chocolate. If 19 list both vanilla and chocolate and 12 list neither of them, how many people participated in the survey?

3. In a survey of 100 students, 50 said that they like rock music, 60 like country music, and 45 like both country and rock. How many students in the survey like country music but not rock?

7.22

1. For each of the following sets, draw a Venn diagram like the one in Display 7.12 and shade in the region that represents the set.

(a) $A \cap B$

(b) $A - B$

(c) $B - A$

(d) $A \cup B$

(e) $(A \cap B)'$

(f) $(B - A)'$

(g) $B - A'$

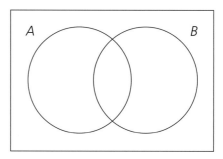

Display 7.12

2. How could you draw a Venn diagram to show that $B \subseteq A$?

7.23

Given a universe U and subsets A and B, use set-builder notation to describe each of the following sets.

(a) $A \cap B$ (b) $A \cup B$ (c) $A - B$ (d) A'

Some Venn diagram questions are easier than others. To see why, start by answering these two questions.

7.24

1. Riverdale Math Company (RMC) makes two products—books on mathematics and video games about mathematics. They have 1520 books and 3417 video games in stock. What is the total number of items RMC has in stock?

2. A local L-Mart sells audio units that play cassette tapes or CDs. The store has 54 units that play cassette tapes and 74 units that play CDs in stock. Of these units, 17 play both tapes and CDs. What is the total number of audio units that L-Mart has in stock?

Which of the two previous problems did you find easier to solve? Why?

7.25

Make up two counting problems like the ones you just did. Write one that you think is easy to solve and one that you think is more difficult. Then write a paragraph about *how* to make such problems easier and how to make them more difficult.

7.26

A Word to Know: Two sets *A* and *B* are **disjoint** if $A \cap B = \emptyset$. That is, *A* and *B* are disjoint if they have no elements in common.

About Words

Something is *joint* if it is common to two or more. A joint account is a bank account that two people have in common. In English the prefix *dis-* means "not," as in *disconnected* (not connected).

For example, let *B* be a set of bicycles and let *R* be a set of rollerblades. Then $B \cap R = \emptyset$, so *B* and *R* are disjoint.

1. Give three different examples of pairs of disjoint sets.

2. How could you draw a Venn diagram to show that *A* and *B* are disjoint sets?

7.27

3. Explain what the idea of disjoint sets has to do with the easy-vs.-difficult problems you did.

You have seen how counting problems about two disjoint sets can be easier. What if you are counting more than two disjoint subsets? Here is an example: A local music store sorts their CDs into four different musical categories—classical, jazz, pop, and rock. Each CD can only belong to one category. In stock they have 380 classical, 450 jazz, 250 pop, and 870 rock CDs. Let *S* be the set of all CDs they have in stock (the universe). Let

$$C = \text{the set of classical CDs}$$
$$J = \text{the set of jazz CDs}$$
$$P = \text{the set of pop CDs}$$
$$R = \text{the set of rock CDs}$$

So

$$\#(C) = 380 \quad \#(J) = 450 \quad \#(P) = 250 \quad \#(R) = 870$$

Every CD is in one of the categories, so $S = C \cup J \cup P \cup R$. Each CD can only belong to one category, so *any two of the sets C, J, P, and R are disjoint*. To show four disjoint sets in a Venn diagram we could draw four circles that do not overlap each other.

Sometimes shapes other than circles are used to picture subsets. Display 7.13 shows a diagram for the CD example that uses squares. The fact that the squares do not overlap indicates that the sets are disjoint.

S

C	J	P	R
380	450	250	870

Display 7.13

To count the total number of CDs in stock we need to find #(S). Since every CD is in exactly one category, all we need to do is add up the number of CDs in each category, right? That is,

$$\#(S) = \#(C) + \#(J) + \#(P) + \#(R)$$
$$\#(S) = 380 + 450 + 250 + 870$$
$$\#(S) = 1950$$

The key to the previous CD problem is that the set we counted, *S*, is the union of subsets that are *all disjoint from each other*. Since no CDs belong to more than one subset we did not have to worry about counting any of them twice when we added up elements in the subsets. This makes the counting quite easy. This idea may seem simple but it is very important for understanding and using more complicated counting methods.

If, *and only if*, each pair of the sets *A*, *B*, *C*, and *D* are disjoint from each other, then

$$\#(A \cup B \cup C \cup D) = \#(A) + \#(B) + \#(C) + \#(D).$$

7.28

Do you think the rule above is true for three disjoint sets? Five?

7.29

How might all the students in your class be divided into four disjoint subsets?

7.30

A set *S* can be divided into 5 subsets *A*, *B*, *C*, *D*, and *E* in such a way that any two of the subsets are disjoint. If each of the 5 subsets has exactly 8 elements, what is #(S)?

Problem Set: 7.2

1. Let A be the set {Hartford, Denver, Miami}. Write all the subsets of A.

2. 48 patients were admitted to an emergency room in a hospital. Some of them had basic medical insurance and some had catastrophic medical insurance.

   What is catastrophic medical insurance?

   Of these 48 patients, 37 had basic medical insurance, 12 had catastrophic medical insurance, and 5 had both types of insurance.

   (a) How many patients had neither of these types of insurance?

   (b) How many of these patients had basic medical insurance but not catastrophic medical insurance?

   (c) Why might a hospital director be interested in these numbers?

3. Display 7.14 shows how a Venn diagram is drawn with *three* main subsets, A, B, and C, in the universe.

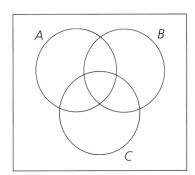

Display 7.14

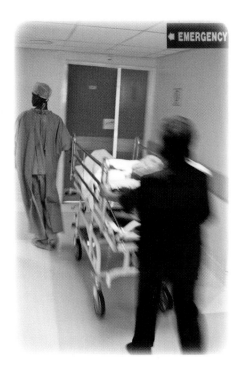

   (a) Draw two copies of Display 7.14. In one, shade the region for $A \cap (B \cap C)$. In the other, shade the region for $(A \cap B) \cap C$. What did you find? What algebraic law does this remind you of? Explain why it makes sense to write $A \cap B \cap C$? How would you describe an element of $A \cap B \cap C$?

   (b) Draw two more copies of Display 7.14. Shade your diagrams to show whether or not $A - (B - C) = (A - B) - C$. What do you find?

   (c) Draw two more copies of Display 7.14. Shade your diagrams to show whether or not $A \cup (B \cup C) = (A \cup B) \cup C$. What do you find?

   Explain why it makes sense to write $A \cup B \cup C$. How would you describe an element of $A \cup B \cup C$?

4. Before selling their products, manufacturers check them for defects. Inspectors look for the type and the number of defect(s) each item has, if any.

The Turniton Co. makes TV sets. Each TV is checked for defects in (i) the picture tube, (ii) the sound system, and (iii) the remote control system. Yesterday they made 1000 sets. They found that 54 units had a defective picture tube, 67 had a defective sound system, and 80 had a defective remote control system. Of these, 26 units had both a defective picture tube and a defective sound system, 20 had both a defective picture tube and a defective remote control system, 31 had both a defective sound system and a defective remote control system, and 14 had all three defects.

If a set has no defects, it is considered "perfect." If a set has only one defect, it can be repaired so it is called "repairable." Sets with two or more defects are considered "scrap" (although some of the parts are reusable). Of the 1000 TV sets made yesterday,

(a) how many sets were repairable?

(b) how many sets were scrap?

(c) how many sets were perfect?

(d) Why might the manager of Turniton be interested in these numbers?

5. A major sports store sells many types of sports equipment, but they specialize in soccer equipment. The manager decides to do some national advertising. She wants a full page ad in sports magazines for a month. She considers three magazines—*Sports Illustrious*, *Popular Sports*, and *Soccer Monthly*. Advertising experts give her the following estimates on numbers of readers:

Sports Illustrious	215,000
Popular Sports	320,000
Soccer Monthly	107,000
Sports Illustrious and *Popular Sports*	198,000
Popular Sports and *Soccer Monthly*	54,000
Sports Illustrious and *Soccer Monthly*	38,000
All Three Magazines	24,000

Display 7.15

The company can only afford to advertise in two magazines. The manager wants to advertise in the two magazines that will have the largest number of people seeing the ad. Which two magazines should the manager choose? Do you think that she should also look at factors other than the total number of readers? If so, what factors?

6. The Rocky Mountain National Bank has 54,000 customers in Colorado and 29,000 customers in other states. It has 45,000 customers with an income of more than $25,000 a year, and 32,000 customers who owe the bank more than $5,000. Of the customers in Colorado, 15,000 owe the bank more than $5,000. Of all the customers with an income of more than $25,000 per year, 10,000 owe the bank more than $5,000. Of the customers in Colorado with an income of more than $25,000 per year, 8,000 owe the bank more than $5,000. Let

   A = the set of customers in Colorado

   B = the set of customers with an annual income of more than $25,000 per year

   C = the set of customers who owe the bank more than $5,000

   This bank considers customers in the set $C - (A \cup B)$ as "high risk" customers.

   (a) Describe, in words, the customers in the set $C - (A \cup B)$. Why do you think the bank considers them "high risk" customers?

   (b) Draw a Venn diagram with the three main subsets A, B, C. (You can copy the diagram in Display 7.14 from problem 3.) Then shade the region for $C - (A \cup B)$.

   (c) Use your Venn diagram to find $\#(C - (A \cup B))$.

7. A set S can be divided into 26 subsets $A, B, C, ..., X, Y, Z$ in such a way that any two of these 26 sets are disjoint. If each of the 26 sets has exactly 15 elements, what is $\#(S)$?

8. Suppose that a set B is a subset of a set A (that is, $B \subseteq A$). What is the relationship between $\#(A)$ and $\#(B)$? Explain.

9. (a) Is $A \cap B$ always a subset of A and of B, for any two sets A and B? Do you think it should be? Write a careful argument to justify your opinion.

   (b) Defend the claim that the empty set, $\varnothing$, is a subset of every set.

   (c) How are parts (a) and (b) of this question related?

7.3 Tree Diagrams and the Fundamental Counting Principle

Learning Outcomes

After studying this section you will be able to:

Draw tree diagrams to represent and solve some counting problems

Determine a set of possible outcomes using a tree diagram

State the Fundamental Counting Principle and use it to solve problems

Use factorial notation.

7.31

Krishna's Deli sells sandwiches. Customers have a choice of one of four types of meat—ham, chicken, beef, or turkey, and one of three types of bread—white, rye, or whole wheat.

Krishna claims that since there are four types of meat and three types of bread, customers have a choice of seven different sandwiches. Is Krishna correct? Why?

One way to count all of the possible sandwiches is to list them. To count correctly, however, you must make sure you don't miss any. A *tree diagram* can be used to help picture this kind of situation and organize the possibilities. (You used tree diagrams with the guessing game in Chapter 5.) The next example shows you how to do this.

Down the street from Krishna's Deli is Dan's Deli. At Dan's, customers can choose one of three types of meat—ham, chicken, or beef—and one of two types of bread—white or rye. Suppose a customer first decides on the type of meat. Each possible choice—ham (H), chicken (C), or beef (B)—can be represented by an arrow that comes from a single starting point, as in Display 7.16.

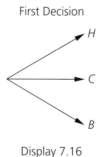

First Decision

H

C

B

Display 7.16

In Display 7.16 we have drawn our arrows from left to right. Sometimes arrows for tree diagrams are drawn in other directions. We often use the left-to-right pattern because its direction matches the usual left-to-right way of reading English.

The next decision for Dan's customer is the type of bread. For each choice of meat, there are two choices of bread—white (W) or rye (R). To show this on the diagram, arrows for each bread choice are drawn at the end of each meat-choice arrow as in Display 7.17.

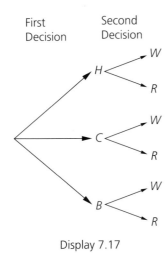

Display 7.17

Why do you think tree diagrams were given that name?

7.32

The tree diagram in Display 7.17 shows all the possible sandwiches at Dan's Deli. The arrows on a tree diagram are called **branches**. Each possibility is represented by a path of branches from the starting point on the left side of the diagram to an ending point on the right. That is called a **complete branch**. For example, the complete branch for the chicken on white bread sandwich is the blue path in Display 7.18.

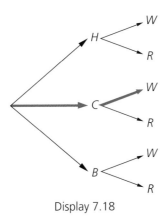

Display 7.18

To count all the possibilities on a tree diagram you need to count all the complete branches. Each end point on the right side corresponds to exactly one complete branch so you can just count those. There are six such end points on the Dan's Deli diagram, so there are six different sandwiches available. That is, if *S* is the set of sandwiches available at Dan's Deli, then #(*S*) = 6. We can write this set *S* = {HW, HR, CW, CR, BW, BR} where HW stands for "Ham on White," HR stands for "Ham on Rye," etc.

1. (a) Draw a tree diagram for choices at Dan's Deli so that the first decision is the type of bread and the second decision is the type of meat.

   (b) Is the number of different sandwiches affected by whether a customer decides on bread or on meat first? Explain.

2. (a) Draw a tree diagram to represent the different sandwiches that are available at Krishna's Deli.

   (b) Let *V* be the set of sandwiches available at Krishna's Deli. Write the set *V* by listing the elements. Did you find the tree diagram helpful in making the list? Why or why not?

   (c) Find #(*V*).

The next example shows how tree diagrams can help you picture the possible outcomes of a sports event.

Mary and Felicia agree to play tennis until one of them wins three games. Make a tree diagram to show the different ways this can happen. How many ways are there?

Here is another example. Suppose you are going to toss a coin twice. Each possible outcome is made up of two steps: the result of the first toss and the result of the second toss. The result of each toss will be a head, (H), or a tail, (T). A tree diagram for this situation is shown in Display 7.19.

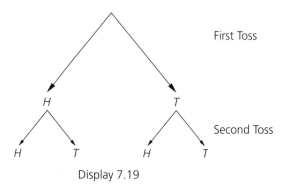

Display 7.19

The possible outcomes are represented by complete branches and we can count them by counting their end points. The diagram makes it easy to see why there are four possible outcomes. *For each* of the 2 possible outcomes of the first toss there are 2 possible outcomes for the second toss. So if S is the set of all possible outcomes, then $\#(S) = 2 \cdot 2 = 4$. We can write this set as

$$S = \{HH, HT, TH, TT\}$$

where the first letter in each pair represents the outcome of the first toss and the second letter represents the outcome of the second toss.

Explain how the tree in Display 7.19 divides the set of outcomes S into a pair of disjoint subsets, each containing two elements.

7.35

Now let's focus on three of the counting problems in this section—sandwiches at Dan's and Krishna's Delis and outcomes for tossing a coin twice. Each of those tree diagrams (we can just call them *trees*) has two levels, one to represent each decision making up an outcome. (You can think of each coin flip as a "decision" where the coin "decides" on which side to land.) Such a tree is called a **two-level tree**. The number of branches at each level depends on the number of choices for that decision. To understand this better, let's look at the Dan's Deli tree in Display 7.20.

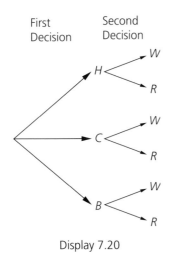

Display 7.20

The first level of this tree represents the meat choice. There are three choices for that decision so there are three branches at that level. The second decision, bread, has two choices, *no matter which choice was made at the first level.* So at the end of *each* first-level branch there are two branches for the second level.

Since there are 3 first-level branches and for each of these there are 2 second-level branches, there are $3 \cdot 2 = 6$ complete branches.

7.36

1. Fill in the blank: If the first level of a two-level tree has n branches and if for each of those there are exactly m second-level branches, the tree has exactly _____ complete branches.

2. For lunch you decide to have a sandwich and a dessert. You have a choice of a ham sandwich or a chicken sandwich. For dessert you have a choice of ice cream, pie, yogurt, cake, or pudding. Think of a tree for this situation but do not draw one. What are your first-level branches? What are your second-level branches? How many different lunches could you have?

This idea is important enough to state as a *principle*. A principle is like an algebraic law. It is a basic rule that we can rely on to solve problems.

Fundamental Counting Principle (for two actions): If one action can be taken in n ways, and if for each of those n ways a second action can be taken in m ways, then the two actions can be taken in $n \cdot m$ ways.

To extend this principle to more than two actions or decisions, just think of them step by step. Try that with the following questions.

7.37

1. You are going to toss a coin 3 times. Two possible outcomes are HTH and THH. Let S be the set of all possible outcomes.

   (a) Draw a tree diagram to show all the possible outcomes.

   (b) List all the elements of S. Did you find your tree useful in writing the list? Why or why not?

   (c) $\#(S) = ?$

2. Suppose a three-level tree has two first-level branches. For each of those there are four second-level branches. For each of those there are two third-level branches. Draw a diagram of such a tree. How many complete branches are there?

3. On your vacation you packed 4 pairs of pants, 7 shirts, and 2 pairs of shoes. How many different full outfits (pants, shirt, and shoes) do you have?

You have seen how trees can help organize and count possibilities made up of two or three decisions or actions of some sort. These are special cases of the general *Fundamental Counting Principle*.

FUNDAMENTAL COUNTING PRINCIPLE

If one of k actions can be taken in n_1 ways, a second action can be taken in n_2 ways, a third action can be taken in n_3 ways, and so on, then there are

$$n_1 \cdot n_2 \cdot n_3 \cdot \ldots \cdot n_k$$

ways to take all k actions.

We sometimes abbreviate the Fundamental Counting Principle by writing FCP.

7.38

1. **Sal, Kim, Mac, Anna, and Jane are responsible for planning a school dance. One of them must be selected as chairperson and another as vice chairperson. In how many different ways can this be done?**

2. **Suppose that in addition to a chairperson and a vice chairperson, a secretary must also be selected from the group. In how many ways can the three positions be filled?**

3. **There is more to be done than the group thought, so they assign each person a position: chairperson, vice chairperson, secretary, treasurer, and decorator. How many different ways are there to do this?**

If you select all of the items in a set S one at a time *without repeating*, then after each decision there is one less to choose from. So if $\#(S) = n$, then by the FCP there are $n(n - 1)(n - 2)\ldots \cdot 2 \cdot 1$ ways to do this. For example, if S is the set of students planning the dance, then $\#(S) = 5$ and there are $5 \cdot 4 \cdot 3 \cdot 2 \cdot 1 = 120$ ways to select them one at a time to fill the five positions. There is another, shorter way to write such a product.

The product of all consecutive positive integers from 1 to n, inclusive, is written ***n*!** and is read "***n* factorial.**" In other words

$$n! = n \cdot (n - 1) \cdot (n - 2) \cdot \ldots \cdot 2 \cdot 1$$

For example, $3! = 3 \cdot 2 \cdot 1 = 6$ and $7! = 7 \cdot 6 \cdot 5 \cdot 4 \cdot 3 \cdot 2 \cdot 1 = 5040$.

Using Technology

Your calculator has a factorial command in it. In the TI-84, it is one of the choices in the **PRB** menu, which you find with the **MATH** key. Look for it and use it to check the result for 7! just given.

7.39 Carmen still begins her puzzles by making a list of all the possible arrangements of the given letters. Then she chooses the ones that are real words.

1. If Carmen's puzzle gives her 3 different letters, how many arrangements are there? Explain. What if she gets 4 different letters? 5 different letters? Do your answers agree with your answers from the beginning of the chapter?

2. How many arrangements are there for 12 different letters? Which puzzle do you think would have more real-word answers, one with 4 different letters or one with 12? Explain.

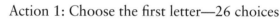

Tree diagrams for many counting problems can be too large or complicated to draw. The FCP let's you solve these problems without the diagram. For example, in the state of Euphoria, license plates have 2 letters followed by 3 digits. Letters and digits may be repeated, so WR135, WW213, CL994, and TT388 are all valid plates. How many license plates are possible? To use the FCP you can imagine the following sequence of actions:

Action 1: Choose the first letter—26 choices
Action 2: Choose the second letter—26 choices
Action 3: Choose the first digit—10 choices
Action 4: Choose the second digit—10 choices
Action 5: Choose the third digit—10 choices

Thus, by the FCP there are $26 \cdot 26 \cdot 10 \cdot 10 \cdot 10 = 26^2 \cdot 10^3 =$ 676,000 possible license plates. Imagine a tree diagram for this problem!

7.40
1. How many license plates are possible in the state of Euphoria if letters and digits may not be repeated?

2. How many license plates are possible in the state of Euphoria if letters and digits may be repeated, but the last digit cannot be 0?

7.41 Mary and Felicia decide to play tennis again. This time they decide to play until one of them wins four games. Can you use the FCP to figure out the number of possible outcomes for the series? If you can, do it. If not, explain why not.

By now you have learned some important tools for counting—Venn diagrams, tree diagrams, and most of all, the Fundamental Counting Principle. As you continue studying this chapter, you will see how important counting is in another area of mathematics—probability.

Problem Set: 7.3

1. A company has centers in New York and San Francisco. A fiber optic line is to be constructed to connect them. It will start in New York and go to either Chicago or Omaha. From that city it will go to Denver, Phoenix, or Albuquerque, and from that city it will go on to San Francisco. Draw a tree to show the different ways in which this line may be routed. How many ways are there?

2. You are going to toss a coin 5 times. Let S denote the set of all possible outcomes. Find #(S) and explain how you found your answer. Did you draw a tree? Did you use the FCP? Why?

3. In the World Series of Baseball one team from the National League (N) plays one team from the American League (A). They play until one team wins four games. Jason says that there are 24 different ways the series can be played. For example, one outcome could be NANNAN, which means the National League team won the first, third, fourth, and sixth games, while the American League team won the second and fifth games.

   (a) Start to draw a tree diagram to represent the possible outcomes. Is Jason correct? Are there 24 different ways the series can be played?

   (b) Do you need to draw a complete tree in order to answer part (a)? Explain.

   (c) Can you use the FCP to solve this counting problem? Why or why not?

4. Display 7.21 represents nine city blocks with the lines as streets. A person at point A (in the lower left corner) needs to get to point B (in the upper right corner) by traveling along those streets. At any corner, the person must go North or East. How many different paths could this person take from A to B? (Problems like this one play a role in routing ambulances, fire trucks, etc.)

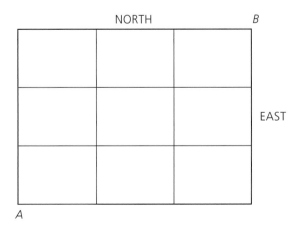

Display 7.21

5. In certain lotteries the player picks 4 digits. (A digit is any number 0–9, inclusive.) For example, a player could pick 2337, 1279, or 9993. How many different ways to pick such lottery numbers are there?

6. Suppose that all license plates in a certain state have three letters followed by three digits.
   (a) If all the digits must be different but the letters may be repeated, how many different license plates can be made?
   (b) If all the letters must be different but the digits may be repeated, how many license plates can be made?

7. Five vice presidents of a company are to be assigned five different offices. How many different ways can the assignments be made?

8. A company has 783 employees. Carefully explain why there must be at least two employees with the same pair of initials.

9. Radio and TV station "call letters," such as WPVI and KYW, begin with a W or K followed by either two or three letters.
   (a) How many station names are possible?
   (b) The FCC is a government agency. What does FCC stand for?
   (c) Why might a person from the FCC be interested in the number of possible station names?

10. A class with 17 students is going to have its picture taken. The photographer asks the students to line up in different orders so that she can select the best arrangement. If the students could form one new line-up every second, how long would it take for them to line up in every possible order? (You may need a calculator!)

11. In a certain computer programming language, an "identifier" is a list (sequence) of symbols where the first symbol is a letter of the English alphabet and each of the remaining symbols may be either a letter or a digit. For example, F43Y2 is an identifier of length 5 (it contains five symbols).
   (a) How many different identifiers of length five are there?
   (b) How many different identifiers are there of length 1 or more, up to and including length 5?

12. One state has 1,570,000 licensed cars and trucks and the number is increasing at a rate of about 10,000 a year. In this state a license must have three letters followed by three digits and no letter or digit can be repeated. A state senator is worried that the state will run out of license plates. If the current rate of increase continues, how many years will it take the state to run out of license plates?

13. In computer science a binary string is a sequence of bits (0s and 1s). For example, 0010110 is a binary string of length 7, 1001 is a binary string of length 4, and 01101 is a binary string of length 5.
    (a) How many binary strings are there of length 7?
    (b) How many binary strings are there of length 7 that begin and end with 0?
    (c) How many binary strings are there of length 7 that begin or end with 0?
    (d) How many binary strings are there of length 7 that have 0 as the second digit?
    (e) How many binary strings of length 7 contain exactly one 0?
    (f) How many binary strings of length 7 begin with 01 and have a 0 as the fourth digit?

14. In Section 7.1 you learned how a computer stores information using the binary digits 0 and 1. One example is the way binary digits can be used to code volume levels of music. An example of how you could code two volume levels is shown in Display 7.22.

Level	Code
soft	0
loud	1

Display 7.22

An example of how you could code four volume levels is shown in Display 7.23.

Level	Code
very soft	00
soft	01
loud	10
very loud	11

Display 7.23

(a) How many volume levels can be coded if each code word contains three bits? What if each contains four bits?
(b) If you want to code 1000 different sound levels, how many bits must each code word contain?

7.4 Probability: What Are the Chances?

Learning Outcomes

After studying this section you will be able to:

Explain probability as a numerical description of the likelihood of an event

Assign probabilities based on intuition or experience

Estimate probabilities by performing experiments.

Last night on the News, a weather forecaster said, "There is a 40 percent chance of rain tomorrow."

Write a paragraph about what the forecaster's statement means to you.

7.42

7.43

1. If a weather forecaster says that there is a 90 percent chance of rain tomorrow, would it affect your plans? How? What plans might other people have that would be affected by this forecast?

2. If a weather forecaster says that there is a 10 percent chance of rain tomorrow, would it affect your plans? How? What plans might other people have that would be affected by this forecast?

Almost every day we hear or use the word "chance." For example, "The soccer team has a good chance to win the league championship." Or, "The chances of it snowing in the Sahara are slim." Rain tomorrow, your team winning the championship, and snow in the Sahara are events with *uncertain outcomes*; they may happen or they may not. Chance refers to the likelihood that such an event will happen. Numbers can be used to describe chances and one way to do this is with percents (like weather forecasters do).

List three other events with uncertain outcomes. For each event, estimate the percent chance that it will happen.

7.44

Some events are certain; they are sure to happen. For example, it is certain that a ball thrown in the air will fall back down. Other events are impossible; they are sure *not* to happen. For example, it is impossible for you to run 500 miles per hour.

7.45

1. List three events that are certain. What is the percent chance that these events will happen?

2. List three events that are impossible. What is the percent chance that these things will happen?

So far you have been using percents to describe chances. An impossible event has a 0% chance. The more likely an event is, the higher its percent chance up to 100%, the chance of a certain event. So, chances can be described numerically on a scale from 0% to 100%. In mathematics, we use the decimal or fraction form of a percentage to do this. This is called the **probability** of an event. So instead of saying "there is a 40% chance of rain" we say "the *probability* of rain is 0.40" or "the *probability* of rain is $\frac{4}{10}$."

7.46

You work for a newspaper. Your next assignment is to report the probabilities of winning different lottery games but you get the data in the form of percents. Write the probability of winning each game as a decimal and as a fraction.

(a) *Try Your Luck* tickets — 10% chance of winning

(b) *It Could Be You* tickets — 13% chance of winning

(c) *Take a Chance* tickets — 2% chance of winning

(d) *Retire for Life* tickets — 0.003% chance of winning

Which of those games do you think offers the biggest prize?

A probability is a number between 0 and 1 inclusive. (Why?) Number lines can help you visualize them. Suppose a weather forecaster says that there is a 40% chance of rain tomorrow. Then the probability that it will rain tomorrow is 0.4, and that can be illustrated by an ✖ on a number line like this:

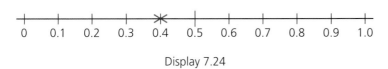

Display 7.24

Capital letters are often used as names for events. Let *E* stand for the event "it rains tomorrow." We abbreviate the statement that the probability of *E* is 0.4 by writing $P(E) = 0.4$.

You probably noticed that the abbreviation $P(\ )$ looks like the notation we use for functions, $f(\ )$. That's right! You can think of P as a function that assigns a probability to events.

If an event *E* is certain, then $P(E) = 1$.

Display 7.25

7.4 Probability: What Are the Chances?

If an event *E* is impossible, then $P(E) = 0$.

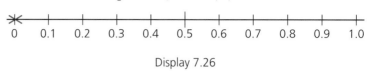

| | | | | | | | | | | |
|0|0.1|0.2|0.3|0.4|0.5|0.6|0.7|0.8|0.9|1.0|

Display 7.26

One way to assign probabilities is to use your *intuition*, your ability to know things based on "gut feelings." This method is especially useful for events with outcomes that are up to you!

7.47

1. Use your intuition to assign each of the following events a probability. Write your answers using function notation, $P(E) = $ [the probability], and then mark the number line to represent the probability you assigned. (Your teacher will give you a handout for this.) Be prepared to explain your choices. In these examples, "I" refers to you.

   (a) *E* is "I will watch TV sometime tomorrow."

   (b) *E* is "I will listen to a CD sometime tomorrow."

   (c) *E* is "I will drink a soda tomorrow."

   (d) *E* is "It will rain tomorrow."

   (e) *E* is "It will snow tomorrow."

   (f) *E* is "I will run 500 miles next weekend."

Here is a review of the important language and notation we have introduced so far. An **event** is something that might or might not happen. To any event, call it *E*, we may assign a number between 0 and 1 inclusive, written $P(E)$. We call $P(E)$ the **probability of** *E*, and often say $P(E)$ is "the probability that *E* will happen."

7.48

1. Describe an event *E* for which you believe $P(E) = \frac{1}{2}$.

| | | | | | | | | | | |
|0|0.1|0.2|0.3|0.4|0.5|0.6|0.7|0.8|0.9|1.0|

Display 7.27

Explain why you believe $P(E) = \frac{1}{2}$.

2. Describe an event *E* for which you believe $P(E) = \frac{1}{4}$. Explain why you believe $P(E) = \frac{1}{4}$.

A medical doctor says, "The patient has a better than even chance of surviving." What does this statement mean to you? How would you make this statement in terms of probability? On what does a doctor base her assessment of a patient's chances?

7.49

The way events have occurred in the past can often help us predict how they will occur in the future. So, previously gathered data, or *history*, can be used to assign probability. For example, suppose a baseball player got 51 hits in the last 300 times at bat. In other words, $\frac{51}{300} = 0.17 = 17\%$ of his past at-bats were hits. From this we can say that he has a 17% chance of getting a hit in the future, or that the probability this player will get a hit next time is 0.17.

1. In the last 8 games, a baseball player walked 13 times, got 11 hits, and struck out 26 times. The player is now coming up to bat. What do you think is the probability that this player strikes out?

7.50

2. Bates Insurance Company sells auto insurance. In the past year, 783 of their customers did not have an accident, 132 had minor accidents, 18 had major accidents, and no customer had more than one accident. Based on this information, what would you say is the probability that a customer has a minor accident next year? Round your answer to two decimal places.

You just saw how past data can be used to assign probability. But what if you do not have any history? One solution is to create your own. To do this, you perform experiments and record the outcomes. Then you can use that data to assign probabilities.

Think about tossing two coins. The outcome is uncertain; it could be two tails, two heads, or one of each. Let's assign a probability to the event of getting two tails. Give this event the name T. So we want to find $P(T)$. To gather data, you perform the experiment of tossing two coins 50 times. Suppose you found that 11 times out of the 50 you got two tails. Now, based on that data you could say that $P(T) = \frac{11}{50} = 0.22$. Your classmate also performed this experiment. He got two tails 14 times out of 50. Based on his data he would say that $P(T) = \frac{14}{50} = 0.28$. Which probability is correct, 0.22 or 0.28? Neither should be considered absolutely correct. *Probabilities based on experiments are estimates, and will usually change from one experiment to another.*

7.51

1. Toss two coins 25 times and count the number of times you get two heads (*H*). What is your estimate of *P*(*H*)? Compare your estimate to those of your classmates.

2. Now decide as a class on an estimate of *P*(*H*). How did you do it? Which estimate do you think is best? Why?

7.52

Think about how you calculated your estimate of *P*(*H*) using data from your experiment. Write a formula to describe how you did it. Be as precise as you can.

Probability is a number between 0 and 1 (inclusive) that describes the likelihood that an event will happen. In this section you learned some ways to assign probabilities—based on intuition, on history, or on data from experiments. In the next sections you will use these ideas to assign probabilities to some more complicated events.

Problem Set: 7.4

1. In the last 24 attempts, a basketball player made 5 field goals.

   (a) Assign a probability to the event that this player makes a field goal, (*F*), on the next attempt. Write your answer using function notation.

   (b) Assign a probability to the event that this player misses, (*M*), on the next attempt. Write your answer using function notation.

2. In the last 3 games, a baseball player walked 4 times, got a hit 3 times, and struck out 10 times. The player is now coming to bat. Base your answers to the following questions on this record.

   (a) What is the probability that this player walks?

   (b) What is the probability that this player gets a hit?

   (c) What is the probability that this player strikes out?

   (d) What is the probability that this player does not strike out?

   (e) What is the probability that this player gets a hit or walks?

   (f) What is the probability that this player walks, gets a hit, or strikes out?

   (g) Write a paragraph about how you think the probabilities you assigned in (a)-(f) are related.

3. Insurance companies use probabilities to determine the rates they charge customers. For example, life insurance rates involve probabilities about how long a person will live while rates for auto insurance depend on probabilities of accidents.

   In a certain state, the probability of a car getting into an accident next year is determined to be 0.09. The Wingate Insurance Company insures 200,000 cars in this state.

   (a) How many of its insured cars does Wingate expect to be in accidents next year? Explain.

   (b) When an insured car gets into an accident, the insurance company pays for the repairs. The mean cost for such repairs is $1,500. How much money can the Wingate Co. expect to pay next year for auto repairs? Explain.

   (c) To be a successful business, the Wingate Co. needs to have $50,000,000 left after paying for auto repairs. If each car owner is charged the same amount, how much must the company charge each of them? Explain.

4. Suppose you have a cup filled with five marbles. Four of them are white and one is green. Without looking into the cup you reach in and pull out a marble. If it is green you stop. If it is white, you put the marble aside and select another marble, and so forth until you pull out the green marble. There is no way to know beforehand which draw is going to get you the green marble. It could be the first draw, the second, the third, the fourth, or the fifth.

   (a) Use your intuition to guess which draw you think is most likely (has the highest probability) to give you the green marble.

   (b) Perform an experiment to see if your guess is correct. Perform as many trials as you can. For each trial, record which draw got you the green marble. (You may use different colors, of course! Just make sure you have four marbles of one color and one of another color.) Now, for each draw, use your data to assign the probability of getting the green marble. Do your answers support your guess from part (a)? Explain.

7.5 Equally Likely Outcomes

Learning Outcomes

After studying this section you will be able to:

Describe a sample space for an experiment

Explain what it means for outcomes to be equally likely

Assign the probability of an event using the ratio of acceptable to total possible outcomes

Use an event's complement to determine its probability

Find the probability of the union and the intersection of events.

In the previous section you learned some ways to assign probabilities—based on intuition, on history, or on data from performed experiments. In mathematics, we call *any* situation with an uncertain outcome an **experiment**, even if we do not actually control or perform it. The set of all the possible outcomes is called its **sample space**. For example, the experiment of tossing a coin has the sample space S containing two outcomes—heads and tails. We write $S = \{H, T\}$.

Think about the experiment of tossing a coin. Use your intuition to assign a probability to the event, T, that you get tails. Explain.

7.53

Most of us believe that the result of a coin-toss is *random*—that one side is just as likely to turn up as the other and that $P(H) = P(T) = 0.5$. This belief is not based on performed experiments, but on intuition and the symmetry of a "fair" coin. A lottery drawing and the gender of a new baby are other situations we may believe have random outcomes. We say outcomes are **equally likely** when each possible outcome has the same chance of happening as every other. In this section we look at experiments with equally likely outcomes and assign probabilities to different events.

7.54

A *die* is a 6-sided cube with its faces marked with 1, 2, 3, 4, 5, or 6 dots. Two of them are a pair of *dice*.

1. **What games do you know that use dice?**

2. **Write the sample space S for the experiment of rolling a die. What is #(S)?**

3. **Is each outcome in the sample space equally likely? Why or why not?**

4. **Use your intuition to assign a probability to each outcome.**

You may have noticed a connection between the number of equally likely outcomes and the probability of each outcome. Let's express that in a general form.

Complete this statement:

If an experiment with sample space *S* has *n* equally likely outcomes, then #(*S*) =_____ and for each outcome *O*, *P*(*O*) = _____.

7.55

This means you can find the probability of equally likely outcomes by *counting* the outcomes in the sample space.

Assume that boys and girls are equally likely to be born. What is the probability that in a family with three children, all three are girls?

7.56

Intuition tells us that if we toss a fair coin *P*(*H*) = *P*(*T*) = 0.5. So, if we toss a coin many times, tails should show half of the time, right?

Toss a coin 10 times and record the outcomes. Use that data to assign a probability to getting tails on a coin toss. Is it the same as the one based on your intuition? Why or why not?

7.57

In reality, experiments do not always turn out precisely the way intuition predicts. (Did everyone in your class get *exactly* 5 tails out of 10 tosses?) That's why probabilities based on performed experiments are only estimates. Intuitive probability tells us what to expect *in the long run*. If a coin is tossed millions of times, we believe that tails would occur about half of the time.

1. If a die is rolled 1000 times, how many times do you expect the 4 to show?

2. If a die is rolled 1000 times, is it possible that a 4 would never show? Use your intuition to assign a probability to that event.

7.58

Now think about this more complicated question: "If you toss a die, what is the probability that you get an even number?" In this case, getting a 2, 4, or 6 would be acceptable. Each outcome is equally likely and there are three acceptable outcomes out of a total of six. So the chances of getting one of the acceptable outcomes are $\frac{3}{6}$. In other words *P*(even number) $= \frac{3}{6} = \frac{1}{2}$. Notice that the acceptable outcomes, {2, 4, 6}, are a subset of the sample space *S* = {1, 2, 3, 4, 5, 6}. Any subset of a sample space is called an **event**. So if *E* represents the event of "getting an even number" on a die-roll, then *E* = {2, 4, 6} and $P(E) = \frac{1}{2}$.

7.59

Think about the experiment of rolling a die. For each given event E, write it as a set by listing its elements and then assign it a probability.

1. E is "getting an odd number."

2. E is "getting a number larger than 2."

3. E is "getting a number smaller than 3."

4. E is "getting a number that is a multiple of 3."

5. E is "getting a number that is divisible by 4."

6. E is "getting a 10."

The die-roll examples show how probability depends on the number of acceptable outcomes and on the number of total possible outcomes. We can write a formula for the probability of an event for an experiment *with equally likely outcomes* like this:

$$P(\text{event}) = \frac{\text{number of acceptable outcomes}}{\text{total number of possible outcomes}}$$

or

$$= \frac{\text{number of outcomes in the event}}{\text{number of outcomes in the sample space}}$$

If E represents the event and S represents the sample space then we get:

$$P(E) = \frac{\#(E)}{\#(S)}$$

This tells us that to assign probabilities we can just count elements in sets!

Consider the experiment of randomly picking a card from a standard deck. What is the probability of picking a king? Let K be the event of "picking a king," so we want to find $P(K)$. The sample space S is the set of 52 cards in the deck and each one is equally likely to be picked. There are four kings in a standard deck, so

$$P(K) = \frac{\#(K)}{\#(S)} = \frac{4}{52} = 0.077 \text{ (to three decimal places)}$$

1. What is the probability of picking a diamond from a standard deck of cards?

2. What is the probability of picking a face card from a standard deck of cards?

3. Think again about the experiment of tossing a die 1000 times. Describe the sample space *S*. What is #(*S*)? Calculate the probability that a 4 never shows. (Was your earlier estimate close?)

4. Suppose an experiment has equally likely outcomes and sample space *S*.

   (a) What is *P*(*S*)? Explain.

   (b) What is *P*(∅)? Explain.

7.60

In a class of 30 students, 7 have blue eyes. A student will be selected at random.

7.61

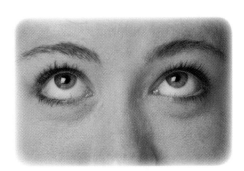

1. What is the sample space *S* for this experiment? What is #(*S*)?

2. If *B* is the event that a blue-eyed student is selected, what is *P*(*B*)?

3. Describe the set *B*′.

Remember that the set *A*′ (read "*A* prime") is the complement of a set *A* in a universal set *U*. It is the set of all elements in *U* that are *not* in *A*. So *A*′ = (*U* − *A*). In probability, the universe is the sample space, *S*. Display 7.28 shows a Venn diagram of these sets. The shaded region represents *B*′.

4. What is *P*(*B*′)? Calculate *P*(*B*) + *P*(*B*′).

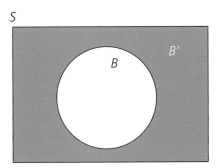

Display 7.28

The sum you found in question 4 of the previous problem illustrates an important property of probabilities. If E is any event for an experiment with sample space S, then

$$P(E) + P(E') = 1$$

or

$$P(E) = 1 - P(E')$$

(Why?) This property is useful because sometimes it is easier to find the probability of an event's complement than to find the probability of the event itself.

7.62

1. You are going to toss a fair coin 5 times. What is the probability that at least one head appears? (*Hint:* First calculate the probability of the complement—that no heads appear.)

2. Suppose you randomly pick a card from a standard deck.

    (a) What is the probability that you do not get a diamond?

    (b) What is the probability that you do not get a face card?

Blaise Pascal

The study of probability began in the 1600s. The Chevalier de Méré was a wealthy French nobleman who liked to gamble. He asked the French mathematician Blaise Pascal various questions about games of chance. Pascal consulted another French mathematician, Pierre Fermat, and they began to develop the theory of probability. See if you can answer one of de Méré's questions.

7.63

Suppose you are rolling two dice. How many rolls must be allowed in order to have a better than even chance of getting two sixes at least once?

Although the study of probability began with games of chance, today it is used in many different areas. For example, life insurance policies consider the probability that a person will live to a certain age, polls determine the probability that a candidate will be elected, and biologists studying heredity look at the probabilities that particular traits are passed on. The list goes on and on. What other uses for probability can you think of?

Research some other modern uses of probability (uses other than gambling or games of chance). Use the Internet (or library) and/or talk to people in various fields. Write a few paragraphs about what you find.

7.64

We have been finding probabilities by counting outcomes (in the event and in the sample space). When events become more complicated, so does the counting. For some problems, Venn diagrams can help you.

In a class of 30 students, 17 play video games, 12 watch MTV, and 5 play video games *and* watch MTV. A student in this class will be selected at random.

7.65

1. What is the sample space S for this experiment? What is #(S)? Draw a Venn diagram to represent the sets in this situation.

2. Let G be the event that a student who plays video games is selected. What is $P(G)$?

3. Let M be the event that a student who watches MTV is selected. What is $P(M)$?

4. Describe the event G'. What is $P(G')$?

5. Consider the event that the selected student plays video games but does not watch MTV. Write this event as a difference of sets. What is the probability of this event?

6. Describe the event $G \cap M$. What is $P(G \cap M)$?

7. Describe the event $G \cup M$. Jason says that $P(G \cup M) = P(G) + P(M)$. Is he correct? Explain. What is $P(G \cup M)$?

8. Now use your results from question 7 to write an equation for the probability of the union of two events, A and B, in a sample space S.

   $P(A \cup B) =$ _____.

   What happens to the equation if events A and B are disjoint? (Such events are called *mutually exclusive*.)

Let's return to the experiment of rolling a pair of (fair) dice. This time we will look at the sum of the two numbers we get. Do you think that the sample space for this experiment should be the set {2, 3, 4, 5, 6, 7, 8, 9, 10, 11, 12}? It's a tempting idea, but there's a catch.

7.66 Are the sum-outcomes in {2, 3, 4, 5, 6, 7, 8, 9, 10, 11, 12} equally likely? Explain. (Think about these questions first: Is a sum of 6 more or less likely than a sum of 2? Is a sum of 12 more or less likely than a sum of 8? Why or why not?)

We have been using the formula $P(E) = \dfrac{\#(E)}{\#(S)}$ to find the probability of an event E in sample space S. However, *it only works if the outcomes in S are all equally likely.* That is not true for the sample space {2, 3, 4, 5, 6, 7, 8, 9, 10, 11, 12} of the dice-sum experiment. Can we find another sample space that allows us to use our definition of probability? Sure.

Suppose the dice are colored—one is red and the other is green. The table in Display 7.29 shows all the possible outcomes from rolling the two dice. The numbers on the outside tell you which numbers appear on each die. The numbers inside are the sums.

		Green die					
		1	2	3	4	5	6
Red die	1	2	3	4	5	6	7
	2	3	4	5	6	7	8
	3	4	5	6	7	8	9
	4	5	6	7	8	9	10
	5	6	7	8	9	10	11
	6	7	8	9	10	11	12

Display 7.29

Each *entry* inside the table represents exactly one possible sum-outcome. The same number appears in several entries when there are different ways to get that sum. These entries form a sample space S of equally likely outcomes—and $\#(S) = 36$. (You can find $\#(S)$ by counting on the table or by the Fundamental Counting Principle—there are $6 \cdot 6 = 36$ possible ways to roll two dice.) Now you can use our definition of probability with this sample space to answer these questions:

You are going to roll two dice.

7.67

1. What is the probability of getting a sum of 7?

2. What is the probability that the sum is an odd number?

3. What is the probability that the sum is greater than 9?

4. What is the probability that the sum is less than 5?

5. What is the probability that the sum is a multiple of 3?

6. If you already know that the sum is greater than 3, what is the probability that it is even? (Be careful!)

7. If you already know that one of the dice showed a 3, what is the probability that the sum is 8?

8. If you already know that one of the dice showed a 4, what is the probability that the sum is greater than 7?

9. What is the probability that the sum is an even number or is a multiple of 3?

In this section you assigned probabilities for experiments with equally likely outcomes. Such experiments involve outcomes that are *random*. In the next section you will learn about using random number lists to model real-world situations.

Problem Set: 7.5

1. The numbers 1 to 100 are written on slips of paper and placed in a box. The slips are mixed and a number is randomly selected from the box.

   (a) What is the probability that the number is greater than 84?

   (b) What is the probability that the number is less than or equal to 10?

   (c) What is the probability that the number is divisible by 7?

   (d) What is the probability that the number is a multiple of 5 and a multiple of 7?

   (e) What is the probability that the number is a multiple of 5 or a multiple of 7?

   (f) What is the probability that the number is greater than 89 if you already know that the number is greater than 75?

   (g) What is the probability that the number is greater than 89 if you already know that the number is odd?

(h) What is the probability that the number is greater than 89 if you already know that the number is a multiple of 3?

2. A science quiz has 10 true-false questions. One student has not studied and simply guesses all of the answers.

   (a) What is the probability that this student will get them all correct?

   (b) What is the probability that this student will get at least one correct?

3. A three-year-old child in your area code dialed a seven-digit phone number at random. What does it mean to you to say that the number was dialed "at random"? What is the probability that she dialed your telephone number?

4. Cards bearing the letters A, M, E, and T are placed in front of a monkey. The monkey successively picks one of the cards at random and does not replace the card. What does it mean to you that the monkey picked a card at random? What is the probability that the monkey picked T E A M (in that order)?

5. A fair coin is tossed seven times.

   (a) What is the probability that the outcome is TTHHHHH?

   (b) What is the probability of all tails?

   (c) What is the probability of getting exactly one head?

   (d) What is the probability of getting at least one head?

   (e) What is the probability that the first toss was a head and the third was a tail?

   (f) What is the probability that the first and third tosses were tails and the last toss was a head?

6. The eleven letters in the word "CONNECTICUT" are written on slips of paper and put into a bowl. Then they are mixed and one of them is picked at random.

   (a) What is the probability that the letter C is picked?

   (b) What is the probability that the picked letter is a consonant?

   (c) What is the probability that the picked letter is in the word "PENNSYLVANIA"?

   (d) What is the probability that the picked letter is in the word "MAMMAL"?

   (e) What is the probability that the picked letter is in the alphabet?

7. A fair die is rolled 120 times. How many times do you expect each of the following events to happen? Be prepared to justify your answers.

   (a) The number 5 is rolled.

   (b) An even number is rolled.

   (c) A number greater than 2 is rolled.

   (d) A number that is a multiple of 3 is rolled.

   (e) A number greater than 7 is rolled.

   (f) A number less than 7 is rolled.

8. When a deer crosses a road there are two things that can happen—either the deer is hit by a car or the deer is not hit by a car. Therefore, the probability of a deer safely crossing a road is $\frac{1}{2}$. Do you agree or disagree? Write a paragraph explaining your answer.

9. The Slot Machine was invented by Charles Fey of San Francisco in 1895 and is sometimes called a "one-armed bandit." (Gambling with these machines is not legal in some states.) To play, you drop a coin into a slot and pull a lever on the side of the machine, which makes a set of reels spin. A standard slot machine has 3 reels, each with 20 pictures. The table in Display 7.30 shows what the pictures are and how many of them appear on each reel of a particular machine.

Picture	Reel 1	Reel 2	Reel 3
Bar	1	3	1
Bell	1	3	3
Plum	5	1	5
Orange	3	6	7
Cherry	7	7	0
Lemon	3	0	4
	20	20	20

Display 7.30

The reels stop randomly with each one showing one of its 20 pictures.

   (a) The Jackpot is the biggest prize and is won when the reels show 3 bars. What is the probability of winning the Jackpot?

   (b) Smaller prizes (other than the Jackpot) are won when the reels show the same three pictures (other than bars). What is the probability of winning a smaller prize?

   (c) What is the probability of not winning any prizes?

10. In a class of 35 students, 8 play in the band, 9 belong to the art club, and 3 are in the band and in the art club. One student in the class will be selected at random. Let A be the event that a student in the art club is selected and B the event that a student in the band is selected.

    (a) Describe the event $A \cup B$. What is $P(A \cup B)$?

    (b) Describe the event A'. What is $P(A')$?

    (c) What is the probability that the selected student is in the band but is not a member of the art club? Write this event in terms of A and B.

    (d) What is the probability that the selected student is neither in the band nor in the art club?

11. In a group of 1000 people, an advertising agency found that 786 people read *Newsweek* magazine, 664 read *Time* magazine, and 461 people read both magazines. One of the people in the group is selected at random.

    (a) What is the probability that the selected person reads at least one of the two magazines, *Newsweek* or *Time*?

    (b) What is the probability that the selected person reads at least one of the two magazines but not both?

    (c) What is the probability that this person reads *Time* magazine if you already know that this person does not read *Newsweek*?

12. In the previous section, you used intuition and experiments to analyze the probability of picking a green marble on a particular draw in the following situation:

    > Suppose you have a cup filled with five marbles. Four of them are white and one is green. Without looking into the cup you reach in and pull out a marble. If it is green you stop. If it is white, you put the marble aside and select another marble, and so forth until you pull out the green marble. There is no way to know beforehand which draw is going to get you the green marble. It could be the first draw, the second, the third, the fourth, or the fifth.

    For each draw, assign the probability of getting the green marble. Justify your answers. Are these outcomes equally likely? Explain.

7.6 Using Random Numbers for Simulation

Have you ever rolled dice, drawn cards, or taken a free-throw in a computer game? Do you know how the computer "does" these things?

Computer games are *simulations*. To **simulate** an activity (or experiment) means to copy or model it without actually doing it. There are many uses for simulations other than games. They model traffic patterns, predict hurricane paths, train astronauts, and many other things. Simulations are often (but not always) done on computers. In this section we look at one of the tools used to run them—random numbers.

We begin by looking at how you could simulate the roll of a fair die. The outcome of a die roll is random—the six possible outcomes, {1, 2, 3, 4, 5, 6}, are all equally likely, with a probability of $\frac{1}{6}$. Now suppose you get a list of digits from 1 to 6 that is also random. That means that each digit is equally likely (also with a probability of $\frac{1}{6}$) to occur in the list. Since the listed digits occur with the same frequencies as the die-roll outcomes, the list can simulate repeated die rolls—each list entry represents one roll outcome.

Jason suggests one way for his class to make such a list: Each student writes a digit from 1 to 6 on a slip of paper. The slips are put into a box and mixed. Then they are drawn out one at a time and the digits are written down. The list can be made as long as you want by repeating the process again and again.

1. **Do you think Jason's method will give you a random list? Why or why not?**

7.68

2. **Come up with your own method for making a random list of digits 1 through 6.**

It can be tricky and time-consuming to create your own random list of numbers. Fortunately, you don't have to. Mathematicians have found efficient ways to make them with computer programs. For example, with a TI-84 you can make a random list of integers between any two integers, and you can

Learning Outcomes

After studying this section, you will be able to:

Explain what it means for a list of integers to be random

Generate random-integer lists on a TI-84

Design random-integer simulation schemes for random and biased experiments

Apply random-integer schemes to simulate various activities.

make that list as long as you need. Suppose you want to simulate 10 rolls of a fair die. You need a random list of 10 integers between 1 and 6, inclusive. To do this on a TI-84:

- Press the **MATH** menu key and scroll right to highlight the **PRB** (probability) menu.

- Then scroll down to **5:randInt(** and press **ENTER**. You will see **randInt(** on your screen.

- Enter three numbers separated by commas and then close the parentheses (closing the parentheses is optional). The first is the first possible integer in the list. The second is the last possible integer. Then enter the number of random integers you want.

- Press **ENTER** to generate the list. Pressing **ENTER** again and again will generate more such lists.

- You will see the first 7 digits of your results. To see the rest, use the ▶ key to move to the right.

So, to get 10 random integers between 1 and 6, inclusive, enter **randInt(1,6,10)**. We did this and got **{2 5 6 3 3 2 4 4 1 5}**.

7.69

1. **Try it. Use your calculator to simulate 12 rolls of a fair die.**

2. **Do four simulations of 8 die rolls each.**

3. **If you simulated 1,000,000 rolls of a fair die, how many times would you expect a 5 to occur? Explain.**

4. **Suppose you actually rolled a fair die 1,000,000 times. How many times would you expect a 5 to occur?**

5. **Are your answers to questions 3 and 4 the same? Should they be? Why or why not?**

7.70

Can you use randInt(on your calculator to simulate 10 tosses of a fair coin? If not, explain why not. If you can, explain how and then do it.

The key to using random-integer lists for simulation is to assign the integers in the list to the outcomes of the simulated activity in a way that "makes sense." For die rolls, the obvious way to do this is to use integers 1-6 to represent die-roll outcomes of the same number. For coin tosses, it makes sense to use two integers and assign one to heads and one to tails. A plan for assigning integers to outcomes for a simulation is called a **scheme**. One easy way to describe a scheme is with a table. The one we used for the die-roll simulation is shown in Display 7.31.

Simulation Scheme A	
Integer	**Die-roll outcome**
1	1
2	2
3	3
4	4
5	5
6	6

Display 7.31

You can create different schemes to simulate an activity.
Two other schemes for die-roll simulations are shown in
Display 7.32. Scheme B uses integers between 1 and 6, inclusive
(like Scheme A). Scheme C uses integers from 10 to 15.

Simulation Scheme B		Simulation Scheme C	
Integer	**Die-roll outcome**	**Integer**	**Die-roll outcome**
1	1	10	1
2	2	11	2
3	3	12	3
4	4	13	4
5	5	14	5
6	6	15	6

Display 7.32

1. Use your calculator and Scheme A to simulate 10 rolls of
   a fair die. Write down the simulated die-roll outcomes.

7.71

2. Use your calculator and Scheme B to simulate 10 rolls of
   a fair die. Write down the simulated die-roll outcomes.

3. Use your calculator and Scheme C to simulate 10 rolls of
   a fair die. Write down the simulated die-roll outcomes.

4. Which of the three schemes, A, B, or C, do you think is
   the best? Explain.

Now let's try simulating rolling two (fair) dice and looking at
the sum of the two numbers we get. The possible sum-outcomes
are {2, 3, 4, 5, 6, 7, 8, 9, 10, 11, 12}. One idea might be to use
a random-integer list from 2 to 12 inclusive and assign each
integer to the sum-outcome of the same number. This scheme is
shown in Display 7.33.

Simulation Scheme 1 Dice-roll sums	
Integer	Sum-outcome
2	2
3	3
4	4
5	5
6	6
7	7
8	8
9	9
10	10
11	11
12	12

Display 7.33

7.72

Do you think that applying Scheme 1 (Display 7.33) to random integers from 2 to 12 gives a good simulation of the sum-outcomes from rolling two dice? To help you decide, first answer these questions:

Suppose you were going to make a random list using **randInt(2,12,100,000)**.

1. How many times would you expect the integer 2 to occur in the list? Explain.

2. How many times would you expect the integer 7 to occur in the list? Explain.

Now suppose you were actually going to roll two dice 100,000 times.

3. How many times would you expect to get a sum of 2? Explain.

4. How many times would you expect to get a sum of 7? Explain.

5. Now go back to our original question: Do you think that applying Scheme 1 to random integers from 2 to 12 gives a good simulation of the sum-outcomes from rolling two dice? Why or why not?

To simulate an activity means to copy or model it *as closely as you can*. For random-integer simulation this means that integers should occur in the list with the same frequency as their assigned outcomes would occur. This is not true for Scheme 1 and the dice-roll sums. The problem is that the integers in a random list are equally likely to occur but the sum-outcomes of a pair of dice are not. An experiment is called **biased** if the outcomes are *not* equally likely. The experiment of rolling two dice and looking at the sum-outcomes is biased.

Is it possible to simulate a *biased* experiment with *random* integers? Yes, it is! The key is to create a scheme that reflects the bias of the experiment. This is done by using probability. To see how, we will do it for the dice-roll experiment with sum-outcomes.

First look at the probabilities of the sum-outcomes. You figured them out in the previous section using a table and the 36 possible outcomes of rolling a red and a green die. They are shown in Display 7.34.

Probabilities of Sum-Outcomes (Rolling two dice)			
Sum-outcome	Probability	Sum-outcome	Probability
2	$\frac{1}{36}$	8	$\frac{5}{36}$
3	$\frac{2}{36} = \frac{1}{18}$	9	$\frac{4}{36} = \frac{1}{9}$
4	$\frac{3}{36} = \frac{1}{12}$	10	$\frac{3}{36} = \frac{1}{12}$
5	$\frac{4}{36} = \frac{1}{9}$	11	$\frac{2}{36} = \frac{1}{18}$
6	$\frac{5}{36}$	12	$\frac{1}{36}$
7	$\frac{6}{36} = \frac{1}{6}$		

Display 7.34

Each of the sum-outcome probabilities can be expressed as a ratio with a denominator of 36. For example, $P(6) = \frac{5}{36}$. So, if we use random integers between 1 and 36 inclusive, we can group them into sets such that the probability of each *set* matches that of a sum-outcome. If a set contains five of the 36 integers, the probability of an integer from that set occurring in the list is $\frac{5}{36}$. The scheme assigns the sets of integers to outcomes with the same probability. Scheme 2 (shown in Display 7.35) is an example of such a scheme.

Simulation Scheme 2 Dice-roll sums	
Random integers	Sum-outcome
1	2
2, 3	3
4, 5, 6	4
7, 8, 9, 10	5
11, 12, 13, 14, 15	6
16, 17, 18, 19, 20, 21	7
22, 23, 24, 25, 26	8
27, 28, 29, 30	9
31, 32, 33	10
34, 35	11
36	12

Display 7.35

Scheme 2 provides a realistic simulation because it reflects the bias of its experiment. For example, integers 31, 32, and 33 all represent a sum-outcome of 10. The probability of one of those integers occurring in a random list of integers between 1 and 36 inclusive equals the probability of actually getting a sum of 10 when you roll two dice— $\frac{3}{36} = \frac{1}{12}$.

To simulate rolling two dice 10 times we entered **randInt(1,36,10)** into the TI-84 and got 11, 4, 5, 5, 20, 9, 4, 17, 9, 34. Applying Scheme 2 to this list gives us these simulated sum-outcomes: 6, 4, 4, 4, 7, 5, 4, 7, 5, 11.

7.73

Are the sum-outcomes from our dice-roll simulation—6, 4, 4, 4, 7, 5, 4, 7, 5, 11—what you expected? Why or why not?

7.74

Use Scheme 2 and your calculator to play this simple game:

Three-Roll Sums (for 2-4 players or teams)—Players take turns simulating rolling two dice three times in a row. Add the sum-outcomes of the three "rolls." The first player to get a total sum of exactly 24 wins.

You just played *Three-Roll Sums* for which the "winning sum" was 24.

7.75

1. How could you change the winning sum so that it might take fewer turns for someone to win? Explain.

2. How could you change the winning sum so that it might take more turns for someone to win? Explain.

Many states sell instant lottery tickets with different levels of prizes. Here is a simplified example; we'll call it *Scratch-2-Win*. The tickets cost $1 each and you can win one of four prizes—$1, $5, $20, or $1,000. The probability of winning each prize is shown in Display 7.36.

Probabilities of Winning with *Scratch-2-Win*	
Prize	Probability
$1,000	0.0001
$20	0.001
$5	0.01
$1	0.1
None	??

Display 7.36

What is the probability of not winning any prize with *Scratch-2-Win*? How do you know?

7.76

To buy lottery tickets you must be at least 18 years old (21 in some states). What you can do instead is simulate playing *Scratch-2-Win*. (You'll probably save money doing it this way!)

Using Technology

7.77

1. Design a random-integer scheme to simulate playing *Scratch-2-Win*. What are the possible outcomes? How many possible random integers do you need? How do you know? Make a table to display your scheme.

2. If you play 20 times (buy 20 tickets), what do you expect to win? Explain.

3. Try it. Simulate playing 20 times. Which prizes, if any, did you win?

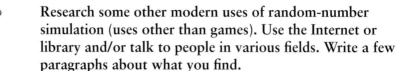

7.6 Using Random Numbers for Simulation

7.78 Research some other modern uses of random-number simulation (uses other than games). Use the Internet or library and/or talk to people in various fields. Write a few paragraphs about what you find.

Using Technology

Problem Set: 7.6

1. You are going to buy a lottery ticket and must choose a five-digit number. The winning number will be chosen at random. Which of these three numbers do you think has the best chance of winning: 99999, 12345, or 84501? Which has the worst chance? Explain.

2. Suppose your computer (or calculator) can only make random lists of digits (0-9 inclusive) such as the one shown in Display 7.37.

List of Random Digits
9 0 4 8 5 3 2 9 5 8 0 8 0 8 9 1 0 4 2 2 6 1 4 9 1 2 6 0 3 0 8 7 2 4 7 2 0 5 0 3 6 8 6 0 3 4 2 1 8 8 5
5 7 3 6 5 0 9 5 3 8 2 4 9 6 4 1 9 8 5 0 7 7 3 8 3 8 8 6 9 6 1 9 4 1 4 1 4 1 4 6 6 3 3 3 2 5 5 2 6 4

Display 7.37

   (a) Can you create a scheme to use with a random-digit list to simulate fair coin tosses? If not, explain why not. If you can, do it. Display your scheme in a table and use it with the list of random digits in Display 7.37 to simulate ten coin tosses.

   (b) Can you create a scheme to use with a random-digit list to simulate (fair) die rolls? If not, explain why not. If you can, do it. Display your scheme in a table and use it with the list of random digits in Display 7.37 to simulate ten die rolls.

3. In basketball there are two possible outcomes for a free throw—the player makes the basket (B) or misses it (M). Free-throw percentages are based on the number of baskets made. At Valley High, the captain of the basketball team has a free-throw percentage of 76%. The captain at Ridge High has a percentage of 71%.

   (a) If each captain is going to take 10 free throws, can you predict who would make more baskets? Explain. What if each takes 100 free throws?

   (b) Create two random-integer simulation schemes (one for each captain) that can be used to simulate free throws for that player.

(c) Simulate a best-of-ten competition between the two players. First simulate 10 free throws by the Valley High captain and then do it for the Ridge High captain. How many baskets are made by each player?

(d) Do the results of your simulation in part (c) support your answer to part (a)? Explain.

4. Set up a scheme to simulate how many hits a baseball player with a .310 batting average might get in five official at-bats in a game. Use your calculator to find the simulated results for seven games. Does this player go hitless in any of the seven games? Explain how you know.

5. The moves for your favorite board game depend on a spinner like the one in Display 7.38. Each player's turn starts by spinning the arrow fast and seeing what color it stops on. You want to play the game, but you've lost the spinner! The box says that $\frac{1}{3}$ of the spinner disk is red, $\frac{1}{4}$ is green, $\frac{1}{5}$ is blue, $\frac{1}{6}$ is yellow, and the rest is purple.

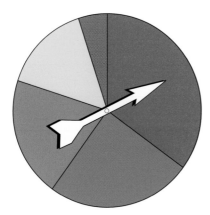

Display 7.38

(a) Design a scheme that will let you play the game by simulating the spinner with the calculator's random integer function.

(b) The instructions on the box say that your spinner tells you to move on the game board like this:

red -- 3 spaces ahead

green -- 4 spaces ahead

blue -- 5 spaces ahead

yellow -- 6 spaces ahead

purple -- 7 spaces backward (or back to Start, whichever is less)

Use your calculator and your simulation scheme to take six turns, and find the total number of spaces you move ahead.

(c) Wally's six turns were {green, red, green, purple, blue, yellow}. Are you ahead of him? If so, by how much? If not, see if you can pass him with one more turn.

6. Some games involve rolling *three* dice and using the sums. The possible sum-outcomes with their probabilities are shown in Display 7.39.

Using Technology

Probabilities of Sum-Outcomes (Rolling three dice)			
Sum-outcome	Probability	Sum-outcome	Probability
3	$\frac{1}{216}$	11	$\frac{27}{216}$
4	$\frac{3}{216}$	12	$\frac{25}{216}$
5	$\frac{6}{216}$	13	$\frac{21}{216}$
6	$\frac{10}{126}$	14	$\frac{15}{216}$
7	$\frac{15}{216}$	15	$\frac{10}{126}$
8	$\frac{21}{216}$	16	$\frac{6}{216}$
9	$\frac{25}{216}$	17	$\frac{3}{216}$
10	$\frac{27}{216}$	18	$\frac{1}{216}$

Display 7.39

(a) Design a scheme for a random-integer simulation of rolling three dice and looking at the sum-outcomes. How many possible random integers do you need? How do you know? Make a table to display your scheme.

(b) Make up your own simple game that you can play by *simulating* the sums you get by rolling three dice. Try playing it with a friend (or friends). Once you have figured out the details, write down the rules. Be sure to carefully explain how to play the game. Do you earn points? Do you move ahead on a board? How do you win? (Don't forget to include the scheme you use for the dice-roll simulation!)

Looking Back

This chapter began with counting. Thinking of counting problems as counting elements in sets lets us use mathematical tools to understand and to solve them.

Some counting problems (like the MTV-video game example) involve related sets and subsets. Sets can be related by union, intersection, difference, or complement. Venn diagrams help to picture such relationships and to count elements. These kinds of problems are often easier when the sets are disjoint.

Other counting problems (like deli sandwich choices or outcomes of a playoff) involve ways to take consecutive actions. Tree diagrams help organize and count possibilities. The Fundamental Counting Principle can be used in some such situations to count without making a tree.

The second half of the chapter was about probability—a numerical way to describe the chances of an event happening. You saw how probabilities can be assigned based on intuition or on data. Experiments considered random (like fair-coin tosses or die rolls) have equally likely outcomes. In that case, probabilities can be found by *counting* outcomes and taking the ratio of acceptable to total possible outcomes. The counting skills from earlier in the chapter are very useful for this. Finally, you saw how probability is used to design random-number schemes for simulation.

You will use the ideas of this chapter again in **MATH** *Connections* for further study of probability and the related field of statistics.

In this chapter you learned how to:

- Use various forms of set notation.
- Describe counting and probability functions.
- Describe the intersection, union, difference, and complement of sets.
- Draw and interpret Venn diagrams to solve some counting problems.
- Draw tree diagrams to represent and solve some counting problems.
- State the Fundamental Counting Principle and use it to solve problems.
- Assign probabilities based on intuition, history, or performed experiments.
- Describe a sample space for an experiment.
- Explain what it means for outcomes to be equally likely.
- Assign the probability of an event using the ratio of acceptable to total possible outcomes.

- Find the probability of an event's complement and of the union and the intersection of events.
- Design and apply random-integer schemes to simulate random and biased experiments.

Along the way, you also learned to:

- Distinguish between finite and infinite sets.
- Use factorial notation.
- Generate random-integer lists on a TI-84 calculator.

Review Exercises

1. Nina surveyed 180 people about which of three types of music players they own. Her results are in the Venn diagram in Display 7.40. Use it to answer the following questions.

   (a) How many own only a tape player?

   (b) How many own CD and MP3 players but not a tape player?

   (c) How many do not own a tape player, a CD player, or an MP3 player?

   (d) How many own all three types of players?

   (e) How many own an MP3 player?

   (f) Describe in words what the unlabeled region represents. Then calculate the number that belongs in that region.

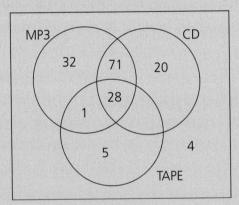

Display 7.40

2. Jeff brought vanilla and chocolate ice cream to the last math club meeting. All 19 members (including Jeff) were at the meeting. Jeff tried to keep track of which flavors everyone ate to help him plan for the next time. He recorded the following information:

    2 members did not have any ice cream. 14 members had at least some chocolate, 12 had at least some vanilla, and 5 had chocolate only.

    (a) How many had both chocolate and vanilla?

    (b) How many had only vanilla?

    (c) Draw a Venn diagram to illustrate this information.

3. Do you know someone (maybe yourself) from a family with four children? If the first child born in a family is a girl (G), the second a boy (B), the third a girl, and the fourth a boy, we could write GBGB to show the order in which the children were born.

    (a) Make a tree diagram and use it to count how many different girl-boy orders are possible for a family with four children.

    (b) Which other counting tool can you use to count the number of possible girl-boy orders there are for a family with four children? Use it and compare your answer with the one you got in part (a).

    (c) Which method do you think is better? Explain.

4. The Valley High School Orchestra includes 16 violinists, 10 violists, and 8 cellists.

    (a) The conductor is going to select students from the orchestra to form a string trio. She needs one violinist, one violist, and one cellist. How many different string trios can she assemble?

    (b) If the conductor decides to assemble a string quartet she will need two violinists (one to play first violin, which plays the melody, and one to play second violin, which plays harmony), one violist, and one cellist. How many different string quartets can she assemble?

5. A teacher has w pieces of white chalk and y pieces of yellow chalk in his desk drawer. Which expression represents the probability of randomly picking a yellow piece of chalk from the drawer?

    (i) $\dfrac{y}{w}$ (ii) $\dfrac{w}{y}$ (iii) $\dfrac{y}{w + y}$ (iv) $\dfrac{w}{w + y}$

6. Diana and Annie are going to play a game of chess. The probability that Diana will win is 46% and the probability that Annie will win is 43%. What is the probability that the game ends in a stalemate (tie)?

7. Amanda randomly selected 30 students from her school and found that 9 of them had blue eyes.

   (a) What is the probability that a randomly selected student has blue eyes?

   (b) What is the probability that a randomly selected student does *not* have blue eyes?

   (c) If Amanda's sample is representative of the school population, about how many of the 1780 students at her school have blue eyes?

8. One of five different prizes can be won with a *Dreaming of Dollars* instant lottery ticket—$2, $5, $25, $100, or $5,000. The probability of winning each prize is shown in Display 7.41.

   (a) What is the probability of winning $5,000?

   (b) What is the probability of winning less than $100?

   (c) What is the probability of winning at least $25?

   (d) A group of friends buy 500 tickets together and plan to share any winnings. How many of their 500 tickets are likely to win nothing at all?

Probabilities of Winning with *Dreaming of Dollars*	
Prize	Probability
None	0.92
$2	0.03
$5	0.025
$25	0.020
$100	0.0045
$5,000	????

Display 7.41

9. The spinner shown in Display 7.42 is used to decide which kind of card will be drawn next in a game—blue, red, or yellow. The spinner is divided into four equal sections. One of the sections is divided in half.

   (a) What is the probability that a yellow card will be drawn?

   (b) What is the probability that a red card will be drawn?

   (c) What is the probability that a red or a yellow card will be drawn?

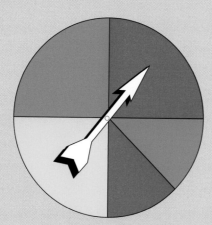

Display 7.42

10. On average, Devon makes 3 foul shots out of every 5 he takes. Which of the following methods could be used to simulate his next foul shot and which could not? Justify your answers.

   (a) Use a random number generator. Let numbers 1, 2, and 5 represent making the shot and numbers 3 and 4 represent missing it.

   (b) Flip a fair coin. Let heads represent making the shot and tails represent missing it.

   (c) Roll a fair die. Let the numbers 1, 2, and 3 represent making the shot and the numbers 4, 5, and 6 represent missing it.

   (d) Spin a spinner with 10 equally sized sections. Let 6 sections represent making the shot and let 4 represent missing it.

   (e) Draw a marble from a bag that contains 12 red and 8 blue marbles. Let a red marble represent making the shot and a blue marble represent missing it.

11. Four best friends, two girls and two boys, are going to line up in a row to have their picture taken.

(a) In how many different ways can the group of friends line up?

(b) In how many different ways can they line up so that a girl is on each end of the row?

(c) If they randomly line up, what is the probability that there will be a girl on each end of the row?

Related Topics

Geometric Probability

Over the course of your mathematical career, you have encountered many formulas for the area of different shapes.

Try to identify which shape is described by each area formula.

7.79

1. $A = s^2$

2. $A = lw$

3. $A = \frac{1}{2}bh$

4. $A = \pi r^2$

Knowing the above formulas is important not only for geometry problems but for other disciplines as well. In this section, we will examine how area can be used to calculate probabilities.

Many games that you might be familiar with rely on chance. Dice are often used to advance a game piece but sometimes spinners are used as well.

1. **What is the probability of getting 4 or greater using the spinner shown in Display 7.43? What assumptions are you making about the sections of the spinner?**

7.80

2. **Did you use area to figure this out? If not, how did you do it?**

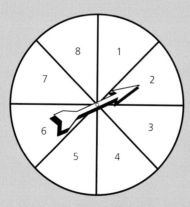

Display 7.43

Area was not needed in the last problem. The definition of probability states that the probability of event *a* happening is:

$$P(a) = \frac{\text{Number of Acceptable Outcomes}}{\text{Total Number of Possible Outcomes}}$$

Because the circle is divided into eighths, a reasonable number of total outcomes would be 8 and the number of acceptable outcomes would be the total of all the numbers 4 or greater. This method will work as long as each slice of pie, known as a sector, is the same size. Is the area at work here? Not really; most of this work can be done using degrees of rotation with 360° degrees being the "total outcomes."

$$P(a) = \frac{\text{Number of Acceptable Degrees}}{360°}$$

7.81

What is the probability that the spinner will land within the 60° sector? What is the probability that it will not land within the 60° sector?

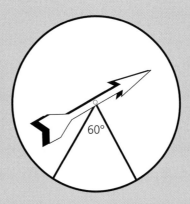

Display 7.44

Both of the previous problems can be solved using area, but that would involve more work. You would have to calculate areas of the sectors as well as the total area of the circle. The definition of probability can be modified to read:

$$P(a) = \frac{\text{Acceptable Area}}{\text{Total Area}}$$

In addition to providing entertainment, games can also be the basis for sophisticated models in the economic and scientific worlds. One example comes from the world of physics. Currently, scientists at the Large Hadron Collider near Geneva, Switzerland, are using particle accelerators to examine the makeup of the universe. By crashing atoms and ions into each other, scientists get a brief glimpse of the basic building blocks that make up everything. Because atoms are extremely small, the chance of two hitting one another is smaller still. Scientists have to use sophisticated methods to make sure these collisions happen.

In the collider, scientists are searching for the "positive" event that the particles will collide. The acceptable outcome can be thought of as the small area of collision and the total outcomes can be represented by all the possible area for where a particle could land.

Imagine using a projectile to try to hit a target represented by the shaded square within the bigger square in Display 7.45. (Note: diagram not drawn to scale.)

7.82

1. The bigger square has a side length of 10 units and the shaded square has a side length of 5 units. Without doing any calculations, predict the probability of hitting the shaded region if the projectile hits somewhere within the big square.

2. Now do the calculations. What is the total area of the bigger square (including the shaded region inside)?

3. What is the area of the shaded region?

4. If you know that you can randomly hit anywhere within the bigger square, what is the probability that the shaded area will be hit?

5. What is the probability that only the unshaded part will be hit by a randomly thrown projectile?

6. Did it match your prediction? If not, describe what happened.

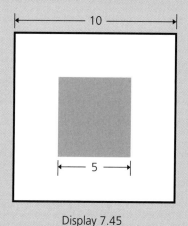

Display 7.45

7.83 Some area problems can be solved without numbers. Display 7.46 is a disk (filled-in circle) that is inscribed inside a square, touching each side at exactly one point.

1. Assign a side length to the square and calculate its area.

2. Use the side length to find the radius of the circle, then calculate its area.

3. Assuming that a projectile randomly hits within the square, find the probability of hitting the disk.

4. Repeat steps 1–3 using a different side length of the square.

5. Did you get the same answer? Why or why not?

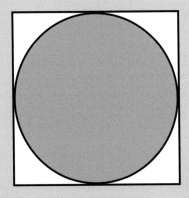

Display 7.46

The previous problem illustrates a problem-solving technique known as "arbitrary values." If the problem does not provide numbers, plug some in. What happens? This works because the ratio of the area of the circle to the area of the square stays the same no matter how big or small you make it.

7.84 Try this problem with arbitrary lengths.

1. Calculate the probability of hitting the smaller circle assuming that a projectile will hit inside the larger circle.

2. Calculate the probability of only hitting the unshaded part assuming that the projectile will hit somewhere within the larger circle.

3. Compare these probabilities to the probabilities in the previous "square within a square" problem. Why do you think they are the same?

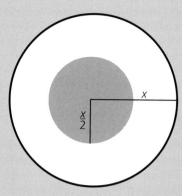

Display 7.47

Some games link probability to point values. The harder it is to hit the target, the more points it is worth. You might be familiar with the game of darts. One of the hardest targets to hit on the board is the inner bullseye.

In this activity, you will examine various probabilities for different spots on the dartboard. In Display 7.48, you are given the diameters of the concentric circles.

7.85

1. Calculate the total area of the board.

2. Calculate the chance of hitting within the outer bullseye (marked 31.8 mm) assuming that a dart will hit somewhere on the board. This would include hitting the inner bullseye.

3. What is the chance of hitting only the inner bullseye (marked 12.7 mm)?

4. What is the chance of only hitting the area of the outer bullseye and not the inner?

5. The number of points for hitting the outer bullseye is 25 whereas the number of points for an inner bullseye is 50. Do you think this is fair based on the probabilities you have calculated? Explain.

6. The first pair of inner rings occurs between 340 mm and 324 mm. This is the "double" ring. Hitting that area with a dart gives double the point value. Find the area of this ring and calculate the chance of a dart hitting the double ring given that it will hit the board.

7. The second pair of inner rings occurs between 214 mm and 198 mm. This is the "triple" ring. Hitting that area with a dart results in triple the point value. Find the area of this ring and calculate the chance of a dart hitting the triple ring.

8. Do the probabilities in questions 6 & 7 match up with the 2 : 3 points ratio? Use numbers to explain.

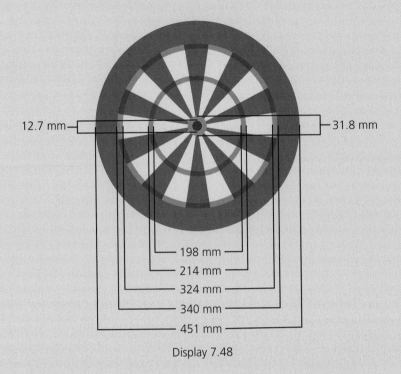

12.7 mm ⎯ 31.8 mm

⎯ 198 mm ⎯
⎯ 214 mm ⎯
⎯ 324 mm ⎯
⎯ 340 mm ⎯
⎯ 451 mm ⎯

Display 7.48

7.86

Write a paragraph explaining whether or not you think that the game of darts uses a "fair" points system. Use numbers to support your view.

Geometric probability is used in the working world in addition to the world of games. There are even mathematical disciplines devoted entirely to the analysis of games. "Game Theory," as it is known, is used for many real-world applications including economic business models. The next time that you play a game, ask yourself, "How can I use this in the real world?"

Problem Set

1. Use the spinner shown in Display 7.49 to calculate the following probabilities.

   (a) Assuming the shaded region is half the spinner, what is the probability of landing in the shaded region with one spin?

   (b) What is the probability of landing in the 40° sector?

   (c) What is the probability of landing in the shaded region but *not* in the 40° sector?

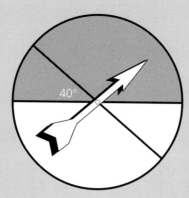

Display 7.49

2. Given the event of a projectile hitting inside the square shown in Display 7.50, find the following probabilities.

   (a) The chance of hitting the shaded region.

   (b) The chance of not hitting the shaded region.

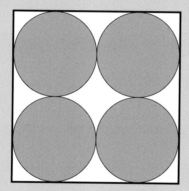

Display 7.50

3. In Display 7.51 there is a square containing four congruent isosceles triangles. Given that a projectile hits inside the square, find the following probabilities.

   (a) The chance that the projectile hits the shaded region.

   (b) The chance that a projectile does not hit the shaded region.

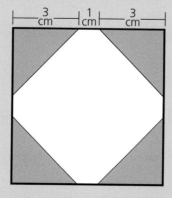

Display 7.51

4. Assuming that a projectile hits somewhere inside the circle shown in Display 7.52, find the probability of hitting inside the square.

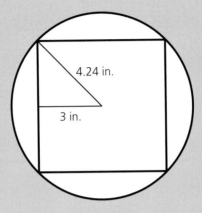

Display 7.52

5. Use Display 7.48 and your previous work to answer the following questions.

(a) There are twenty numbers in darts and therefore 20 (roughly) even pie-shaped divisions of the board. What is the chance of hitting just one of the rounded rectangles in the doubles ring?

(b) What is the probability of hitting just one of the 20 rounded rectangles in the triples ring?

Absolute Value Revisited

Earlier, we looked at absolute value numerically and graphically. You saw how absolute value was used to find the distance between two points on a number line. You were also asked to solve problems like $|x - 2| = 4$. We are now going to look at problems similar to this but in the form of an inequality.

Let's start by looking back at problems you have seen before.

Graph each of the following inequalities.

7.87

1. $x < 4$

2. $x \leq -3$

3. $x \geq 2$

Now let's look at two key words in mathematics: "and" and "or." The word "and" is often used to mean that the solution must meet all requirements (such as intersection of sets) where "or" means that the solution must meet at least one of the requirements but does not need to meet all of them (such as union of sets). So, if you are asked to find a number x that meets the following requirement, $(x < 4)$ *and* $(x > -2)$, the solution must meet both conditions. If you selected $x = -5$, the first condition would be met (-5 is less than 4) but not the second condition, as -5 is not greater than -2.

1. **Can you find a number that meets both of these conditions?**

    7.88

2. **How many numbers can you select?**

3. **Let's be a little more detailed with question 2. What natural numbers work? What integers work? What real numbers work?**

4. **Graph the solutions to question 3 on separate number lines.**

In Chapter 2, when you did these problems, you left the answers in graph form. Now we need to look at writing the solutions in set-builder notation and interval notation. If we first look at the natural number solution of question 3, we see that the only solutions are 1, 2, and 3. There are a few ways that we can write this in set-builder notation:

- $\{x \mid x \in \mathbb{N}, x < 4\}$. In words, the set of all x such that x is an element of the natural numbers and x is less than 4.

- $\{x \mid x \in \{1, 2, 3\}\}$. In words, the set of all x such that x is an element of the set that includes 1, 2, 3.

Let's look at changing the set of numbers to integers.

- $\{x \mid x \in \mathbb{Z}, -2 < x < 4\}$
- $\{x \mid x \in \{-1, 0, 1, 2, 3\}\}$

Finally, let's look at the real numbers. We cannot list each of the members as we have in the previous two examples.

- $\{x \mid x \in \mathbb{R}, -2 < x < 4\}$

We could also write the real-number solution in interval notation, which would be $(-2, 4)$. This form looks like an ordered pair but it is not. This notation shows that all numbers between the endpoints are solutions. You use parentheses to indicate that an endpoint is not included and you use brackets to indicate that an endpoint is included.

What if we changed the problem to $(x < 4)$ or $(x \geq 8)$ and chose $x = 10$ as a solution? Well, 10 is greater than or equal to 8, but 10 is not less than 4. The word "or" indicates that only one of the conditions needs to be true in order for the solution to work, so 10 would be a solution.

7.89

1. **What natural numbers work?**

2. **What integers work?**

3. **What real numbers work?**

4. **Graph the solutions to questions 1 through 3 on separate number lines.**

Now can we record these answers in set-builder notation? Can we list each element of the solution set? The answer to the first question is Yes but the second is No. We cannot list each element as there is no end to the list of natural numbers greater than or equal to 8.

7.90

Write in set-builder notation the solutions to questions 1 though 3 of Lightning Icon 7.89.

Interval notation for this problem would be a little more difficult as we need all real numbers less than 4 or all real numbers greater than or equal to 8. The operation would be the union of both these sets. So, we would write that as $(-\infty, 4) \cup [8, \infty)$. That means that you want the numbers from negative infinity up to 4, but not including 4, and the numbers from 8, including 8, up to positive infinity. These two intervals are joined together by the set operation union. When we use infinity, we must use a parenthesis on that side of the interval.

Write interval notation for the following intervals.

7.91

1. $-2 \le x \le 6$

2. $4 \le x < 20$

3. $x \ge 3$

4. $(x < 3)$ or $(x \ge 6)$

Now let's go back to investigating absolute values with inequalities. If we have the inequality $|x| < 5$, how would we go about finding the solution? Well, up to this point we have solved many problems numerically, algebraically and geometrically. Let's try the numerical method first by guess and check.

Answer the following questions based on the inequality $|x| < 5$.

7.92

1. From the set $\{-10, -9, ..., 9, 10\}$, which values would be solutions?

2. Can you find any integer solutions outside the above set that would work?

3. How would you describe the real-number solution set for this problem?

4. Graph the real-number solutions.

5. Write the real-number solutions in set-builder notation.

Algebraically, you would need to rewrite the inequality without the absolute value symbols. First, you will need to know that $<$, "and," and "intersection" are all intertwined in this concept. In rewriting the absolute value, we need to break it up into two components that we will call cases. As you may recall the definition of absolute value is as follows.

$$|x| = \begin{cases} x \text{ for } x \ge 0 \\ -x \text{ for } x < 0 \end{cases}$$

This definition shows us that we have to deal with two cases when working with absolute value. The first will be the positive case ($x \ge 0$) and the second the negative case ($x < 0$). Let's look at what it will look like for this problem.

$$|x| < 5$$

Positive Case   Negative Case

$$x < 5 \quad \text{and} \quad x > -5$$

As you recall, when we see the word "and," we need to meet both conditions or, in other words, the intersection of both sets.

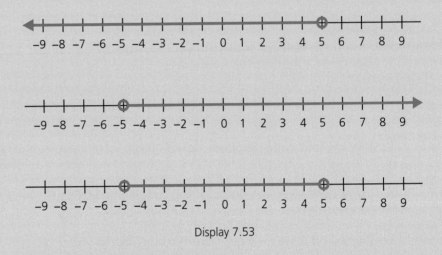

Display 7.53

From the graphs in Display 7.53, you see the first graph is the solution to the positive case, the second graph is the solution to the negative case and the third graph is the intersection of these two graphs (that is, where these two graphs overlap each other). This graph indicates that any number between -5 and 5 works. We could rewrite this solution into a compound statement as $-5 < x < 5$, in set-builder notation as $\{x \mid x \in \mathbb{R}, -5 < x < 5\}$, or in interval notation as $(-5, 5)$.

7.93

Solve the last example over the following sets. Graph the solutions on a number line and write the solution in set-builder notation.

1. **Natural numbers**

2. **Integers**

Now we can find a graphical solution using your graphing calculator. The graphing calculator has a provision in it that allows you to enter an inequality into the **Y=** list. You can find inequality symbols under the **TEST** menu (**2ND, MATH**). When an x-value is substituted into an inequality and it forms a true expression, then the output is the value 1, otherwise it yields 0. So, using the **Y=**, the **MATH,** and the **TEST** menus you should see the screens in Display 7.54.

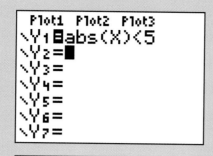

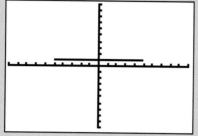

Display 7.54

You can see on the graph that y-values from -5 to 5 have 1 as a result and all other x-values have 0. This may not be evident from the graph but you can see it in the table on the calculator. Looking at the screens in Display 7.55, you can see that at $x = 5$ and $x = -5$, the y-value is 0. The endpoints are not included in this graph.

Display 7.55

Now let's change the inequality to $|x| > 5$.

7.94

1. From the set $\{-10, -9, ..., 9, 10\}$, which values would be solutions?

2. Can you find any integer solutions outside the above set that would work?

3. How would you describe the real-number solution set for this problem?

4. Graph the real-number solutions.

5. Write the real-number solution in set-builder notation.

Algebraically, again we will break this inequality into two cases. But in this situation, the $>$ symbol lets us know the word "or" and the operation "union" are going to be used. So, we will have the following breakdown.

$$|x| > 5$$

Positive Case   Negative Case

$x > 5$ or $x < -5$

From our previous work, you know that any value you choose must meet just one of the requirements. So, we need to join the two solution sets together (union). The graphs of this operation are shown in Display 7.56.

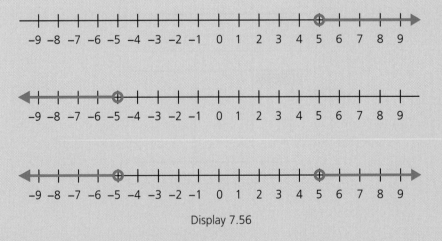

Display 7.56

The final graph shows us that any number less than -5 or any number greater than 5 works for this problem.

The numbers between -5 and 5, inclusive, do not work. In set-builder notation, the answer would look like $\{x \mid x \in \mathbb{R}, (x < -5) \text{ or } (x > 5)\}$. How would you write this in interval notation? It would need the union operation for the word "or" and would look like $(-\infty, -5) \cup (5, \infty)$.

> **Solve the last example over the following sets. Graph the solutions on number lines and write the solution in set-builder notation.**
>
> 1. **Natural numbers**
>
> 2. **Integers**

7.95

The graphing calculator approach to this problem is similar to the previous problem. Use the screens in Display 7.57 below to check your work as you try this problem on your calculator.

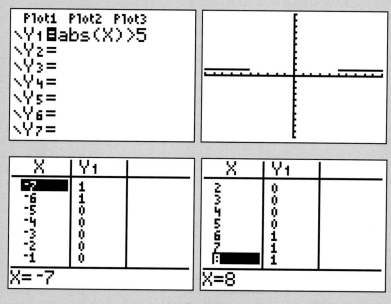

Display 7.57

Now it is time to introduce a few additional concepts. What if something was added or subtracted from the x-term inside the absolute value? How does it change the problem? Let's look at $|x + 2| < 5$. Again, you could substitute values into x using the guess and check method of solving the problem. We could also use the algebraic and graphical methods.

Algebraically, we get two cases: $x + 2 < 5$ *and* $x + 2 > -5$. We need to solve each of these before we can graph a solution.

$$x + 2 < 5 \quad \text{and} \quad x + 2 > -5$$
$$x < 3 \quad \text{and} \quad x > -7$$

This can be rewritten as $-7 < x < 3$ and the graph is shown in Display 7.58.

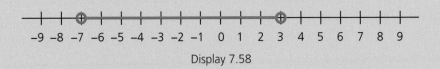

Display 7.58

Let's check this out with our calculator. You should see the graph and tables in Display 7.59.

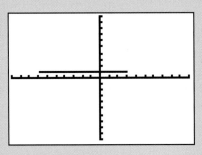

Display 7.59

Let's make one change to the problem. If the problem was $|x + 2| \leq 5$, what changes? The endpoints would now be included. Look at how the tables in Display 7.60 change when the inequality is changed.

Display 7.60

You should notice that the endpoints, $x = 3$ and $x = -7$, are now included in the solution.

Now let's look at $|x + 2| > 5$. We have the algebraic expansion as $x + 2 > 5$ or $x + 2 < -5$, which simplifies to $x > 3$ or $x < -7$. The graph is shown in Display 7.61.

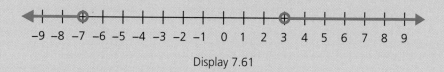

Display 7.61

Let's summarize what we have done so far.

If we are given an inequality in the form of $|ax + b| < c$, then we need to convert it to the compound inequality: $ax + b < c$ and $ax + b > -c$.

If we are given an inequality in the form of $|ax + b| > c$, then we need to convert it to the compound inequality: $ax + b > c$ or $ax + b < -c$.

In both cases, we then need to solve these compound inequalities to determine the final solution.

Solve the following inequalities.

7.96

1. $|x + 4| > 5$

2. $|x - 2| < 4$

We have now handled the basic forms of absolute value inequalities. If we are given variations of the form, all we need to remember is to get the absolute value term alone on one side of the inequality and the value on the other. Then the inequality is set to be broken down into the separate cases.

Let's try another variation, $2|x - 1| < 6$. This inequality does not have just the absolute value on the left-hand side. We have the 2 being multiplied to the absolute value. If we divide both sides by 2, we will have $|x - 1| < 3$. You can now solve this from here, using the techniques from this section.

What if we rewrote the above problem to $-2|x - 1| < 6$? If we divide by -2 we get $|x - 1| > -3$ (remember when you multiply or divide both sides of an inequality by a negative number, you change the direction of the inequality). If we break this inequality into its two cases, we have:

$$x - 1 > -3 \quad \text{or} \quad x - 1 < 3$$
$$x > -2 \quad \text{or} \quad x < 4$$

If we graph these separately and join them together, we get the solution "all real numbers," as shown in the last graph in Display 7.62. We would write this in set-builder notation as $\{x \mid x \in \mathbb{R}\}$. How would this be written in interval notation? The real numbers range from negative infinity to positive infinity, so it would be $(-\infty, \infty)$.

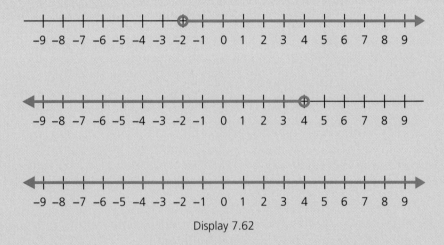

Display 7.62

When we were at the step $|x - 1| > -3$, we should have recalled that the absolute value always yields a positive number. Thus all real numbers will work for x. If we changed the problem to $-2|x - 1| > 6$, we would find out that there are no values of x that will work.

Show why $-2|x - 1| > 6$ has no solutions.

7.97

Solve the following inequalities over the real numbers. Graph the solutions on number lines and write the answers in both set-builder notation and interval notation.

7.98

1. $3|x - 1| + 2 < 11$

2. $2|x + 4| - 3 > 9$

As we have done throughout the textbook, we have encompassed many skills within the frameworks of a problem. Let's think about the following problem.

Say we want to find all the values of x on a number line within 5 units of 4. As you recall, the distance between any two points on a number line can be represented by $|x_2 - x_1|$. So, for this problem, we are trying to find all values that are less than or equal to 5 units away from 4 which translates to the following inequality.

$$|x - 4| \leq 5$$

Solving for x we must first convert the inequality to the compound inequality $|x - 4| \leq 5$ and $x - 4 \geq -5$. Solving both cases, the solution simplifies to: $-1 \leq x \leq 9$. Thus, all the points on the number line between -1 and 9, inclusive, are within 5 units of 4. Now it's your turn.

Find all the values of x on a number line that are more than 6 units away from -3. First, write the inequality that goes along with the problem, then solve it.

7.99

Problem Set

For problems 1–4, solve for x over the given set, graph the solution on a number line, and write the solution in set-builder notation.

1. $3x - 5 < 16$ {Integers}

2. $6 - 2x > 14$ {Integers}

3. $9 - 3x > 12$ {Natural numbers}

4. $|x - 4| \leq 7$ {Natural numbers}

For problems 5 and 6, answer the same questions as in problems 1–4 *and* also write the solution in interval notation.

5. $|2x - 4| \geq 8$ {Real numbers}

6. $3|2x - 4| + 2 \geq 8$ {Real numbers}

Stafford Thompson
Predicting the Unknown

Stafford Thompson is a senior actuarial analyst at CIGNA Health Care. "I really enjoy being a mathematician," he explains. "I like being able to identify problems, put them into a mathematical context, and then solve them!"

Stafford had always liked math. The summer after 11th grade found him at a camp for actuarial science. "I had no idea what an actuary was, but I knew they offered calculus and linear algebra, so I wanted to go." He went on to Florida Agricultural and Mechanical University in Tallahassee. He earned a B.S. in Mathematics with a concentration in Actuarial Science.

It's commonly believed that actuaries just help insurance companies predict when policyholders will get sick or die. In fact, actuaries perform many interesting types of statistical analysis. They can figure the probability of a baseball player hitting a fan on the head with a foul ball. They can predict the chance that space shuttle debris will land on your house. They can also calculate the probability of serious injury to Michael Jackson, whose voice is insured for millions.

Stafford uses his actuarial skills to predict how profitable an investment will be. "We use the law of large numbers. We can't really predict what a person will do. But with many millions of individuals, we can do a very reliable job." Using probability, averages and measures of variance, Stafford forecasts the values of various investments. "We look at current and past rates over a 10 to 15 year history," he explains. "We try to predict the rate of inflation. There's a lot of educated guesswork."

Stafford's long-term goal is to teach Actuarial Science at a university. "I want to prepare other students for an actuarial career."

"I like my job," he concludes. "I like the opportunity to use my skills. I enjoy making money, and actuarial science provides a foundation for any entrepreneurial dreams you may have. Using financial analysis, I've learned how to build a business from the ground up."

Quadratic Functions and Equations

8

8.1 Combining Linear Functions

Learning Outcomes

After studying this section, you will be able to:

Add, subtract, compose, and multiply two linear functions

Explain what a quadratic function is

Describe how quadratic functions are related to linear functions

Put any quadratic function into a standard form.

Earlier in **MATH** *Connections* you worked a lot with linear functions. Do you remember what they are? Let us help you out:

> **A Phrase to Know:** A **linear function** is a function that can be put in the form $f(x) = ax + b$, where a and b are specific real numbers (constants).

Linear functions are used to describe many situations. They are useful because they are easy to work with and their graphs are simple straight lines. When different parts of a situation are described by linear functions, combining them in one way or another can lead to simpler, more useful formulas. Here are some examples.

Francine has a part-time office job that pays her $12 an hour. It costs her $2 per day to ride the bus to and from work. Before she goes to work each day, she has to drop off her daughter Gloria at day care. Day care costs $3 an hour, and it takes Francine half an hour to get to work from the day care center (and half an hour to get back).

8.1

1. If Francine works 5 hours on Monday, how much will Gloria's day care cost? How much money will Francine make on Monday before she pays for day care? After she pays for day care?

2. If Francine only works 3 hours on Tuesday, how much will Gloria's day care cost? How much money will Francine make on Tuesday before she pays for day care? After she pays for day care?

3. Write a linear function (call it g) for how much Gloria's day care costs if Francine works x hours on Wednesday. Put it in the form $g(x) = ax + b$.

4. Write a linear function (call it f) for how much money Francine will make before paying for day care if she works x hours on Wednesday. Put it in the form $f(x) = cx + d$.

5. Combine these two functions to get a single function (call it h) for how much money Francine will make after paying for day care if she works x hours on Wednesday. Is the result a linear function? How can you tell?

6. Use your formula from part 5 to compute how much Francine makes after paying for day care if she works 8 hours.

8.2

A construction company needs to move a small bulldozer to various job locations during a week. They rent a truck and a trailer to do it.

1. The truck rental costs $150 for the week, plus $0.40 per mile. Write a linear function f for the total cost of renting this truck for x miles. Use it to calculate the cost for 90 miles and for 230 miles.

2. The trailer rental costs $75 for the week, plus $0.25 per mile. Write a linear function g for the total cost of renting this trailer for x miles. Use it to calculate the cost for 90 miles and for 230 miles.

3. Add the functions f and g to form a single cost function, $f + g$, for moving this bulldozer. Write your answer in $ax + b$ form. Then use it to calculate the cost for 90 miles and for 230 miles. Do your answers for these mileages agree with the sums of your answers in parts 1 and 2? (They should.)

As you can see from these questions, to add two functions, you just add the two images for each domain element. To do that more efficiently, you can write a single formula for the sum by adding the two algebraic expressions for the functions. The same kind of thing works for subtraction. In symbols, this is what we have just said:

The **sum** $f + g$ of two functions f and g is the function defined by

$$(f + g)(x) = f(x) + g(x)$$

for every domain element x. The **difference** $f - g$ is the function defined by

$$(f - g)(x) = f(x) - g(x)$$

for every domain element x.

$f(x) = 2x + 5$ and $g(x) = 3x - 1$ are two linear functions. Write the functions $f + g$, $f - g$, and $g - f$ in the form $ax + b$.

8.3

Is the sum of two linear functions *always* linear? What about the difference? Give a persuasive argument to justify your answers.

8.4

Were you able to convince yourself (and maybe someone else) that the sum and difference of linear functions is always linear? If not, did someone convince you? We hope so, because it's true.

Another way to put two linear functions together is by composition. That is, you apply the second function to the results of the first one. For instance, in Chapter 3 you found this linear function for changing temperature measurement from Fahrenheit degrees to Celsius degrees:

$$C(x) = \frac{5}{9}x - \frac{160}{9}$$

where x is a temperature in degrees Fahrenheit. You also learned that a Kelvin temperature measurement can be found from a Celsius measurement by adding 273.2. That is a linear function, too. If we call it K, then

$$K(x) = x + 273.2$$

for any Celsius temperature x. You can convert a temperature from Fahrenheit to Kelvin in these two steps, or you can use the composite function $K \circ C$ that does it all at once, like this:

$$(K \circ C)(x) = K(C(x)) = (\tfrac{5}{9}x - \tfrac{160}{9}) + 273.2$$

By combining the constant terms you get the standard linear form, $ax + b$, for this composite function:

$$K(C(x)) = \tfrac{5}{9}x + \frac{22{,}988}{90}$$

For most purposes, this can be simplified and rounded to

$$K(C(x)) = 0.556x + 255.42$$

8.5

1. Calculate the Kelvin temperature for 72°F in two steps, using the functions C and then K. Then calculate it again using the composite function. Do your answers agree?

2. Water boils at 212°F. What is that in Celsius degrees? What is it in Kelvins? Use the composite function to calculate the answer in Kelvins. Does it agree with what you think it should be?

3. $f(x) = 2x + 5$ and $g(x) = 3x - 1$ are two linear functions. Write the composite functions $f \circ g$ and $g \circ f$ in the form $ax + b$.

8.6

Justify the claim that the composite of two linear functions is always linear.

Still another way to combine two linear functions is by multiplying them together. You can find the product of the images of two linear functions efficiently by making a single product function, like this:

The **product** $f \cdot g$ of two functions f and g is the function defined by

$$(f \cdot g)(x) = f(x) \cdot g(x)$$

for every domain element x.

Suppose, for example, you are trying to make up plans for a rectangular storage shed. The outside of this shed needs to be three times as long as it is wide, and the walls will be 1 foot thick all around. To figure out the usable floor space inside, you need to multiply the inside width by the inside length. Now, each of these dimensions depends on the outside width. If you call the outside width x, then the inside width is $x - 2$ (allowing for the wall thickness) and the inside length is $3x - 2$.

1. Find the amount of inside floor space (in square feet) if the outside width is 10 feet. What if the outside width is 15 feet?

8.7

2. Write a function $A(x)$ that will tell you the inside floor space for any outside width x. Then use it to check your answers from part 1.

3. Write A as a linear function, in $ax + b$ form, if possible. If that is not possible, explain why not.

The answer to question 3 is important. Did you say that it is not possible to write A as a linear function? If so, you're correct! But why? Let's take a closer look. To find the area of a rectangle, you multiply its length times its width, right? So the area function in this case should be

$$(3x - 2) \cdot (x - 2)$$

The distributive law allows us to rewrite this as

$$(3x - 2) \cdot x - (3x - 2) \cdot 2$$

(Do you see why?) This looks a bit like a linear function, but the coefficient of x is not a constant number; it's an expression that has a variable in it. To simplify it further, we can use the distributive law again—twice—to get

$$3x \cdot x - 2 \cdot x - 3x \cdot 2 + 2 \cdot 2$$

By the laws of algebra you learned in Chapter 2, this area function can be rewritten in a more compact form:

$$3x^2 - 8x + 4$$

The x^2 term tells us that this cannot be a linear function. That is, the product of two linear functions is *not* always a linear function! We have a different kind of function here, a kind that has a name of its own.

About Words

The prefix *quad-* comes from the Latin word for "four," as in *quadrangle, quadruplet,* and *quadruped* (a four-footed animal). The word *quadratic* here reflects the connection between these functions and areas of rectangles, which are four-sided polygons.

A Phrase to Know: A **quadratic function** is a function that can be put in the form

$$f(x) = ax^2 + bx + c,$$

where a, b, and c are specific real numbers and a is not 0.

1. $f(x) = 2x + 5$ and $g(x) = 3x - 1$ are two linear functions. Write their product as a quadratic function in the standard form $ax^2 + bx + c$.

2. Make up two linear functions in any way you choose. Write their product as a quadratic function in the standard form $ax^2 + bx + c$, if you can. If you cannot, explain why it is not possible to do that.

Can the product of two linear functions ever be linear? Justify your answer.

Multiplying two linear functions using the distributive laws can be tedious. There is a quicker method, but before you use it, you should understand why it works. We will show you this using algebraic symbols, rather than particular numbers, because the symbols make the pattern clearer. (That's one of the things algebra is good for!) Follow along carefully; if you run into a line you can't figure out, ask your teacher or a classmate to help you.

We start with two linear functions, $a_1x + b_1$ and $a_2x + b_2$. (Yes, we know subscripts can be annoying, but they will help you keep track of which coefficients come from which functions.) Now we'll multiply them, using the distributive law several times and then tidying up:

$$(a_1x + b_1) \cdot (a_2x + b_2)$$
$$a_1x \cdot (a_2x + b_2) + b_1 \cdot (a_2x + b_2)$$
$$a_1x \cdot a_2x + a_1x \cdot b_2 + b_1 \cdot a_2x + b_1 \cdot b_2$$
$$a_1a_2 \cdot x^2 + a_1b_2 \cdot x + b_1a_2 \cdot x + b_1b_2$$
$$a_1a_2 \cdot x^2 + (a_1b_2 + b_1a_2) \cdot x + b_1b_2$$

Now look carefully at the pattern of the subscripts:

*   The coefficient of x^2 is the product of the "first" coefficients of the two linear functions.

*   The first part of the x coefficient is the product of the "outer" numbers of the linear functions, a_1 and b_2.

- The second part of the x coefficient is the product of the "inner" numbers of the linear functions, b_1 and a_2.

- The constant term is the product of the "last" numbers of the two linear functions.

Display 8.1 is a picture of this pattern. For years, math teachers have called this the "FOIL rule"—First, Outer, Inner, Last—and that's a pretty good way to remember it. But you have to remember, too, that it really is just an efficient way of applying the distributive law and regrouping a bit.

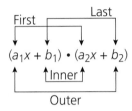

$$(a_1x + b_1) \cdot (a_2x + b_2)$$

First

Last

Inner

Outer

The FOIL Rule

Display 8.1

1. Use the FOIL rule to find the product of $7x + 5$ and $3x + 4$. Write the product function in standard quadratic form.

8.10

2. $f(x) = 2x - 5$ is a linear function. If you put it in the form $ax + b$, what is a? What is b?

3. Use the FOIL rule to find the product of $2x - 5$ and $3x - 4$. (Be careful! Part 2 gives you an important fact you need for this.) Write the product function in standard quadratic form.

4. Find the product of $x + 9$ and $4x - 3$ and write it in standard quadratic form.

Several laws of algebra were used in deriving the FOIL rule. Write down which laws were used at each step and explain how they were used.

8.11

Problem Set: 8.1

1. For each of these pairs of linear functions f and g, find $f(x) + g(x)$, $f(x) - g(x)$, $f(g(x))$, and $f(x) \cdot g(x)$. Write your answers in the appropriate standard form.

(a) $f(x) = x + 5,$ $g(x) = 2x + 3$

(b) $f(x) = 2x - 5,$ $g(x) = 3x + 1$

(c) $f(x) = 5x - 4,$ $g(x) = 3x - 5$

(d) $f(x) = -x + 7,$ $g(x) = 3x - 2$

(e) $f(x) = x + 3,$ $g(x) = x - 3$

(f) $f(x) = 7x - 4,$ $g(x) = 7x + 4$

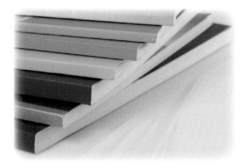

2. A small publishing company is preparing a children's workbook. It will have 32 black-and-white inside pages and a full-color cover. The black-and-white pages will cost 80 cents per workbook plus a press setup charge of $30. The color covers will cost 60 cents each plus a press setup charge of $50. Let w stand for the number of workbooks they plan to print.

   (a) Write two linear functions that describe the cost of the insides and of the cover. Then combine them to get a function for the total printing cost per workbook.

   (b) The publisher sells these workbooks to a bookstore chain for $2.60 each. The bookstore chain charges a $100 placement fee for displaying these workbooks in their stores. Assuming that all the workbooks that are printed will be sold to the bookstores, write a function for the amount of money the publisher will receive. Put the function in standard form. Is it linear? Why or why not?

   (c) Combine your answers to parts (a) and (b) to write a function for the amount of gross profit the publisher will make when the workbooks are sold. Put it in standard form. Is it linear?

   (d) How many workbooks will the publisher have to sell before it starts making some gross profit? Explain your answer.

3. Fritz's Frame Shop is designing a large series of rectangular picture frames of various sizes, but with the same relative proportions. Their width-to-height ratio is 7 to 5. Fritz wants a formula for the number of square centimeters of picture canvas that will actually be visible inside each frame. The frame stock he is using will use up 2 cm of the rectangle along the top and each of the sides, and it will use up 3 cm along the bottom. (See Display 8.2.)

   (a) Write a formula for Fritz.

   (b) Use your formula to calculate the visible canvas areas for frames of heights 15 cm, 30 cm, and 50 cm.

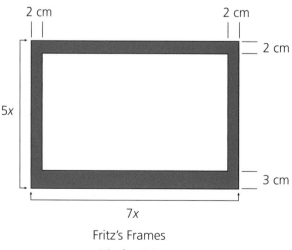

Fritz's Frames

Display 8.2

4. The pattern of the FOIL rule suggests a challenge: Can you do it backwards? That is, if we give you a quadratic function that we calculated by the FOIL method, can you figure out the linear functions we started with? Here are a few to try. To make the game fair, we will guarantee that all the linear functions we used have integer coefficients and constant terms. How many of them can you find?

(a) $x^2 + 3x + 2$

(b) $x^2 + 6x + 8$

(c) $x^2 - 5x + 6$

(d) $x^2 + 3x - 40$

(e) $x^2 - 3x - 40$

(f) $2x^2 + 5x + 2$

(g) $6x^2 + 17x + 12$

(h) $56x^2 + 11x - 15$

5. The square of a linear function is just that function multiplied by itself. For instance, $(x + 1)^2 = (x + 1) \cdot (x + 1)$.

(a) Write in standard form the quadratic functions $(x + 1)^2$, $(x + 2)^2$, $(x + 3)^2$, $(x + 4)^2$, and $(x + 5)^2$. Describe any pattern you see in the coefficient of the quadratic functions. Use that pattern to predict what $(x + 50)^2$ ought to be. Check your prediction using FOIL.

(b) Write the pattern you found in part (a) in symbols by completing this statement: For any natural number n, $(x + n)^2 = $ _____.

(c) Write in standard form the quadratic functions $(x - 1)^2$, $(x - 2)^2$, $(x - 3)^2$, $(x - 4)^2$, and $(x - 5)^2$. Describe any pattern you see in the coefficient of the quadratic functions. Use that pattern to predict what $(x - 50)^2$ ought to be. Check your prediction using FOIL.

(d) Write the pattern you found in part (c) in symbols by completing this statement: For any natural number n, $(x - n)^2 = $ _____.

(e) Write in standard form the quadratic functions $(x + 1) \cdot (x - 1)$, $(x + 2) \cdot (x - 2)$, $(x + 3) \cdot (x - 3)$, $(x + 4) \cdot (x - 4)$, and $(x + 5) \cdot (x - 5)$. Describe any pattern you see in the coefficient of the quadratic functions. Use that pattern to predict what $(x + 50) \cdot (x - 50)$ ought to be. Check your prediction using FOIL.

(f) Write the pattern you found in part (e) in symbols by completing this statement: For any natural number n, $(x + n) \cdot (x - n) = $ _____.

8.2 The Quadratic Shape

Learning Outcomes

After studying this section, you will be able to:

Use quadratic functions to solve problems about gravity

Calculate first and second differences of functions

Describe the shape of a quadratic graph

Explain how to tell if a curve is a parabola.

Why does anyone care about quadratic functions? There are lots of reasons. Most of them are connected to the fact that some of the most important ideas of science and business can be described by quadratic functions. Here is one that you may already know from your science classes. Gravity is a fundamental force in our world. It affects the motion of the planets, the length of a home run, the path of a bullet or an arrow, the distance of a ski jump, and many, many other things. And the effect of gravity on a free-falling object can be measured by this simple quadratic function:

The distance that a free-falling object falls in t seconds, if you ignore air resistance, is approximately $4.9t^2$ meters.

For some things in our everyday world, ignoring air resistance is not very realistic. Feathers or paper, for example, fall much more slowly because the air affects them a lot. But for other things, such as rocks or baseballs, air resistance doesn't matter very much. If you are peering over the edge of a steep cliff and you want to know how high you are above the river below, you could drop a small stone and time how long it takes to make a splash. If it takes 3 seconds, the cliff is about $4.9 \cdot 3^2 = 44.1$ meters high. (Of course, the accuracy of this distance depends on the accuracy of your timing.)

8.12

If it takes 4 seconds for the stone to make a splash, how high is the cliff?

Forensic scientists who investigate the paths that bullets take deal with this function all the time. As soon as a bullet is fired, gravity starts to pull it down. If it is aimed directly parallel to the flat ground, it will hit the ground at the same time as a free-falling bullet dropped from the same height. This means that a bullet aimed directly at a target will hit too low. And the further away the target is, the lower the bullet will hit. Why? Because it takes the bullet longer to get to the target, so it has more time to fall. (See Display 8.3.)

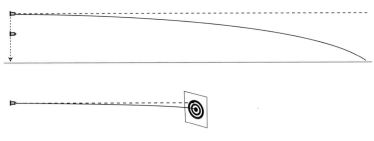

Display 8.3

For example, this is how gravity affects a .22-caliber bullet used for target practice. This bullet takes about 0.1 sec. to hit a target 100 feet away. In that time, the bullet falls $4.9 \cdot 0.1^2$ m., about 1.9 inches. So the aim has to be adjusted upward by that amount.

1. **If you ignore air resistance (which is not much over such a short distance), a bullet traveling at the same speed will take twice as long to hit a target 200 feet away. By how much must the aim be adjusted in this case?**

   8.13

2. **Is that more than, less than, or the same as twice the adjustment for the 100-foot distance?**

Your answer to question 2 should remind you that the free-fall function is not linear. That is, the function outputs are not proportional to the inputs. Here is another way to look at that. We will compare the free-fall distance function $d(t) = 4.9t^2$ with a linear function that has the same coefficient, $f(t) = 4.9t$. The chart in Display 8.4 shows the values for these two functions for every second from 0 to 10.

t(sec.)	$f(t) = 4.9t$	$d(t) = 4.9t^2$
0	0	0
1	4.9	4.9
2	9.8	19.6
3	14.7	44.1
4	19.6	78.4
5	24.5	122.5
6	29.4	176.4
7	34.3	240.1
8	39.2	313.6
9	44.1	396.9
10	49.0	490

Display 8.4

Display 8.4 shows that the quadratic function *d* grows *much* faster than the linear function *f*. But there's more useful information hiding in this data. You just have to know how to look for it. The differences from each step to the next form an interesting pattern.

$f(1) - f(0) = 4.9 - 0 = 4.9$ $d(1) - d(0) = 4.9 - 0 = 4.9$

$f(2) - f(1) = 9.8 - 4.9 = 4.9$ $d(2) - d(1) = 19.6 - 4.9 = 14.7$

$f(3) - f(2) = 14.7 - 9.8 = 4.9$ $d(3) - d(2) = 44.1 - 19.6 = 24.5$

$\vdots$ $\vdots$

These are called **first differences**. They are the differences between successive values of a function for a sequence of equally spaced domain values (such as 0, 1, 2, 3, …). By taking the differences between successive first differences, you get **second differences**. That may seem a little confusing at first, but it's not hard. Try it with this data.

8.14

Your teacher will give you a Blackline Master that begins like Display 8.5. Fill it in with all the first and second differences for the functions *f* and *d*, using the data of Display 8.4. Then describe any patterns you see.

t	f(t)	1st diffs.	2nd diffs.	d(t)	1st diffs.	2nd diffs.
0	0			0		
		4.9			4.9	
1	4.9		0	4.9		9.8
		4.9			14.7	
2	9.8			19.6		
3	14.7			44.1		
4						

First and Second Differences

Display 8.5

First and second differences tell you something about the shape of the function you're dealing with. We will come back to that idea a little later. Now let us look a little more closely at the shape of a quadratic function.

1. Set the **WINDOW** on your graphing calculator so that both **X** and **Y** go from 0 to 10. Then graph the free-fall function $d(t) = 4.9t^2$.

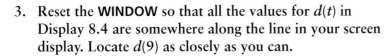

Using Technology

8.15

2. Think of the graph of d as extending beyond your calculator screen. Is there a point on that graph for every value of t, no matter how large? Why or why not?

3. Reset the **WINDOW** so that all the values for $d(t)$ in Display 8.4 are somewhere along the line in your screen display. Locate $d(9)$ as closely as you can.

4. Does your work on part 3 change your answer to part 2? Why or why not?

5. The function d describes free fall. Why does its graph go up?

The free-fall function is just one example of a simple quadratic function of the form $f(x) = ax^2$. All of them have similar shapes.

EXPLORATION 1

YOUR CALCULATOR: Set your graphing calculator **WINDOW** with $-5 \leq X \leq 5$ and $-50 \leq Y \leq 50$. Set the **X-scale** to **1** and the **Y-scale** to **10**.

Using Technology

TRY IT YOURSELF:

1. Graph the functions x^2, $2x^2$, $5x^2$, and $10x^2$.

2. Describe the shape of graphs of functions of the form ax^2, where a is a positive real number. How does the shape change as a changes?

3. See if $0.5x^2$ and $100x^2$ fit your description. Adjust it if they don't.

4. Predict the shape of graphs of functions $-ax^2$, where a is a positive real number. Then graph $-x^2$, $-2x^2$, $-5x^2$, $-12x^2$, and $-0.3x^2$ to see if they fit your prediction. Adjust your description if they don't.

5. How does the picture change if you add a constant to ax^2? Test your answer by graphing $2x^2 + 10$, $2x^2 - 10$, $-5x^2 + 20$, and $-5x^2 - 20$. Adjust your description, if necessary.

So far we have looked at quadratic functions of the form $f(x) = ax^2 + c$. But what about that middle term? When does that show up, and what does it do? To answer that, let's go to the State Fair.

The Test-Your-Strength game at the State Fair is a tall iron rod with a doughnut-shaped weight around it. (See Display 8.6.) The weight sits on a see-saw plank at the bottom. When you hit the plank, the weight shoots up the rod. The distance it travels depends on two things: its starting speed and the force of gravity dragging it back toward the ground. (We are ignoring the very small effect of air resistance.) The starting speed is called *initial velocity* in physics; it is measured in feet per second, meters per second, miles per hour, or something like that.

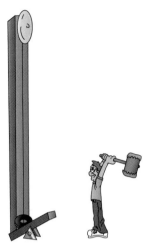

Test-Your-Strength

Display 8.6

The harder you hit the plank, the faster the initial velocity and the farther up the weight goes. In this case, a strong whack will start the weight moving at about 22 mph, or about 9.8 meters per second. (Yes, we chose this number to make the example work easily, but it is very close to what would happen in real life.) We can combine the gravity function and the linear velocity function to get a formula for how high the weight is at any time during its brief trip. Gravity is pulling down, so we make that part of the function negative. The initial velocity is pushing up, so we make that part positive. This gives us the function

$$h(t) = -4.9t^2 + 9.8t$$

for the height in meters at any time t, measured in seconds. If a video of this showed the moving weight every tenth of a second, you would see something like Display 8.7.

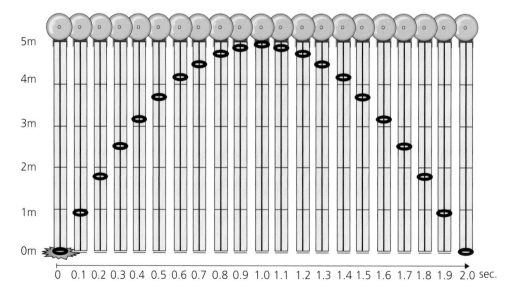

$h(t) = -4.9t^2 + 9.8t$

Display 8.7

Set your graphing calculator **WINDOW** to $0 \leq X \leq 2$ and $0 \leq Y \leq 5$. Then graph $h(t) = -4.9t^2 + 9.8t$. Compare your result to Display 8.7. What does **X** stand for? What does **Y** stand for?

8.16

Here is one more gravity example to illustrate how the constant term is useful. Flash Fastball is a baseball pitcher. He bets a teammate that he can throw a ball straight up 300 feet above the ground. He winds up and lets go of the ball at head height, 6 feet above the ground, at an initial velocity of 90 miles per hour.

Did Flash win the bet? Work through these questions to find out. We'll help. In this case the measurements are in feet and miles, so we must use a gravity coefficient for feet per second squared. 4.9 meters is approximately 16 feet. Set up a quadratic function, $h(t)$, for the height in feet above the ground t seconds after it is thrown. (We will ignore air resistance, even though it would probably have some measurable effect in this case.)

8.17   **Using Technology**

1. The t^2 term represents the effect of gravity on the ball. What is it? Is it positive or negative?

2. The t term accounts for the initial velocity. What is it? (Be careful!)

3. How can you account for the fact that the ball starts out 6 feet above the ground?

4. Write the formula for the function $h(t)$. Then graph it on your calculator using the **WINDOW** settings $0 \leq X \leq 10$ and $0 \leq Y \leq 300$. Did Flash win the bet? Why or why not?

5. Use your calculator to help you answer these questions: About how high did the ball go? (Assume that air resistance did not affect it much.) How long was it in the air before it hit the ground?

Gravity is not the only idea for which quadratic functions are useful. They appear in business, science, engineering, and statistics. Later in this chapter you will see more real-world uses of quadratic functions. For the rest of this section, we will look a little more carefully at the shape of their graphs. We said "shape," not "shapes," because the graphs of all quadratic functions have a single, distinctive U-shape. It is called a *parabola*.

8.2 The Quadratic Shape

Using Technology

Of course, there are many different parabolas. Sometimes the U opens upward, sometimes downward. Sometimes the curve is tight and steep; sometimes it is shallow. But they all share some very special properties. You have already seen one of them:

The second differences of any parabola are constant.

That is, if you take successive steps of the same size along the x-axis and calculate the second differences of their images, you will get a constant number. Try some examples.

EXPLORATION 2

YOUR CALCULATOR: Begin by setting your graphing calculator **WINDOW** to $-3 \leq X \leq 3$ and $-1 \leq Y \leq 4$. (The **X** and **Y** scales can be set to **1**.) Your teacher will give you a worksheet to help organize your work on some of these questions.

TRY IT YOURSELF:

1. Enter the function x^2 in the **Y=** list and graph it. Do you think it is a parabola? Why or why not?

2. Using the same **WINDOW** settings, turn off (but keep) the x^2 function. Then enter the function $0.1x^4 + 0.7x^2$ and graph it. Do you think it is a parabola? Why or why not?

3. Now turn the x^2 function back on and graph both together. Are they both parabolas? Can you tell from their pictures?

   It is not easy to tell from the calculator pictures whether or not both of these functions are parabolas. But there is a numerical way to decide if a graph is not a parabola. The second differences for a parabola must be constant.

4. Fill in tables (1) and (2) on your worksheet. Start by putting the images of the numbers 0 through 6 in the second column. (We've done that part of the first table for you.) You can use the **Value** function or the table on your calculator to help you do that. Then work out the first and second differences. Are they both parabolas?

5. When you check for constant second differences, you do not have to start at $x = 0$, and you do not have to take 1-unit steps, as long as all of the steps are the same size. Tables (3) and (4) show two different sizes of steps and two different starting points. Use the function $2x^2 - 3x + 1$ to fill in these two tables. Do you get constant second differences both times?

6. Are you suspicious that our examples have been "rigged" to work out? Not this time. Try your own examples in tables (5) and (6). Make up any quadratic function you want for table (5) and choose any steps you want (as long as they are the same size, of course). See if you get constant second differences. Then make up a function with an x^3 term in it and try the experiment again in table (6). See if you get constant second differences this time, too.

Here are the main ideas about parabola-shaped graphs of functions:

- A **parabola** is a U-shaped curve, opening upward or downward. It is symmetric about a vertical line through its lowest or highest point; that point is called its **vertex**. It has nonzero constant second differences everywhere. This last property distinguishes parabolas from other symmetric, U-shaped curves.

- The graph of every quadratic function is a parabola.

- Every function that has a parabola-shaped graph is a quadratic function.

Later in **MATH** *Connections* you will meet up with parabolas again. At that time you will have to define these very important curves without using differences of function values. But that will have to wait until you have more experience with geometry.

You have just seen how all parabolas are alike, in some sense. Now we will take a brief look at how different they can be. You know that a quadratic function has the form

$$f(x) = ax^2 + bx + c$$

where a, b, and c can be any real numbers and $a \neq 0$. How do a, b, and c affect the shape of the graph? In Exploration 1 you saw the effects of changing a and c. The effect of the bx term is harder to describe easily. What can you say about it?

Set the **WINDOW** of your graphing calculator to $-10 \leq X \leq 10$ and $-40 \leq Y \leq 40$. Set the **X** scale to **1** and the **Y** scale to **10**. Enter these functions into the **Y=** list in order:

Using Technology

8.18

$$x^2 \qquad x^2 + 2x \qquad x^2 + 4x \qquad x^2 + 6x \qquad x^2 + 8x$$
$$x^2 + 10x \qquad -x^2$$

Graph them all at once. Now enter

$$x^2 \qquad x^2 - 2x \qquad x^2 - 4x \qquad x^2 - 6x \qquad x^2 - 8x$$
$$x^2 - 10x \qquad -x^2$$

and graph them all again. Write a short paragraph explaining how you think changing the bx term affects the graph of the quadratic function.

Problem Set: 8.2

1. Gravity on the Moon is much weaker than it is on Earth. On the Moon, the distance that a free-falling object falls in t seconds is approximately $0.8t^2$ meters. That is, $d(t) = 0.8t^2$.

   (a) A bullet aimed level with the ground takes 0.15 seconds to reach its target. How far has the path of the bullet dropped below the horizontal level when it hits the target? Express your answer in cm and also in inches.

   (b) An astronaut working on the Moon Lander dropped a wrench. It took 2 seconds to reach the ground. How far did it fall? Express your answer in meters and also in feet.

   (c) The astronaut tossed a rock into the air with an initial velocity of 28 miles per hour. When it left her hand it was 5 feet above the ground. Write a quadratic function for the height $h(t)$ (in meters) of the rock above the ground at time t (in seconds).

   (d) Use your answer to part (c) and your calculator to answer these questions approximately. How high did the rock go? How long was it in the air?

2. The planet Jupiter is much bigger than the Earth. It is more than 1000 times as large as the Earth in volume! Its gravity is much stronger, too. Near its surface, the free-fall function for t seconds is approximately $d(t) = 12t^2$ meters.

   (a) An astronaut lands on Jupiter in some future age. (Unlikely, but who knows?) When the side hatch of the spaceship opens, a small tool falls to the ground. It reaches the ground in 0.6 seconds. How high above the ground is the hatch?

   (b) The astronaut climbs down to the ground, and then tries to jump. He jumps upward with an initial velocity of 3.6 meters per second. (On Earth, that initial velocity is enough for a jump more than 2 feet high.) Write a quadratic function for the height $h(t)$ (in meters) of the astronaut above the ground at time t (in seconds). Then use your function and the calculator to see how far up he jumps and how long he is in the air.

3. In Section 8.1 you saw that quadratic functions are products of linear functions.

   (a) Write $4.9t^2$ as a product of linear functions. Can you do it in more than one way? If so, write at least one more product. If not, explain why not.

   (b) Write ax^2 as a product of linear functions, for any nonzero real number a. Can that always be done in more than one way? Why or why not?

   (c) Write the function $h(t) = -4.9t^2 + 9.8t$ as a product of linear functions in at least two different ways. What basic law of algebra allows you to do this?

   (d) Write the function $f(x) = ax^2 + bx$, for any nonzero real numbers a and b, as a product of linear functions. What basic law of algebra allows you to do this?

4. (a) For this part, $f(x) = 3x^2 - 5x + 4$. Make a chart of the images, first differences, and second differences for $x = 0, 1, 2, 3, 4, 5, 6, 7, 8$.

   (b) What do you think *third differences* are? Write a one-sentence description of them. Then extend your chart of part (a) to include the third differences for f.

   (c) Using the function $g(x) = x^3 + 1$, make a chart of the images, first, second, and third differences for $x = 0, 1, 2, 3, 4, 5, 6, 7, 8$.

   (d) Display 8.8 is a chart for images and first and second differences of a quadratic function q. Fill in the missing values.

x	q(x)	1st diffs.	2nd diffs.
0	4		
		−3	
1			10
2			
		17	
3			
4			
5			
6			
7			
8			

Display 8.8

5. For each part, write the formula for a parabola that fits the given description. Check your answer by graphing it on your calculator.

(a) It opens upward, its vertex is on the y-axis, and it does not touch the x-axis.

(b) It opens downward, its vertex is on the y-axis, and it crosses the x-axis in two places.

(c) It opens upward and crosses the positive side of the x-axis in two places.

(d) It opens downward and crosses the positive side of the x-axis in two places that are at least 5 units apart.

(e) Its vertex is below -5 on the y-axis and it crosses the x-axis between -1 and 1.

(f) It opens downward, the x- and y-coordinates of its vertex are both between -2 and -1, and it crosses the x-axis once on each side of 0.

(g) It opens upward and its vertex is on the x-axis, but not on the y-axis.

8.3 Using Quadratic Equations

The yearbook committee at Great Ridge School is making plans for their next yearbook. Jeff, the treasurer, has met with the printing company. He tells the committee, "The printer said that if we order 500 books, the cost will be $17,500; 1000 books will cost us $25,000; and 2000 books will cost us $40,000."

Jolene, the sales manager, asks, "But what if we want to order a different number of books. How much will it cost for, say, 750?"

8.19

1. Display 8.9 shows a graph of the total cost y versus the number x of yearbooks, using the three prices given by the printer. The three points appear to lie in a straight line. How can you be sure?

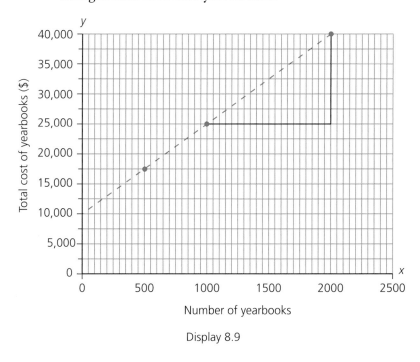

Display 8.9

2. Write a function $y = f(x)$ that calculates the total cost for any number of yearbooks ordered. Is $f(x)$ linear? Is it quadratic? How do you know?

3. The dotted line in Display 8.9 appears to show that if the school orders no yearbooks, there would still be a total cost of $10,000. Is this correct? Explain.

Learning Outcomes

After studying this section, you will be able to:

Explain what a quadratic equation is

Use quadratic equations to describe real-world questions

Solve quadratic equations graphically

Use graphs to explain why some quadratic equations have no solutions

Use graphical methods to find the maximum or minimum value of a quadratic function.

Now Jolene can calculate the total cost for any number of yearbooks, and so can you.

8.20

1. Use the formula above to calculate the total cost of

   (a) 200 yearbooks

   (b) 750 yearbooks

   (c) 1250 yearbooks

2. Can you calculate a value for y if x is 150.5? If so, do it. If not, explain why not.

3. Can you calculate a value for y if x is -200? If so, do it. If not, explain why not.

There is often a difference between what makes sense mathematically and what makes sense in reality. The equation makes mathematical sense for any real number x. However, in this situation, the fact that x represents the number of yearbooks means that it must be a whole number.

The situation restricts this function in other ways, too. Recall that the set of possible x-values for a function is called its *domain*, and its set of possible y-values for a function is called its *range*. For example, if the printer only takes orders in multiples of 50, the domain could be {50, 100, 150, 200, ...} The range would then be the set {\$10,750, \$11,500, \$12,250, \$13,000, ...}. It would also make sense to limit the maximum number of yearbooks to something related to the number of students in the school.

Back at the yearbook club meeting, another problem has arisen. Jolene says, "That's great, we can figure out how much it will cost us for any number of yearbooks. The problem is we don't know how many to order because we aren't sure how many we can sell!"

At this point José speaks up. "I have the sales figures from the last 10 years. It seems that the number of yearbooks sold depended on the price of a yearbook."

1. José presents the figures for the number of yearbooks sold and the corresponding prices. His data appears in Display 8.10. Enter the data into two lists of your calculator, and then find the line of best fit. Write down its equation.

8.21

2. Do the data all lie exactly on the straight line of part 1? How do you know?

3. It appears that this straight line describes the number of yearbooks sold as a function of the price. By this function, if the price of the yearbook were $40, how many would they sell?

Number of Yearbooks Sold

Price ($)	30	28	26	31	33	34	27	32	38	29
Number Sold	1000	1020	1040	990	970	960	1030	980	920	1010

Display 8.10

José has noticed a basic law of economics. If the price goes up, sales go down, and if the price falls, sales increase. In this case, notice that 1000 books will sell at $30 each and that every $1 price reduction results in the sale of 10 more yearbooks. Every $1 price increase results in the sale of 10 fewer yearbooks.

Jeff is really excited now. This year, the profit that the yearbook committee makes will go to hurricane flood relief, so the committee wants to make as much profit as possible. He knows that too high a price will cause sales to suffer, and too low a price will not make much money. He thinks that he can use José's data to decide how to maximize the profit. He also thinks that this information may help them decide how many yearbooks to order and what price to charge.

1. Your teacher will give you a copy of the chart in Display 8.11. Use the yearbook committee's information to complete it. We filled in the row with the $30 selling price for you, like this:

8.22

Number of yearbooks to be sold: 1000

Total printing cost: $1000 \cdot 15 + 10{,}000 = \$25{,}000$

Total sales income: $1000 \cdot 30 = \$30{,}000$

Profit (income − cost): $30{,}000 - 25{,}000 = \$5{,}000$

Number of yearbooks to be sold	Total printing cost ($)	Selling price ($)	Total sales income ($)	Profit ($) (sales income – printing cost)
1100		20		
1000	25,000	30	30,000	5,000
900		40		
800		50		
700		60		
600		70		
500		80		
400		90		

Display 8.11

2. Think of the profit as a function—call it $P(x)$—of the selling price, which we'll call x. That is, the entries in the last column on the right are images of the entries in the middle column. State in terms of price and profit the meaning of $P(60) = 21,500$. Does this agree with a row of your table?

Using Technology

3. Enter the price data from Display 8.11 into one list of your calculator and enter the corresponding profit data into a second list. Then use **STAT PLOT** to plot the data points on a graph. (What **WINDOW** settings should you use?)

4. What kind of function do you think P is: linear? quadratic? something else? Give reasons for your answer.

What did you answer in part 4? Did you say that P is quadratic? Did you suspect that from the pattern of points on the graph? Did you check the first and second differences? If you did (of course you did!), you saw that the second differences for these equally-spaced prices are constant. As you know from Section 8.2, that tells you that these points lie on a parabola, the graph of a quadratic function. But which one? Your calculator can tell you, if you know how to ask it.

Remember the line of best fit from Chapter 4? You found it by using a calculator function called **LinReg**, an abbreviation for "Linear Regression." Just below it (in the TI's **STAT CALC** menu) is **QuadReg**, short for "Quadratic Regression." This choice will find the quadratic function that best fits your data. In this case, if the points really do lie on a parabola, the graph of the quadratic regression function will go right through them. Let's find out.

1. Press **STAT** and go to the **CALC** menu. Choose **QuadReg**, followed by the names of the two data lists. (If you put the price data in **L1** and the profit data in **L2**, your entry should look like **QuadReg L1,L2**.) Write in standard form the quadratic function you get.

8.23

2. Press **GRAPH** to see that you still have the separate data points displayed, and nothing else. Enter that function into your **Y=** list; then press **GRAPH** again. What happens?

3. Use this graph and the **TRACE** function to estimate the maximum profit that the yearbook committee could make. What price would they have to set to do it? Do you think they should put that price on the yearbooks? Why or why not?

The yearbook committee is worried that the price they would have to charge for maximum profit would be too high for some students. Those students might want a yearbook, but would not be able to afford it. Nevertheless, they do want to make a lot of money to help the families who lost their homes in the flood. They decide that $20,000 would be a big enough profit for that. Now they need to know what yearbook price will make this much profit for them. That is, they want to know the x value for which

$$P(x) = \$20{,}000.$$

1. Use the function $P(x)$ that you found in part 1 of Lightning Icon 8.23 to write the equation $P(x) = \$20{,}000$ in the form $ax^2 + bx + c = 20{,}000$.

8.24

Using Technology

2. Enter $y = 20000$ into the **Y=** list of your calculator. Then graph it along with $P(x)$.

3. Use **TRACE** to approximate two possible solutions for this equation. Which one should the committee pick? Why?

4. Round your answer to part 3 to the nearest whole dollar and then calculate the profit predicted by the function P. How close is it to $20,000?

Notice that the yearbook committee's last question is a little different than most of the ones we have seen so far. Up to now, most questions about quadratic functions have asked about the images of domain elements. That is, you were given an x value for a function $f(x) = y$ and asked to calculate y. Now we are asking the reverse question:

> If you know the y value you want, what x value will get it for you?

In other words, we set a function $f(x)$ equal to some particular number k and ask what domain element x results in that image. If the function is quadratic, the equation is called a *quadratic equation*. Usually, the equation is put into a standard form by subtracting k from both sides, so that one side becomes 0. That is, a **quadratic equation** is an equation that can be put in the form

$$ax^2 + bx + c = 0$$

where a, b, and c are specific real numbers and a is not 0.

8.25

1. How is the graph of $P(x)$ related to the graph of $P(x) - 20{,}000$?

2. If $f(x)$ is some function and k is some fixed number, how is the graph of $f(x)$ related to the graph of $f(x) - k$? Explain briefly.

3. When a function equals 0, where are those points on its graph?

8.26

In Section 8.2 you saw that a bullet aimed parallel to flat ground will hit the ground at the same time as a free-falling bullet dropped from the height at which it was fired. The free-fall gravity function is $d(t) = 4.9t^2$ for t seconds and the distance in meters.

1. A bullet is fired horizontally 1.5 meters above the ground at the Bonneville Salt Flats. How long does it take to hit the ground? Write this question as a quadratic equation in standard form. Then solve it graphically to the nearest hundredth of a second.

2. If the bullet moves at an average speed of 320 meters per second, about how far will it travel? Give your answer in both meters and feet. How does this compare to the length of a football field?

3. The Bonneville Salt Flats is an area in which western state? For what is this location famous?

A rock is thrown straight up into the air with an initial velocity of 30 meters per second. It leaves the thrower's hand 1.2 meters above the ground. The free-fall gravity function, $-4.9t^2$, is "pulling down" on it. How long is it in the air? Ignore air resistance and give your answer to the nearest tenth of a second.

8.27

Solving a quadratic equation $ax^2 + bx + c = 0$ means finding where the parabola $ax^2 + bx + c$ intersects the x-axis. Does every parabola intersect the x-axis somewhere? Let us help you explore some examples.

EXPLORATION 3

YOUR CALCULATOR: Clear your **Y=** list and set the **WINDOW** to **Standard**.

Using Technology

TRY IT YOURSELF:

1. Put these functions into the **Y=** list and graph them:

$$0.3x^2 \qquad 0.3x^2 + 1 \qquad 0.3x^2 - 1 \qquad 0.3x^2 + 2$$
$$0.3x^2 - 2 \qquad 0.3x^2 + 3 \qquad 0.3x^2 - 3$$

2. When you set each quadratic function of part 1 equal to 0, you get a quadratic equation. Which of those equations have solutions and which do not?

3. Now replace 0.3 with 4 in each function in the **Y=** list and graph them again. When you set each of these functions equal to 0, which of the resulting equations have solutions? How are they related to the equations in part 2?

4. If you replace the 4 in each function by any other positive number a, which of the equations $ax^2 + c = 0$ have solutions and which do not? Explain why you think your answer is true.

5. If a is negative, which of the equations $ax^2 + c = 0$ have solutions and which do not? Explain why you think your answer is true.

6. Now graph these functions: x^2, $x^2 + x$, $x^2 - x$, $x^2 + 2x$, $x^2 - 2x$, $x^2 + 3x$, $x^2 - 3x$. Which of their quadratic equations have solutions? How many solutions in each case?

7. What if you make -1 the coefficient of x^2 in each of the functions in part 6? Before graphing anything else, predict which equations have solutions. Explain why you think your prediction is correct. Then check it by graphing.

8.3 Using Quadratic Equations

You can see from this Exploration that some quadratic equations have solutions and some do not. In fact, if you put a quadratic equation into standard form and then graph the parabola described by its nonzero side, you can see from the picture whether or not there are any solutions.

Using Technology

8.28

Which of the following quadratic equations have solutions? Be prepared to explain your answers.

1. $x^2 + 5 = 0$
2. $3x^2 - 8 = 0$
3. $-5x^2 + 2 = 0$
4. $-5x^2 = 0$
5. $-5x^2 = 3$
6. $2x^2 + 3x = 0$
7. $-7x^2 = 3x$
8. $x^2 + 2x + 6 = 0$
9. $x^2 + 2x - 6 = 0$
10. $-3x^2 + 5x = 9$

8.29

In your own words, explain the difference between a quadratic function and a quadratic equation. Also explain how they are related. How are parabolas related to these two kinds of things?

Problem Set: 8.3

1. As you have seen, the distance (in meters) that a free-falling object (on Earth) falls in t seconds is $d(t) = 4.9t^2$. How long does it take a rock dropped off a high cliff to fall 100 meters? 200 meters? Answer these questions to the nearest tenth of a second by graphing.

2. Rewrite each of the following quadratic equations in standard form. Then say which ones have solutions and which do not.

   (a) $5x^2 = 7$
   (b) $x^2 + 4 = 3x$
   (c) $x^2 + 1 = 2x$
   (d) $-x - 5 = 2x^2$
   (e) $-0.5x^2 + 10 = 6x$
   (f) $(x + 2) \cdot (x + 1) = 0$
   (g) $(x + 3) \cdot (2x - 5) = 12$
   (h) $(x - 3)^2 = 0$

3. This is an example of a common marketing problem that can be solved with the tools of this section:

   A farmer has 10,000 pounds of potatoes that he can sell right now for 20 cents per pound. For every week that he waits to sell, the price will go up by 2 cents per pound. However, each week he will lose 200 pounds of potatoes because of spoilage. When should he sell his potatoes to get the most money for selling them?

   (a) What will the price per pound be 3 weeks from now? What will it be x weeks from now?

(b) How many pounds of good potatoes will he have 3 weeks from now? x weeks from now?

(c) How many dollars would he receive for the potatoes if he sold them 3 weeks from now?

(d) Write the number of dollars he would receive x weeks from now as a quadratic function, $A(x)$, and put it in standard form.

(e) Solve $A(x) = 0$ any way you can. You should get two solutions.

(f) How can you use the solutions from part (e) and symmetry to compute the answer to the farmer's problem? Do it. Check that your answer is reasonable by graphing $A(x)$ and finding its highest value.

4. Begin by setting your graphing calculator **WINDOW** to **Standard**. Adjust the settings, if necessary, to help you answer these questions.

Using Technology

(a) Enter these quadratic functions in your calculator's **Y=** list and graph them all together:

$$x^2 - 1 \quad x^2 - 4 \quad x^2 - 9 \quad x^2 - 16 \quad x^2 - 25$$

(b) Write the coordinates of the vertex of each of these parabolas. How are these coordinates related to the constant term in each case?

(c) Find the solutions to each of these equations. (You can do this without graphing.)

$$x^2 - 1 = 0 \quad x^2 - 4 = 0 \quad x^2 - 9 = 0$$
$$x^2 - 16 = 0 \quad x^2 - 25 = 0$$

(d) Describe in words any patterns you notice that relate the equation solutions to the constant terms and the graphs. Then make a conjecture about the solutions of any equation of the form $x^2 - c = 0$, where $c > 0$.

5. When Ali hits the Test-Your-Strength plank, the weight starts up with an initial velocity of 8.4 meters per second. As in the previous section, the height of the weight in meters is given by $h(t) = -4.9t^2 + 8.4t$, for t in seconds.

(a) To the nearest tenth of a second, how long did it take the weight to go up and come back down?

(b) You can use your answer to part (a) and symmetry to calculate without graphing how high the weight got. Explain how; then do it.

Test-Your-Strength

8.4 Solving Quadratic Equations

Learning Outcomes

After studying this section, you will be able to:

Solve equations of the form $ax^2 + bx = 0$

Explain why some equations of the form $ax^2 + c = 0$ do not have real-number solutions

Solve equations of the form $ax^2 - c = 0$ for $c > 0$

Explain how the algebraic solutions of quadratic equations relate to their graphs

Solve some equations of the form $ax^2 + bx + c = 0$ where a, b, and c are all nonzero.

8.30

1. If $5a = 0$, what is a? How do you know?

2. If $ab = 0$, must either a or b equal 0? Must they both equal 0?

3. If $ab \neq 0$, can either a or b equal 0?

4. If $ab = 2$, must either a or b equal 2?

5. If $ab = c$, where c is some nonzero real number, must either a or b equal c?

Explain your answers.

Did you get question 2 right? It's the most important one in the list. It's so important that we display it as a fundamental fact of this section.

A Fact to Know: If the product of two numbers is zero, then one or the other of those numbers *must* be zero. In symbols,

$$ab = 0 \text{ implies } a = 0 \text{ or } b = 0.$$

You already knew that from arithmetic, right? This is just a reminder because that idea is the key to solving quadratic equations with algebra. Why do that? Two reasons:

- Graphical solutions are only approximate, which sometimes is not good enough.

- Finding graphical solutions can be tedious and awkward.

An algebraic solution is always more accurate. Sometimes it is easier and faster, too. Here is an example from the previous problem set.

When Ali hit the Test-Your-Strength plank, the weight started up with an initial velocity of 8.4 meters per second. The height of the weight in meters is given by $h(t) = -4.9t^2 + 8.4t$, for t in seconds. How long did it take the weight to go up and come back down?

1. To solve this problem, you need to find a time t for which $-4.9t^2 + 8.4t = 0$. Rewrite the left side of this equation as the product of t and something else. What basic law of algebra allows you to do this?

8.31

2. By the Fact to Know on the previous page, the height $h(t)$ equals 0 if either $t = 0$ or the "something else" equals 0. At what time does the "something else" equal 0?

3. Graph $h(t) = -4.9t^2 + 8.4t$ and see if your answer agrees with the place where $h(t)$ crosses the positive x-axis.

That wasn't hard, was it? Sometimes algebra saves you time and effort. Here are the major steps for solving a quadratic equation algebraically:

1. Rewrite the quadratic equation so that one side is 0.

2. Rewrite the other side as a product of linear factors.

3. Set each linear factor equal to 0 and solve it.

4. Check to see which solutions satisfy the conditions of the problem.

Find a positive solution for $5x^2 = 12x$ by following the four steps above. Then show graphically that your answer makes sense.

8.32

OK, we confess. One of the four steps is not always so easy. In fact, one of them sometimes cannot be done (with real numbers). But often it can be done easily. We'll look at some of those cases first.

1. Solve these five equations by the first three steps above:

$$x^2 = x \quad x^2 = 2x \quad x^2 = 3x \quad x^2 = 4x \quad x^2 = 5x$$

8.33

What patterns do you notice?

2. Use the patterns from part 1 to write down the solutions for $x^2 = 7843.705x$ without doing any algebraic steps.

3. Complete this statement: If b is any positive real number, then the solutions to the equation $x^2 = bx$ are _____.

4. Now complete this statement: If a and b are any positive real numbers, then the solutions to the equation $ax^2 = bx$ are _____. Does this answer agree with your answer to Lightning Icon 8.32? Why or why not?

When you rewrite an equation of the form $x^2 = bx$ so that 0 is on one side, the other side is the quadratic function $x^2 - bx$. As you know, the graph of this function is a parabola that opens upward. And because $x^2 - bx = x \cdot (x - b)$ [by what law?], that parabola crosses the x-axis at 0 and b. For instance, $x^2 - 3x$ crosses the x-axis at 0 and 3, the two solutions to the equation $x^2 - 3x = 0$.

Using Technology

8.34

1. Set your calculator's **WINDOW** to **Standard** and graph the five quadratic functions for the equations in part 1 of Lightning Icon 8.33.

2. What if you change the $-$ signs in the middle of each of these functions to $+$ signs? Can you predict what their graphs look like? Try predicting first; then graph the five functions to check your predictions.

3. Do equations of the form $x^2 + bx = 0$ for any number b always have solutions? If so, what are they? If not, give an example of an equation of this form that doesn't have a solution. Justify your answer.

8.35

If a and b are nonzero numbers, then the equation $ax^2 + bx = 0$ always has a nonzero solution. What is it? Sometimes that solution is positive, sometimes it is negative. Sometimes the graph of the parabola opens upward, sometimes it opens downward. Write a paragraph describing when each of these things happens. Include an example for each case. (For instance, if a is positive and b is negative, is the solution positive or negative? Does the parabola open upward or downward?)

Quadratic equations without a constant term are easy to solve because you can always factor them as $x \cdot$ (some linear function) $= 0$. Quadratic equations without an x term are almost as easy, if you think of them in the right way. We'll begin by looking at some graphs you have seen before.

8.36

Remember: A solution to a quadratic equation is a point where the graph of the function crosses (or touches) the x-axis.

1. Solve $x^2 = 0$. Then graph it.

2. Now choose a positive number—call it c—and graph $x^2 + c$. What does your graph tell you about solutions for $x^2 + c = 0$?

3. Graph $x^2 - c$ for that same positive number c. What does your graph tell you about solutions for $x^2 - c = 0$?

Question 3 of Lightning Icon 8.36 is related to a pattern you've seen before (and will see again). Before we tell you more about it, we need to refresh your memory.

1. Multiply $(x + 3)(x - 3)$ and $(x + 5)(x - 5)$.

2. Complete this statement for the general pattern of part 1:

   For any positive number k, $(x + k)(x - k) =$ _____.

3. Write $x^2 - 4$ as a product of linear factors. (Think about parts 1 and 2 backwards.)

4. Write $x^2 - 5$ as a product of linear factors.

5. Recall your positive number c from Lightning Icon 8.36. Write $x^2 - c$ as a product of linear factors.

6. Now solve the equation $x^2 - c = 0$. Find your answers on your graph from part 3 of Lightning Icon 8.36.

A quadratic function of the form $x^2 - k^2$ is called a *difference of squares*. As you just saw, it factors easily:

$$x^2 - k^2 = (x + k)(x - k)$$

This makes solving the quadratic equation $x^2 - k^2 = 0$ very easy. When you set each factor equal to 0 and solve for x, you get $x = -k$ or $+k$ right away. That is, the two solutions are the two square roots of k^2.

Quadratic equations like this come up in many places. Here is an example based on a real TV commercial for pickup trucks.

A pickup truck will be dropped from a helicopter onto a target. A second truck has to start up and drive across the target just before the first one hits and smashes. It is very important to know how much time the second truck has to get past the target area! (It would be important to know this even if the stunt was done with special effects.) Help the film crew figure it out.

1. The free-fall gravity function is $d(t) = 16t^2$, where $d(t)$ is the distance in feet that something falls in t seconds, ignoring air resistance. A falling pickup truck is not slowed down much by air resistance, so we can ignore that. If the helicopter drops the truck from a height of 1600 feet, the equation you need to solve is $16t^2 = 1600$. Do it.

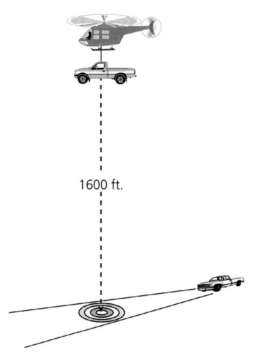

1600 ft.

Display 8.12

2. The helicopter pilot says that 1000 feet is as high as she will go with such a heavy load. How much time will that give the second truck? Answer to the nearest tenth of a second.

8.39

How can $7x^2 - 29 = 0$ be solved as a difference of squares? How can any equation of the form $ax^2 - c = 0$, where a and c are positive, be solved as a difference of squares?

Here is a summary of the main ideas about solving equations of the form $ax^2 \pm c = 0$ for a and c positive:

- $ax^2 + c = 0$ has no real-number solutions. The parabola for that function is entirely above the x-axis.

- $ax^2 - c = 0$ always has two real solutions, one positive and one negative, with the same absolute value. The vertex of the parabola is on the negative y-axis, and it crosses the x-axis on each side of the origin.

- You can always find the solutions for $ax^2 - c = 0$ by rewriting the left side as a difference of squares, as follows:

  – Divide both sides of the equation by a, getting $x^2 - \frac{c}{a} = 0$. (Remember that 0 divided by any nonzero number is 0.)

– Rewrite the (positive) number $\frac{c}{a}$ as $\left(\sqrt{\frac{c}{a}}\right)^2$. (Remember that squaring and taking the square root are inverse processes; each one undoes what the other one does.)

– Then, because $x^2 - \left(\sqrt{\frac{c}{a}}\right)^2 = \left(x + \sqrt{\frac{c}{a}}\right)\left(x - \sqrt{\frac{c}{a}}\right) = 0$, the two solutions are $\pm\sqrt{\frac{c}{a}}$.

What if a is negative? Explain solving equations of the form $ax^2 \pm c = 0$ when $a < 0$ and $c > 0$.

8.40

Caution: When you solve an equation with one side 0 by multiplying or dividing both sides by the same number, *you are changing the function on the other side*. For instance, we can solve $-2x^2 + 6 = 0$ like this:

Multiply both sides by -1:	$2x^2 - 6 = 0$
Divide both sides by 2:	$x^2 - 3 = 0$
Now solve this last equation:	$x = \pm\sqrt{3}$

The solutions for the last equation are also the solutions for the first one because we have preserved equality at every step. But the three quadratic functions are all different!

Do This: Set your calculator **WINDOW** to **Standard** and graph these three functions together:

$$-2x^2 + 6 \qquad 2x^2 - 6 \qquad x^2 - 3$$

See? All three functions have different graphs. Multiplying or dividing by a constant exchanges the original function for a "nicer" one *that crosses the x-axis in the same places*. The functions are different, but the solutions to their equations are the same.

OK. So now you know about the quadratic equation forms $ax^2 + bx = 0$ and $ax^2 \pm c = 0$. It's time to tackle $ax^2 + bx + c = 0$, where a, b, and c are all nonzero. The approach is the same as before: Factor the quadratic side into linear factors, set each one equal to 0, and solve them. The hard part is the factoring!

Factor these quadratics into products of linear functions, if you can. (Three of them can be done with integers. The other one cannot be done, even allowing any real numbers.)

8.41

1. $x^2 + 3x + 2$

2. $x^2 + 7x - 18$

3. $x^2 + 5x + 10$

4. $3x^2 + 11x + 10$

How did you do? Was it easy to spot the one that can't be done? Probably not. They all look pretty much alike. Figuring these out is like doing a Sudoku puzzle. There are certain rules to play by, and you try to rule out possibilities that won't work. In this case, the "rules" come from thinking about undoing the "First-Outer-Inner-Last" process for multiplying two linear functions.

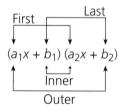

FOIL again

Display 8.13

Here is an example. To factor $x^2 + 5x + 4$, say, you want two factors like this

$$(a_1x + b_1)(a_2x + b_2) = x^2 + 5x + 4$$

for some numbers a_1, b_1, a_2, and b_2. By FOIL (see Display 8.13), this means

$$(a_1a_2)x^2 + (a_1b_2 + b_1a_2)x + (b_1b_2) = x^2 + 5x + 4$$

That is, $a_1a_2 = 1$ and $a_1b_2 + b_1a_2 = 5$ and $b_1b_2 = 4$. That's the puzzle. Can you find four numbers that fit together like this? Now, *if* your math book or teacher or test is nice enough to tell you that the four numbers are integers, that isn't too hard. You can reason like this:

- $a_1a_2 = 1$, so either both a_1 and a_2 are 1, or they are both -1.

- b_1b_2 is positive, so b_1 and b_2 must have the same sign. The product of these two numbers is 4, so either they are both 2 (or -2) or they are 4 and 1 (or -4 and -1).

- Make all these numbers positive for now (because it's simpler), and try to find a combination that fits. Look at the possibilities for $a_1b_2 + b_1a_2$: $1 \cdot 2 + 2 \cdot 1$ or $1 \cdot 4 + 1 \cdot 1$. The second one adds up to 5, as required, so that's it!

$$(x + 4)(x + 1) = x^2 + 5x + 4$$

Written out like that, the process looks much harder than it really is. There are really just three "rules" for this game:

- The product of the first linear terms must equal the first quadratic term.

- The product of the last linear terms must equal the last quadratic term.

- The sum of the inner and outer linear products must equal the middle quadratic term.

The rest is up to your own skill in finding combinations of numbers that work.

Try solving these quadratic equations, just for fun. All factors (but not all solutions) use integers only.

8.42

1. $x^2 + 8x + 15 = 0$

2. $x^2 - 5x - 14 = 0$

3. $x^2 - 7x + 6 = 0$

4. $x^2 + 2x - 8 = 0$

5. $2x^2 - 15x - 27 = 0$

6. $6x^2 + 17x + 5 = 0$

The bad news is that most quadratic equations are not as nice as the ones you just worked on. Most of the time, the coefficients are not integers. Even when they are, the factors do not always work out nicely. You may not be able to find the factors by playing this game, but that doesn't mean there aren't any solutions! The good news is that there is a way to solve quadratic equations that works all the time. It is called the *Quadratic Formula*. The next section shows you how and why this formula works.

Problem Set: 8.4

1. Solve each of these quadratic equations, if possible. If it is not possible, explain how you know that.

   (a) $5x^2 = 3x$

   (b) $12x^2 + 3x = 0$

   (c) $0.5x - 7x^2 = 0$

   (d) $2.7x^2 - 9x = 0$

   (e) $x^2 - 36 = 0$

   (f) $x^2 = 9$

   (g) $x^2 + 9 = 0$

   (h) $5x^2 = 3$

   (i) $1.65x^2 - 32.34 = 0$

   (j) $1.65x^2 + 32.34 = 0$

   (k) $x^2 + 12x + 35 = 0$

   (l) $x^2 - 4x = 12$

   (m) $4x^2 + 16x = 9$

   (n) $3x^2 - 34x + 40 = 0$

Using Technology

2. (a) The graph shown in Display 8.14 was made on a TI-84 calculator with **Standard WINDOW** settings. Write the four quadratic functions that formed it.

   (b) When you set each of these functions equal to 0, you get four equations. All four equations have one solution in common. What is it?

   (c) Pair up these equations according to which ones have the same other solution.

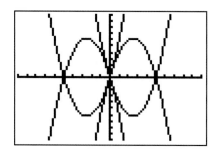

Display 8.14

3. A small company is trying to decide whether or not to produce a new video game. They have done a survey to estimate how many of their potential customers would buy this new game at various prices. The line of best fit for the data on the number of customers who would buy a game was approximately $n(p) = -25p + 1000$, for prices p (in dollars).

(a) The gross revenue from sales of this game is the price times the number of games sold. Write this as a function $r(p)$.

(b) According to your function $r(p)$, what price will be too high to make any gross revenue?

(c) The company must take in a gross revenue of at least $7,500 to make it worthwhile to produce the game. What price should they set to reach that amount? Justify your answer algebraically.

(d) For what price range will they make more than $7,500? Justify your answer.

4. A company that makes solar roofs needs to make rectangular panels with an area of exactly 340 sq. in. To fit properly, each panel must be 3 inches longer than it is wide. What should the length and width of each panel be? (Reminder: The area of a rectangle equals its length times its width.)

5. A lead weight in free fall travels $4.9t^2$ meters in t seconds from the time it is dropped. How long does it take the weight to fall...

(a) 98 meters?

(b) 200 meters?

(c) 500 meters?

(d) 1000 meters?

Answer to the nearest hundredth of a second. Calculate your answers algebraically.

8.5 The Quadratic Formula

Learning Outcomes

After studying this section, you will be able to:

Solve quadratic equations by "completing the square"

Explain why the Quadratic Formula works

Use the Quadratic Formula to solve quadratic equations

Explain what it means to say that a quadratic equation "has no solution."

In the previous section you saw that quadratic equations are not always easy to solve by factoring. But they are valuable mathematical tools, so people searched for a better way to solve them. They looked for a formula that would work for any quadratic equation. This section shows you what they found.

The story begins in ancient Baghdad, capital of the Islamic Empire in the 9th century. One of the scholars at the "House of Wisdom" there was Muhammad ibn Musa al-Khwarizmi. Al-Khwarizmi studied and wrote about astronomy, geography, and mathematics. His most famous mathematics book was *al-jabr w'al muqabalah*, about how to solve equations. It was translated into Latin in the Middle Ages, and the word *algebra* comes from its title.

Algebra in the 9th century did not use symbols. All the problems and all the solutions were stated in words! Here is the first problem in al-Khwarizmi's book:

What must be the square which, when increased by ten of its own roots, amounts to 39?

8.43

Think of "the square" as x^2. Then "its own roots" are copies of x. Write al-Khwarizmi's problem as an equation. Then solve it.

Here is al-Khwarizmi's solution (translated from Arabic, of course):

You halve the number of roots, which in the present instance yields 5. This you multiply by itself; the product is 25. Add this to 39; the sum is 64. Now take the root of this, which is 8, and subtract from it half the number of the roots, which is 5; the remainder is 3. This is the root of the square which you sought for; the square itself is 9.

Did he get it right? Why or why not?

8.44

We guess that you solved al-Khwarizmi's problem more easily than he did. You probably found a second solution, too. But you have some tools that he didn't have. Back in the 9th century, zero was not used as a number. Neither were negatives. Al-Khwarizmi did not know about setting linear factors equal to 0, so he had to find another way. And the way he found is better than factoring, *because it works every time!* His solution was a pattern for solving any quadratic equation. To use it well, you have to understand what he did and why it works.

1. Write the steps of al-Khwarizmi's solution to $x^2 + 10x = 39$ using modern arithmetic symbols.

8.45

2. Now think of the equation as $x^2 + bx = k$, where b and k are numbers that you don't know. Rewrite your answer to part 1 in terms of b and k.

Puzzled? That's OK. In a way, we hope so. We hope you are trying to figure out how these steps solve the equation. The algebra by itself doesn't help you see that. But al-Khwarizmi had a picture in mind! The picture is the key to the puzzle. Here is his picture, redone with modern notation.

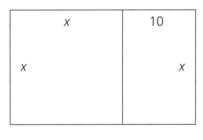

$x^2 + 10x$

Display 8.15

Remember the original problem: You have a square (x^2) and 10 of its roots ($10x$). Now, to al-Khwarizmi and everyone else in the 9th century, "square" meant a geometric shape. So that part of the problem looked like Display 8.15. Now follow these steps.

a. You do not know the side length x of the original square. But $10x$ is a rectangle with one side equal to 10. Divide this rectangle in half, so that you have two $5x$ rectangles, as in Display 8.16(a).

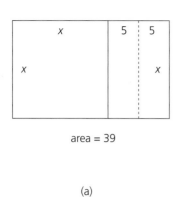

area = 39

(a)

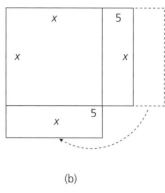

(b)

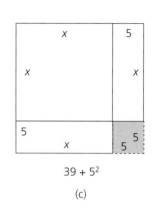

$39 + 5^2$

(c)

Display 8.16

b. Now move one of them to the bottom of the original square, as in Display 8.16(b). The resulting figure has the same area as the original one (39) and is almost a square.

c. It has a missing corner, as in Display 8.16(c). The side length of that missing square piece is 5, which is half of "the number of the roots." Its area is $5^2 = 25$, so the area of the completed square is $39 + 25 = 64$.

d. The rest is easy. The side length of the completed square is $\sqrt{64} = 8$, which is $x + 5$, so $x = 8 - 5 = 3$.

8.46 In al-Khwarizmi's diagram, the original square looks much bigger than the missing square corner, but it turns out to be smaller. Does that matter? Why or why not?

8.47 Your turn. Your teacher will give you a sheet with three unlabeled copies of the diagram in Display 8.16. The first two are for these questions. The third one is to help you with the explanation that comes later.

1. The quadratic equation $x^2 + 6x = 50$ does not factor nicely, but it can be solved using al-Khwarizmi's method. Do it by filling in the first copy of the diagram. Then complete the computation for the length x. Round your answer to two decimal places.

2. Fill in the second copy of the diagram for the general form of al-Khwarizmi's equation, $x^2 + bx = k$. Compare your answer for x with the one you got for part 2 of Lightning Icon 8.45. Do they agree?

Al-Khwarizmi's method of solving quadratic equations of the form $x^2 + bx = k$ is called **completing the square**. You can see why. He imagined $x^2 + bx$ as a large square region of area k with a small square corner missing. By figuring out the size of the missing piece and adding it in, he found the side length of the large square. Then the original length x was a simple matter of subtraction.

Now we can show you how this method can be used to solve any quadratic equation. Fill in the third diagram on your worksheet as you follow the steps.

- Start with a quadratic equation in standard form, $ax^2 + bx + c = 0$, where $a \neq 0$. To put it into the form that al-Khwarizmi used, subtract c from both sides; then divide both sides by a. Write the result on your worksheet. You should get the equation

$$x^2 + \frac{b}{a}x = -\frac{c}{a}$$

Now work through al-Khwarizmi's steps, as follows:

- Divide the "number of roots" in half; you should get $\frac{b}{2a}$.
- Rearrange the rectangles to form the incomplete square.
- Find the area of the missing square corner, $\left(\frac{b}{2a}\right)^2$, which is $\frac{b^2}{4a^2}$.

- The area of the large square is the sum of the original area and the area of the missing corner:

$$-\frac{c}{a} + \frac{b^2}{4a^2}$$

- The side length of the large square is the square root of that:

$$\sqrt{-\frac{c}{a} + \frac{b^2}{4a^2}}$$

- The value of x is the result of subtracting $\frac{b}{2a}$ from the side length of the large square. Write that on your worksheet.

If you got the correct answer for x, you should be able to rewrite it as

$$x = \frac{-b + \sqrt{b^2 - 4ac}}{2a}$$

8.48

Write a step-by-step explanation of how to do this.

Hang on; we're almost done. Completing the square has led to this general formula. Because we derived it using letters, instead of numbers, it tells us how to find a solution for *any* quadratic equation. In fact, it really tells us how to find *two* solutions. A number such as 9 actually has two square roots, $+3$ and -3. If we extend this idea to that formula for x, we

should allow for $+\sqrt{b^2 - 4ac}$ and $-\sqrt{b^2 - 4ac}$. This is the final step. Now we can state the result that this section is named for.

> **The Quadratic Formula:** The solutions of any quadratic equation in the form $ax^2 + bx + c = 0$, where $a \neq 0$, are
>
> $$x = \frac{-b \pm \sqrt{b^2 - 4ac}}{2a}$$

1. The left side of $x^2 - 2x - 3 = 0$ factors easily. Solve this equation by factoring; then solve it with the Quadratic Formula. Do your answers agree? If not, what went wrong?

2. Use the Quadratic Formula to solve $2x^2 + 3x - 5 = 0$. Check your answers by putting them into the equation.

3. Try one more. Use the Quadratic Formula to solve $3x^2 - 6x + 2 = 0$. Round your answers to two decimal places. Then check by substituting them for x in the original equation. Do you get approximate equality?

Something about the statement of the Quadratic Formula should be bothering you. What is it? If you can't think of anything, try solving $x^2 + 2x + 3 = 0$.

Were you bothered by the claim that the Quadratic Formula will solve any quadratic equation? What about the ones with parabolas completely above or completely below the x-axis? How can they have solutions?

It depends on the kinds of numbers you allow. In al-Khwarizmi's time, people didn't believe in negative numbers because they thought of numbers only as lengths or areas or volumes. They would have said that $x^2 + 3x + 2 = 0$ (which is $x^2 + 3x = -2$) has no solution, even though $x = -1$ and $x = -2$ satisfy it. To them, $x^2 + 3x$ was the sum of a square and a rectangle, which could not be negative.

Later, as quadratic equations were used in different ways, negative solutions made sense, so they were accepted. But people did not accept square roots of negatives. After all, the square of any real number must be positive, so how can any negative number have a square root?

As with negatives, the answer came from expanding the number system. Square roots of negative numbers make sense in a number system larger than the reals, called the *complex numbers*. You will learn more about that number system in Year 3. For now, it is enough to know that such a system exists. A quadratic equation may not have a real-number solution, but it will always have a complex-number solution.

A Word to Know: A solution of an equation is also called a **root** of the equation.

1. A quadratic equation may have two real solutions or two non-real, complex solutions, but it can never have one of each. Why not?

8.51

2. There is another possibility for the solution of a quadratic equation. What is it? When does it happen?

Use the Quadratic Formula to solve each of the following equations. Which ones have real-number solutions? Truncate (cut off) each real root after two decimal places. Check your answers by graphing these equations on your calculator.

8.52

Using Technology

1. $x^2 + 8x + 5 = 0$

2. $3x^2 - 4x - 1 = 0$

3. $9x^2 + 12x + 4 = 0$

4. $-2x^2 - 3x - 6 = 0$

5. $7x^2 + 2x + 5 = 0$

6. $-3x^2 + 6x - 3 = 0$

A company is planning a security system for its computer network. As part of that system, it needs a code number to identify each possible two-way connection between each pair of computers on the network.

8.53

1. Right now the company has 10 computers. How many pairs of computers are there? (Recall the Fundamental Counting Principle, and then ignore the order in the pair.)

2. The company is adding more computers to its network as it grows, so it wants a formula for the number of pairs if they have *n* computers. Find it. (Generalize your answer to part 1.)

3. How many pairs can be identified using a three-digit code, from 000 to 999? What is the maximum number of computers that this system can have? (Use your answer to part 2 to write a quadratic equation for this. Then solve it.)

4. If they use a four-digit code, from 0000 to 9999, what is the maximum number of computers that the system can have?

Quadratic equations are powerful tools in many areas of science and business, as well as in mathematics. But that is a story for another time.

Problem Set: 8.5

1. (a) If you think about $x^2 + 18x = 40$ the way al-Khwarizmi did, what is the size of the missing square piece?

   (b) Solve $x^2 + 18x = 40$ by completing the square.

   (c) In this case, is the missing square piece bigger or smaller than the square of x?

   (d) This equation also has a negative solution (which al-Khwarizmi would not have accepted). What is it?

   (e) Check both your solutions by substituting them back into the original equation.

2. Solve $3x^2 - 7x + 2 = 0$ by factoring and then by the Quadratic Formula. Which way do you like better? Why?

3. Use the Quadratic Formula to solve each of the following equations. Which ones have real-number solutions? Truncate (cut off) each real root after three decimal places.

   (a) $x^2 + x - 1 = 0$

   (b) $x^2 + x + 1 = 0$

   (c) $x^2 + 7x - 12 = 0$

   (d) $5x^2 + 10x + 5 = 0$

   (e) $5x^2 - 3x + 20 = 0$

   (f) $2x^2 + 9x + 1 = 0$

   (g) $x^2 - 6x = 17$

   (h) $9x^2 - 30x + 25 = 0$

   (i) $0.5x^2 + 0.3x + 1.8 = 0$

   (j) $3.6x^2 - 4.9x = 2.5$

4. In Section 8.3 you saw how the yearbook committee at Great Ridge School found the profit function $P(x)$ for selling their yearbooks at price x (in dollars):

$$P(x) = -10x^2 + 1450x - 29{,}500$$

(a) You graphed this function to find two prices that would give them a $20,000 profit. Use the Quadratic Formula to get those prices, and see if they agree with what you found in Section 8.3.

(b) Use your answer to part (a) to help you find the price that would give them maximum profit. (Remember: The parabola $P(x)$ is symmetric with respect to the vertical line through its vertex, which is its highest point. How does that tell you what x value you need?) What would the maximum profit be?

5. Casey hit a towering pop fly, straight up. It left his bat $4\frac{1}{2}$ feet above the ground with an upward velocity of 80 feet per second. The downward pull of gravity is $\frac{-16 \text{ ft.}}{\text{sec.}^2}$.

(a) Ignoring air resistance, how long did it take for the ball to hit the ground? (The catcher missed it.)

(b) How high did the ball go?

Looking Back

Quadratic functions are related to many important ideas in science and business. This chapter began by showing you what a quadratic function is and how to recognize the shape of its graph. Then you learned various ways to solve problems that can be described by quadratics.

A function is *quadratic* if it can be put in the form $f(x) = ax^2 + bx + c$, where $a \neq 0$. One way to get a quadratic function is to take the product of two non-constant linear functions. You used the distributive law for that and learned how to do it efficiently. You wrote quadratic functions to describe situations about gravity and profit and used graphs to answer questions about them.

The graph of a quadratic function is a *parabola*, a U-shaped curve opening up or down that is symmetric about the vertical line through its vertex. Constant, nonzero second differences distinguish them from other U-shaped graphs. Through Explorations you saw how changing the values of a, b, and c affects the shape and position of a parabola.

You then focused on solving *quadratic equations*, which can be put in the form $ax^2 + bx + c = 0$. You solved them graphically by finding where the parabola $y = ax^2 + bx + c$ intersects the x-axis. This helped you picture why all quadratic equations have either one, two, or no real solutions. Solving by graph gives only approximate solutions, so you learned algebraic ways to find exact ones. The factoring method can be a quick way to find solutions, but it doesn't always work easily. Finally, you saw how al-Khwarizmi's method of completing the square leads to the Quadratic Formula, which can be used to solve any quadratic equation.

In this chapter you learned how to:

- Explain what a quadratic function is and how to put one into standard form.
- Describe how quadratic functions are related to linear functions.
- Write quadratic functions and equations to describe real-world situations.
- Describe the shape of a quadratic graph.
- Use second differences to determine whether a curve is a parabola.
- Find the maximum or minimum value of a quadratic function using its graph.
- Explain what a quadratic equation is.
- Solve quadratic equations graphically.

- Explain how the solutions of quadratic equations relate to their graphs.
- Solve some quadratic equations by factoring.
- Solve quadratic equations by "completing the square."
- Explain why the Quadratic Formula works and use it to solve quadratic equations.
- Explain graphically and algebraically why some quadratic equations have no real-number solutions.

Along the way, you also learned to:

- Add, subtract, compose, and multiply two linear functions.
- Calculate first and second differences of functions.
- Explain and use the Zero Product Property: If $ab = 0$ then $a = 0$ or $b = 0$.

Review Exercises

1. Solve each equation by factoring. If it is not possible, explain how you know that.

   (a) $x^2 + 2x - 15 = 0$

   (b) $4x^2 + 12x = 0$

   (c) $4x^2 - 9 = 0$

   (d) $x^2 + 16 = 8x$

   (e) $2x^2 + 6 = 0$

   (f) $3x^2 = 7x - 4$

2. Use the Quadratic Formula to solve each of the following equations. Which ones have real-number solutions? Truncate (cut off) each real root after three decimal places.

   (a) $3x^2 + 2x - 4 = 0$

   (b) $4x^2 + 1 = -6x$

   (c) $-2.6x^2 + 1.5x - 2 = 0$

   (d) $4x^2 - 11 = 5x$

   (e) $x^2 + 3x = 28$

   (f) $3x^2 + 30x + 75 = 0$

3. Check your answers to problems (1) and (2) by finding solutions using graphs on your calculator.

4. A rectangle and an equation representing its area, A, are shown in Display 8.17. Which of the following could represent b, the length of the base of the rectangle, and h, the height of the rectangle?

$$A = x^2 - 8x + 15 \quad h$$

b

Display 8.17

(i) $b = (x - 3)$; $h = (x + 5)$

(ii) $b = (x - 3)$; $h = (x - 5)$

(iii) $b = (x + 3)$; $h = (x + 5)$

(iv) $b = (x + 3)$; $h = (x - 5)$

5. Police officer Hewins is analyzing an accident scene. She uses the formula $d = 0.06s^2 + 0.5s$, which gives the distance in feet d that it takes a car to stop if it is traveling s miles per hour when the brakes are applied.

(a) Use the formula to determine the stopping distance for a car traveling 10 mph.

(b) The car in the accident left a skid mark 150 feet long. The speed limit on that road is 40 miles per hour. Was the driver speeding? About how fast was the driver traveling?

6. The first five terms in a quadratic sequence are shown below.

$$4, 7, 12, 19, 28, \ldots$$

(a) What is the next term in the sequence?

(b) Write an algebraic formula for this sequence.

(c) Use your formula from part (b) to find the 17th term in the sequence.

7. Moira and Jeff's new house has a fenced, square pen in the backyard where the previous owners kept their dog. The pen is 12 feet on each side. Moira and Jeff want to increase the fenced area and put a kiddie pool in it. They are going to remove two sides of the square and add fencing to make a new rectangular pen. The dimensions of the square pen and the new rectangular pen are shown in Display 8.18.

(a) Write an expression in terms of x to represent width, in feet, of the new pen.

(b) Write an expression in terms of x to represent length, in feet, of the new pen.

(c) Use your expressions from parts (a) and (b) to write an equation for the area of the new rectangular pen, A, in square feet.

(d) Moira and Jeff want the new pen to have area of 500 square feet. Substitute this value into your area equation from part (c) and solve for x.

(e) What should be the length and the width of the new, 500-square-foot pen?

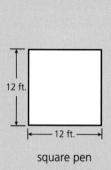 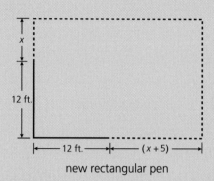

square pen   new rectangular pen

Display 8.17

8. Anya is training for the 10-meter platform dive in the next Olympics. She is now able to jump up off the platform with an initial upward velocity of 2.8 meters per second.

(a) Write a quadratic function that describes Anya's height above the water at any time during her dive. Ignore air resistance and recall that the downward pull of gravity is $\frac{4.9\text{ m}}{\text{sec.}^2}$.

(b) How long is Anya in the air, from the time she jumps until she enters the water? Round your answer to the nearest 100th of a second.

(c) How high above the level of the platform is Anya at the highest point of her dive? Round your answer to the nearest decimeter (10th of a meter).

(d) If Anya builds up her strength so that she can jump upward at 3 meters per second, how much more time will her dive take?

9. Passing Tone Music Co. is trying to decide on the price to charge for a new CD. Their survey of 100 possible customers shows that, for prices between $5 and $22, they will lose about 5 sales for every $1 increase in price. They found that 95 customers would buy the CD for $5, but only 10 would buy it for $22.

(a) Write a linear function for the number of customers that would buy the CD at price p, for $\$5 \le p \le \$22$. Call this function $n(p)$.

(b) It costs $2 per copy to make the CDs. Its gross profit is the total amount of money it receives from sales, minus the cost of making the CDs sold. Write a function $g(n)$ for the gross profit if n CDs are sold at a particular price p.

(c) The composite function $g(n(p))$ will tell you the gross profit as a function of the price. It is a quadratic function. Write it in standard form.

(d) What price should the company charge in order to get the most gross profit?

10. Determine which graph(s), if any, in Display 8.19 match each of the following descriptions. (Some statements may match more than one graph.) The tick marks on the axes are the integer points.

(a) a quadratic function with vertex at $(0, 4)$

(b) a quadratic function with vertex at $(-1, 4)$

(c) a quadratic function with range $\{y \mid -4 \leq y < \infty\}$

(d) a quadratic function with range $\{y \mid -\infty < y \leq 4\}$

(e) a quadratic equation with no real-number roots

(f) a quadratic function with minimum at $(0, 4)$

(g) a quadratic function with a maximum value of 4

(h) the function $y = -(x - 1)(x + 3)$

(i) the function $y = 4 - x^2$

(j) the function $y = -(x^2 + 4)$

(k) the function $y = (x - 4)^2$

(l) the function $(x + 1)(x - 3)$

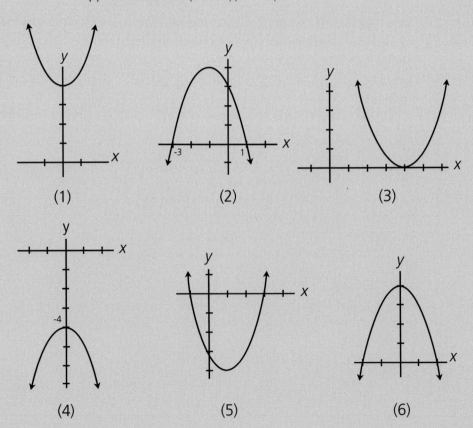

(1)

(2)

(3)

(4)

(5)

(6)

Display 8.19

Related Topics

Families of Functions

Back in Chapter 6 (in Sections 6.4 and 6.5), some basic algebraic equations in the form of $y =$ are reintroduced as $f(x) =$ functions. The familiar $y = mx + b$ is brought back as $f(x) = ax + b$. Both can be used to graph a line and are linear functions, but with different notations.

Compare $y = mx + b$ with $f(x) = ax + b$. What does each variable represent?

8.54

One might ask, "Why introduce a new notation when the old one works perfectly well?" If algebra consisted of solving linear functions and graphing lines, then there might not be need for $f(x)$ notation, but the human imagination allows us to envision much more complicated shapes.

The function $f(x) = ax + b$ is a member of a class of functions with varying degrees of complexity called polynomials. Here are some members of this class:

Zero Degree (constant) $f(x) = a$

First Degree (linear): $f(x) = ax + b$

Second Degree (quadratic): $f(x) = ax^2 + bx + c$

Third Degree (cubic): $f(x) = ax^3 + bx^2 + cx + d$

Fourth Degree (quartic): $f(x) = ax^4 + bx^3 + cx^2 + dx + e$

Fifth Degree (quintic): $f(x) = ax^5 + bx^4 + cx^3 + dx^2 + ex + f$

There are many patterns in the names and notation of the polynomials. Explore these by answering the questions below.

8.55

1. The word *degree* is a characteristic of each polynomial. Describe what number in the $f(x)$ notation represents degree.

2. How is $f(x) = a$ related to $y = c$? What will each graph look like?

3. Why is $f(x) = a$ considered a zero degree polynomial?

4. What would be the notation for a sixth-degree polynomial?

5. A certain variable coefficient appears in each polynomial and is called the *leading coefficient*. What variable is represented by the leading coefficient?

6. Examine the fifth-degree equation. Describe the order of the letters used as coefficients.

7. Using the fifth-degree as an example, describe the pattern in the powers of x.

8.56

Answering all of the previous seven questions should provide a common understanding of how the class of polynomials can be notated. Please fill in the following blanks to test your knowledge.

Polynomials are a class of _____ with the form:

$$f(x) = ax^n + bx^{n-1} + cx^{n-2} + dx^{n-3} + ...$$

The degree of this polynomial is represented by the variable ____.

The leading coefficient is the number that multiplies the x-term with the _____ power and is represented by the variable ____.

Powers of x are displayed in _____ order from left to right.

Coefficients for each power are represented by letters that are in _____ order from left to right.

The degree of each polynomial can tell us a lot about its graph. Within polynomials there are subgroups called *families of functions*. All the members of particular families have similar properties to each other.

8.57

1. The function $f(x) = a$ represents a family of functions that would include all possible values of a. Three members of this family are: $f(x) = 0$, $f(x) = 1$, and $f(x) = 2$. What do the graphs of each of these look like? How are they similar and how are they different? Write up a general description for the family $f(x) = a$.

2. Setting $b = 0$ in $f(x) = ax + b$ creates a family of functions with the form: $f(x) = ax$. List three members of this family. What does each member have in common graphically? What does changing the variable a do?

3. Setting $a = 1$ in $f(x) = ax + b$ creates a family of functions with the form: $f(x) = x + b$. List three members of this family. What does each member have in common graphically? What does changing the variable b do?

4. Fill in a table similar to Display 8.20 with sketches containing at least 3 family members for each.

Family	$f(x) = a$	$f(x) = ax$	$f(x) = x + b$

Display 8.20

Our next step in examining polynomials involves looking at what are known as **even** and **odd functions**.

1. Graph the following on the same screen of your graphing calculator.

8.58

$$y = x^2 \qquad y = x^4 \qquad y = x^6$$

2. It might not surprise you to learn that the above functions are called even functions. Why is this name appropriate?

3. Each of these functions passes through the same three points. What are they? Would this pattern continue for higher powers such as the eighth or the tenth power?

4. On the graph, there is a line that divides the graph *evenly* called a *line of symmetry*. If the graph was printed on paper, the paper could be folded along this line. Each side of the graph would match up, point for point, with the other side. Which axis is the line of symmetry?

5. The description of an even function may be written algebraically as: $f(x) = f(-x)$. Consider $y = x^4$. Plug at least four x-values into a chart like the one in Display 8.21 to numerically examine this property.

	X = _____	X = _____	X = _____	X = _____
$f(x)$				
$f(-x)$				

Display 8.21

6. Using question 5 as a guide, write out your own description of an even function.

7. Not all functions with even powers in them are even functions. Use your graphing calculator to examine which of the following functions are even.

$$f(x) = x^2 - 4x - 5 \qquad g(x) = -x^4 + 6$$
$$h(x) = x^2 - 4x$$

8.59

1. Graph the following on the same screen of your graphing calculator.

$$y = x^1 \qquad y = x^3 \qquad y = x^5$$

2. The above functions are called odd functions. Why is this name appropriate?

3. Each of these functions passes through the same three points. What are they? Would this pattern continue for higher powers such as the seventh or the ninth power?

4. There is a certain symmetry to the graphs, but not one as obvious as the symmetry of even functions. It could be described as double reflection, reflecting across both sets of axes. It could also be thought of as having a rotational symmetry of 180°. Invert your graph by turning your graphing calculator 180°. How do the inverted graphs compare to the right-side-up graphs?

5. The description of an odd function may be written algebraically as: $f(x) = -f(-x)$. Consider $y = x^3$. Plug at least four x-values into a chart like the one in Display 8.22 to numerically examine this property.

	X = _____	X = _____	X = _____	X = _____
$f(x)$				
$f(-x)$				
$-f(-x)$				

Display 8.22

6. Using question 5 as a guide, write out your own description of an odd function.

7. Not all functions with odd powers in them are odd functions. Use your graphing calculator to discover if the following are odd functions. Remember that the graph would have to look identical (not similar) when rotated 180°.

$$f(x) = -6x^3 + 3x \qquad g(x) = -2x^3 + 3x + 2$$
$$h(x) = x^3 - 3$$

The **end behavior** of a polynomial can be described as what happens to the value of the polynomial when you plug a very large positive number or a very small negative number into x. For instance, if you plug 1,000,000 (10^6) into $f(x) = x^2$, the value of the function is a very large number, 1,000,000,000,000 (10^{12}). Plug a larger number into the function and the output is even greater. This trend can be summed up as saying, "As x gets larger, $f(x)$ gets larger." On the negative side, plugging a very small negative number into x yields a large positive number for $f(x)$.

The phrase "end behavior" can be misleading, because there is no end to how big or small a number can be. For mathematicians, there is a "virtual" end known as "infinity." Written as a sideways eight (∞) infinity can describe very large positive numbers, ∞, or very small negative numbers, $-\infty$. The end behavior of $f(x) = x^2$ can be described this way:

As $x = \to \infty$, the function $f(x) \to \infty$ and

As $x = \to -\infty$, the function $f(x) \to \infty$.

In words, "As x gets very large, so does the does value of the function. As x gets very small, the value of the function becomes large." We can also see this illustrated in Display 8.23 on the next page.

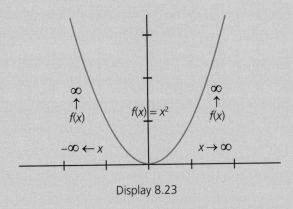

Display 8.23

Odd and even functions have differing end behaviors. Knowing these behaviors can help you sketch the shape of an unknown polynomial even without the help of a graphing calculator.

8.60

1. Fill in Display 8.24 to describe the end behaviors of even and odd functions. The first line has been done for you.

Function	Even/Odd	Left Side $x \to -\infty$	Right Side $x \to \infty$
$f(x) = x^2$	Even	$f(x) \to \infty$	$f(x) \to \infty$
$f(x) = -x^2$			
$f(x) = x^3$			
$f(x) = -x^3$			

Display 8.24

2. The two even functions suggest a pattern. What is it?

3. Would this pattern hold for $f(x) = x^4$ and $f(x) = -x^4$?

4. The two odd functions suggest a pattern. What is it?

5. Would this pattern hold for $f(x) = x^5$ and $f(x) = -x^5$?

6. What is the main difference in the end behaviors of even functions versus odd functions?

Quadratic functions of the form $f(x) = ax^2 + bx + c$ have two basic shapes that are determined by whether a is positive or negative. In the function $f(x) = x^2$, a is positive and it is a parabola, which always have a U shape. When a is negative, as in $f(x) = -x^2$, the graph is also a parabola but in this case the shape is an upside-down U. When sketching quadratics, knowing the value of a is one of the most important considerations.

In other polynomials, the value of a helps describe the end behavior and can give a good hint at the general shape of the polynomial.

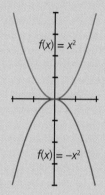
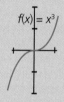

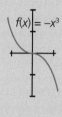

Display 8.25

Use the graphs in Display 8.25 to help answer the following questions.

8.61

1. In an even function, what does a positive a-value tell you about the end behaviors of the function?

2. In an even function, what does a negative a-value tell you about the end behaviors of the function?

3. In an odd function, what does a positive a-value tell you about the end behaviors of the function?

4. In an odd function, what does a negative a-value tell you about the end behaviors of the function?

Whereas quadratic functions have two basic patterns, cubic equations are much more complex. When graphing $f(x) = -6x^3 + 3x$ earlier, you may have noticed a pattern resembling a sideways S. These "bumps" in the function are known as **turning points**. The polynomial $f(x) = -6x^3 + 3x$ is said to have two turning points (as shown in Display 8.26). The higher the power of a polynomial, the more turning points it could possibly have.

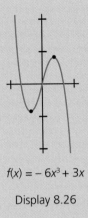

$$f(x) = -6x^3 + 3x$$

Display 8.26

8.62

1. Fill in a chart similar to Display 8.27 by exploring the following graphs on your graphing calculator.

Function	Turning Points	Degree	Sketch
$f(x) = x^2$	1	2	
$f(x) = 6x^3 - 3x$			
$f(x) = 0.2x^4 - 1.8x$			
$f(x) = x^5 + 4.4x^4 + 3x^3 - 5x^2 - 4.5x$			

Display 8.27

2. What is the relationship between the degree of a polynomial and the number of possible turning points?

3. How many turning points would a linear function have? Does this fit with your answer to question 2?

In summing up what we have done in this section, we discovered some of the properties for families of functions. First, various linear families were examined, then higher-powered polynomials were explored. Even and odd functions were compared along with their end behaviors and the relationship with the leading coefficient a. Finally, the number of possible turning points was linked to the degree of a polynomial.

Combine all of the above information by creating sketches in a chart similar to Display 8.28.

8.63

Function	Degree	Sketch for Positive a	Sketch for Negative a
Linear			
Cubic			
Quartic			
Quintic			

Display 8.28

Problem Set

1. Consider the following function: $f(x) = ax^2$ where $a > 0$.
   (a) Sketch at least three family members.
   (b) What do all members in this family have in common?
   (c) If $a < 0$, what would that family look like?

2. Consider the following function: $f(x) = x^3 + c$ where $c \neq 0$.
   (a) Sketch at least three family members.
   (b) What do all members in this family have in common?
   (c) Write a description of this family.

3. Draw sketches of the following:
   (a) A cubic function with a positive leading coefficient and two turning points.
   (b) A quartic function with a negative leading coefficient and three turning points.
   (c) A cubic function with no turning points and a negative leading coefficient.

4. Consider the function: $f(x) = 0.5x^3 + 3x^2 + 2x - 4$.
   Without graphing, address the following:

   (a) Describe the end behavior.

   (b) How many turning points could it have?

   After you've finished the two parts above, graph to check your work.

5. For each of the following:

   (i) Describe the end behavior.

   (ii) State whether a is positive or negative.

   (iii) State whether it is an even or odd function.

   (a)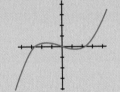

   (b)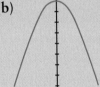

   (c)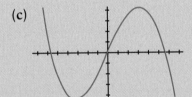

6. Consider the absolute value function: $f(x) = |x| + c$.

   (a) Sketch at least three family members.

   (b) Describe the shapes of these graphs.

7. Examine the rational function: $f(x) = \frac{1}{x} + c$.

   (a) Sketch at least three family members.

   (b) Describe the shapes of these graphs.

Special Factors

When you are given a polynomial and asked to factor it, it is very important to remove any **common monomial factors** (or **CMF**) as a first step. Here are some examples of that process.

$$3x + 6 \qquad 2x^3 - 18x \qquad x^2y^2 + 8xy^2 + 16y^2$$

The two terms in the first example each have 3 as a common factor. The two terms in the second example each have $2x$ as a common factor. The three terms in the third example each have y^2 as a common factor. These common monomial factors can be factored out of each polynomial. The results after CMF factoring are shown here.

$$3(x + 2) \qquad 2x(x^2 - 9) \qquad y^2(x^2 + 8x + 16)$$

It is a good idea to use your knowledge of the distributive law to check to see if the factored form of the polynomial is correct. If you use the distributive law to multiply the CMF back in and it matches the original, you have probably factored it correctly.

After you have removed any common monomial factors from a polynomial, you should look to see if the polynomial is one of several special cases. Here are examples of special cases.

$$x^2 - 16 \qquad x^2 + 8x + 16 \qquad x^2 - 8x + 16 \qquad x^2 + 16$$

The first example is called the **difference of squares**. It is a quantity squared ($4^2 = 16$) being subtracted from another quantity squared (x squared or x^2). Subtraction is often referred to as a "difference." Consequently, the name for this pattern is the "difference of squares." This example can be factored into two binomials. The factored form is shown here.

$$(x + 4)(x - 4)$$

If you use your knowledge of multiplying two binomials, you can check to see that the factored form is equivalent to the original non-factored form. Using FOIL you get $x^2 - 4x + 4x - 16$. Because $-4x$ added to $4x$ is equal to zero, there is no middle term (or $0x$) in the original non-factored form.

Try a couple of these on your own.

8.64

1. $x^2 - 25$

2. $a^2 - 49$

The second and third special cases shown are examples of a pattern called "a perfect square." The first and last terms are some quantity squared (just like the difference of squares example) but these polynomials have an additional middle term as well. In other words, the middle terms did not cancel out as they did with the difference of squares. If $4x$ and $4x$ were added together the answer would be $8x$. If $-4x$ and $-4x$ were added together the answer would be $-8x$. Perhaps only the signs need to be changed for perfect squares. Here are the factored forms of the above two perfect square examples.

$$x^2 + 8x + 16 = (x + 4)(x + 4)$$

$$x^2 - 8x + 16 = (x - 4)(x - 4)$$

If you use your knowledge of multiplying two binomials, you will see that the factored form for each matches the original non-factored form. Note that the middle term in a perfect square (in these examples, $8x$ or $-8x$) is always double the product of the first and last terms ($4x$ or $-4x$). This will always be true in a perfect square. Now, why is it called a perfect square? Look at the factored form of each. These factored forms may be written as follows:

$$(x + 4)(x + 4) = (x + 4)^2 \qquad (x - 4)(x - 4) = (x - 4)^2$$

Thus, they are called perfect squares.

Try factoring a couple.

8.65

1. $a^2 - 14a + 49$

2. $x^2 + 6x + 9$

What combination of signs would work to factor the fourth example given as a special case?

$$x^2 + 16 = (x \; ? \; 4)(x \; ? \; 4)$$

Multiply the following binomials.

8.66

1. $(x + 4)(x + 4)$

2. $(x - 4)(x - 4)$

3. $(x + 4)(x - 4)$

4. $(x - 4)(x + 4)$

Are there any other combinations that may work? You should be convinced that the sum of two squares can't be factored. You have used all of the possible combinations of signs with the difference of squares (one $+$ and one $-$) and the perfect squares (two $+$ or two $-$). This information might save you some time in the future. If you know that the sum of two squares can't be factored, you shouldn't waste time trying to factor that pattern.

Let's summarize what we have learned about special cases.

$x^2 - 16 = (x + 4)(x - 4)$ Difference of Squares

$x^2 + 8x + 16 = (x + 4)(x + 4) = (x + 4)^2$ Perfect Square

$x^2 - 8x + 16 = (x - 4)(x - 4) = (x - 4)^2$ Perfect Square

General Rules for Special Quadratics:

Difference of Squares $a^2 - b^2 = (a + b)(a - b)$

Perfect Squares $a^2 + 2ab + b^2 = (a + b)(a + b) = (a + b)^2$

                  $a^2 - 2ab + b^2 = (a - b)(a - b) = (a - b)^2$

So, when the directions tell you to factor and you are given a polynomial, what should you do? First, you should remove any common monomial factors. Often this will cause patterns to be more apparent in the polynomial. Then you should check the result to see if any special cases (patterns like the difference of squares, perfect squares, or the sum of two squares) exist. If you find a pattern, go ahead and factor. What do you do if you do not find any patterns? In that event, you just have to use trial and error to find factors that will work (assuming that the polynomial can be factored). Here is an example where you would have to to use trial and error.

$$x^2 - 3x + 2$$

First, there is no common monomial factor to factor out. Also, this is not a special case (as 2 is not an integer squared). If this is factored into a binomial times a binomial, the first terms of each could be x. The possible integer factors of 2 are 2 and 1 (or -2 and -1). So you could try $(x\ ?\ 2)(x\ ?\ 1)$ as possible binomial factors. The question remains as to what signs would work to make the factored form equivalent to the original form. You can't use one of each (one $+$ and one $-$) because the 2 in the original form is positive. A positive 2 has to come from either a positive times a positive or a negative times a negative. If you try two positives for the signs, the middle term becomes $3x$ (from $2x + 1x$). That will not fit because the middle term in the original is $-3x$ (not $+3x$). If you try both signs as negatives, it matches. So

$$x^2 - 3x + 2 = (x - 2)(x - 1)$$

Practice a few factoring problems.

8.67

1. $x^2 - 6x + 5$

2. $x^2 - 6x - 7$

3. $x^2 + 6x + 5$

To reinforce how important it is to first remove any CMF before attempting to look for patterns in a polynomial, look back at the first three examples on page 677 where you were given polynomials that needed to have a CMF removed. Did any special cases examples appear after the CMF was removed?

In the second example, $x^2 - 9$ emerged. This can be factored some more because it is the difference of squares, so

$$2x^3 - 18x = 2x(x^2 - 9) = 2x(x + 3)(x - 3)$$

It would have been difficult to see the difference of squares pattern before removing the CMF.

In the third example, $x^2 + 8x + 16$ (a perfect square) emerges after the CMF is removed. So the polynomial can be additionally factored:

$$x^2y^2 + 8xy^2 + 16y^2 = y^2(x^2 + 8x + 16) = y^2(x + 4)^2$$

Again, it would have been difficult to see the perfect square pattern before factoring out the common monomial factor.

Does it matter if you have two variables in the factors? Let's look at the quadratic expression $x^2 - 4xy + 4y^2$. The first and last terms are perfect squares with factors x and $2y$. If you multiply these and double them, you get the middle term. So, this factors out to $(x - 2y)(x - 2y) = (x - 2y)^2$.

Try factoring these.

8.68

1. $x^2 - 16y^2$

2. $x^2 + 6xy + 9y^2$

3. $x^2 + 6xy + 5y^2$

Another question that arises out of factoring is: "Does the order matter?" Let's take a quick look at that. John and Paul were working on factoring $x^2 - 4x - 12$. John determined that the factored form was $(x - 6)(x + 2)$ and Paul said it was $(x + 2)(x - 6)$. Are they both correct? Verify your answer by using the FOIL method to check their work. If we go back to our basic mathematical laws about numbers, we may better understand this. If you were asked to write 12 in terms of two factors, you could write $2 * 6$ or $6 * 2$ since multiplication is commutative. This concept works for algebraic expressions as well.

One way to check if your factored form is correct is to graph both the original form and the factored form on your calculator. If the graphs are the same, you have factored the polynomial correctly. Here is an example of this using the quadratic expression $x^2 + 4x - 5$ and its factored form $(x - 1)(x + 5)$.

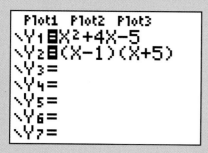 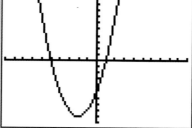

Display 8.29

You can see that there is only one graph because they overlapped each other. Thus, they are the same equation in different forms.

Problem Set

Here are some examples for you to factor. Remember, first factor out any CMF, then look for special cases. If all else fails, use trial and error.

1. $5x - 30$
2. $4x^2 + 36$
3. $x^2 + 4x + 4$
4. $6x^2 - 6$
5. $x^2 - 14x + 49$
6. $x^2 - xy - 12y^2$
7. $2x^2 + 14x + 24$

8. $x^2 - y^2$

9. $3x^3 + 30x^2 + 75x$

10. $3x^2 - 6x + 3$

11. A student factored problem 10 in the following way: First she factored out the CMF of 3. The result was $3(x^2 - 2x)$. Then the student realized that she had missed the CMF of x. So the student continued factoring by stating that $3(x^2 - 2x) = 3x(x - 2)$. When the student graphed the original form and the final factored form of the polynomial, the graphs did not match. Obviously, the student had made an error. Can you figure out what she did wrong?

Quadratic Inequalities

In this chapter, you studied quadratics and the graphs of parabolas. Earlier, you studied linear inequalities. In this section, we are going to look at quadratic inequalities and systems of inequalities. You will need your graphing calculator or a graphing utility on a computer. If you are using your TI-84 graphing calculator to graph inequalities, you will need to go to the **APPS** menu and select the **Inequalz** application. The application will automatically turn on.

Display 8.30

Your $\boxed{Y=}$ screen will now look like Display 8.31. If you want to reset your $\boxed{Y=}$ menu back to its original form, you need to go back to the **APPS** menu, select **Inequalz**, then choose **Quit Inequal**.

Display 8.31

The top row of commands still leaves you with access to each of the three stat plots but it adds in another command **(X=)**. This option allows you to type in equations with x as the dependent variable, in other words, $x = 3y + 2$. In order to select an inequality symbol on this screen, your cursor needs to be over the equal sign when you press $\boxed{ALPHA}$ and then one of the menu keys on the top row: $\boxed{Y=}$ for $=$; $\boxed{WINDOW}$ for $<$; $\boxed{ZOOM}$ for $\leq$; $\boxed{TRACE}$ for $>$ and $\boxed{GRAPH}$ for $\geq$. So, if you want to graph $y < x^2$, you would press the $\boxed{ALPHA}$ key then the $\boxed{WINDOW}$ to get $<$. Then, you need to arrow over one space to the right and type in x^2. Your screen will look like Display 8.32, on the next page.

Display 8.32

Finally, press GRAPH and you will see the solution. The graphing calculator will plot a dotted line when the curve is not included in the solution.

EXPLORATION

Let's start by looking at the following inequalities:

(a) $y \geq x^2$ (b) $y > x^2$ (c) $y \leq x^2$ (d) $y < x^2$

Graph $y = x^2$ on your calculator or on your computer, then predict what the graphs of each of the above inequalities will look like in relationship to $y = x^2$.

For each of the above, graph the inequality on your calculator to check your predictions and answer the following questions.

1. How well did you do in predicting these graphs?

2. What is the difference between graph (a) and graph (b)?

3. What is the difference between graph (a) and graph (c)?

4. Are there any points of intersection between graph (a) and graph (c)?

5. Are there any points of intersection between graph (b) and graph (d)?

8.69

Given the equation $y = (x - 2)^2 + 1$, graph each of the four inequalities that can be derived from this equation on separate axes (be sure to label them clearly).

Given the following graphs of inequalities, write the inequality that represents each graph.

8.70

1.

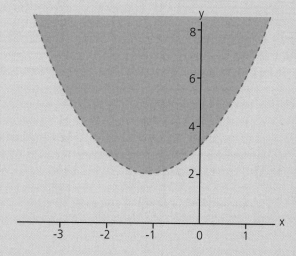

2.

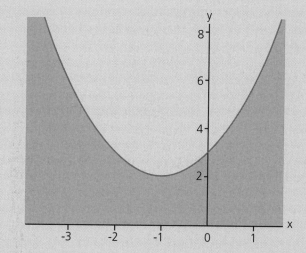

Graph the following two inequalities: $y > -x^2$ and $y > x^2$.

8.71

1. What do these graphs have in common?

2. What are their differences?

3. Do their solutions intersect each other?

4. On graph paper, clearly highlight the points both inequalities have in common.

If you use your graphing calculator for this problem, you can use the **Shades** menu on the graphing screen to help make your graph clearer. In Display 8.33 on the next page, you will see three screenshots: the original graph, the **Shades** menu, and finally (after **Ineq Intersection** is chosen), the graph of the intersection.

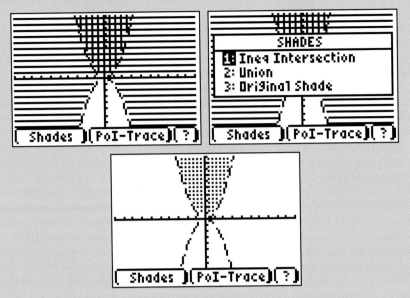

Display 8.33

Now we will look at more complex systems of equations. You should be able to graph these systems by hand as well as through the use of technology.

8.72

1. If you are given two parabolas in the form of $y = ax^2 + bx + c$, how many points of intersection could there be? Graphically show your answer.

2. Given $y \le x^2$ and $y \ge x^2 - 2$, graph each inequality and shade the overlapping region. Do the graphs intersect?

3. Graph the following systems of inequalities by hand and verify the solution with your calculator.

    (a) $y \le x^2 - 2$
    $y \ge (x - 4)^2$

    (b) $y \le x^2 + 1$
    $y \ge x^2 - 1$

    (c) $y > -x^2 - 1$
    $y < (x + 2)^2 + 2$

Appendix A: Using a TI-84 Plus Graphing Calculator

A graphing calculator is a useful tool for doing many different mathematical things. Once you begin to use it, you'll find that it is powerful, fast, and friendly. In fact, your biggest difficulty may be just getting started for the first time! Because this machine can do a lot, it has lots of complicated looking buttons. But you don't have to know about *all* of them before you start to use *any* of them! The sooner you make friends with your electronic assistant, the more it will be able to help you. Let us introduce you to each other by trying a few simple things.

The Cover

The face of the calculator is protected from dirt and scratches by a cover that slides on and off from the top. When you're using the calculator, this cover slips on the back so that you won't lose it. Always put the cover back over the face of the calculator when you finish using it.

ON, OFF, 2ND, and CLEAR

To get the calculator's attention, just press ON (at the lower left corner of the calculator). What happens? Do you see a dark block blinking in the upper left corner of the screen? That's the cursor, which tells you where you are on the screen. The cursor is always at the spot that will be affected by the next button you push.

Notice that the word **OFF** is printed in blue above the ON button. Notice also that there is one key of the same color. It is the key marked 2ND at the top of the first column of buttons.

When you push 2ND, it makes the next key that you push behave like what is marked above it in blue.

Try it. Push 2ND. What has happened to the cursor? Do you see an up arrow (↑) inside it as it blinks? That's to remind you that 2ND key has been pushed and will affect the next key you choose. Now push ON. What happens? Did the cursor disappear? You should have a blank screen; the calculator should be off.

It's always a good idea to turn your calculator off when you finish using it. If you forget, the calculator will turn itself off after a few minutes to save its batteries. Sometimes when you are using it, you may put it aside and do something else for a little while. If it is off when you pick it up again, don't worry; just press [ON]. The screen will show what was there before it shut down.

Pressing [CLEAR] gives you a blank screen that is ready for new work. But the last thing you did is still stored. Press [2ND] then [ENTRY] (bottom right corner) to bring it back.

Basic Arithmetic

Doing arithmetic on a graphing calculator is no harder than on a simpler calculator. In fact, it's easier. This calculator has a screen that lets you keep track of the problem as you enter it. Let's try a few simple exercises. Turn your calculator on.

- Pick two 3-digit numbers and add them. To do this, just key in the first number, press [+] and then key in the second number. Your addition problem will appear on the screen. Press [ENTER] to get the answer.

If you make a mistake when entering a number, you can go back and fix it. The [◀] key lets you move back (left) one space at a time. When you get to your mistake, just key in the correct number over the wrong one. Then move forward (right) to the end of the line by using the [▶] key.

For instance, to add 123 and 456, press **1 2 3** [+] **4 5 6** [ENTER]. The screen will show your question on the first line and the answer at the right side of the second line, as in Display A.1.

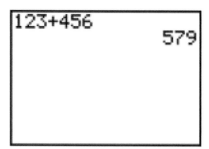

Display A.1

- Now let's try the other three basic arithmetic operations. To clear the screen, press CLEAR. Then try subtracting, multiplying, and dividing your two 3-digit numbers. For instance, if your numbers are 123 and 456, press

123 − 456 ENTER

123 × 456 ENTER

123 ÷ 456 ENTER

Your screen should look like Display A.2.

```
123-456
           -333
123*456
          56088
123/456
     .2697368421
```

Display A.2

Notice that the display uses * for multiplication (so that it is not confused with the letter X) and / for division.

- Here are two button-pushing shortcuts.

  If you want to redo a problem with just a small change in it, you don't have to reenter the whole thing. 2ND [ENTRY] will bring back the last problem you entered. Just move to the place you want to change, key in the change, and press ENTER. For instance, add 54321 and 12345, as in Display A.3.

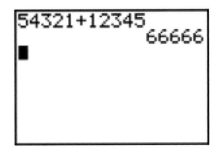
```
54321+12345
          66666
■
```

Display A.3

Now, to subtract 12345 from 54321, press [2ND] [ENTRY]; the next line will show **54321 + 12345**. Move your cursor back to the + sign (using [◄]) and press [−]; then press [ENTER]. Did you try it? Your screen should look like Display A.4.

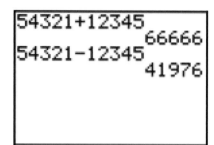

Display A.4

Let's check to see that 41976 is the correct answer by adding 12345 to it and seeing if we get the first number back again. Since you want to do something to the last answer, *you don't have to reenter it*. Press [+]. Does your calculator show **Ans+** and the cursor? It should. If you press an operation key right after doing a calculation, the machine assumes that you want to perform this operation on the last answer. It shows that last answer as **Ans**. Now key in **12345** and press [ENTER]. You should get back the first number, 54321.

A.1

1. **Pick two 7-digit numbers and add them. What do you get?**

2. **Now subtract the second number from the first. Can you do it without rekeying the numbers? What do you get?**

3. **Now multiply your two 7-digit numbers. What do you get? What does the E mean?**

4. **Check the last answer by dividing the second of your 7-digit numbers into it. Do it without rekeying the last answer. Do you get your first number back again?**

A.2

Multiply 98765432 by 123456. Now check the product in two ways.

• Divide by pressing [÷] then entering **123456**. Does it check?

• First reenter the product; then divide it by 123456. The product is in scientific notation. To enter it as a regular number, remember that the positive number after the E tells you to move the decimal that many places to the right. Does it check?

1. Divide 97533 by 525 and by 625. One of the answers you get will be exactly right, and the other one will be a very close approximation.

A.3

- Which is which?

- How can you tell?

- If you hadn't been told that one of the answers is an approximation, how could you know?

2. When an answer is too long to be displayed with ten digits, the calculator shows a 10-digit approximation. Does it do this by just chopping off (truncating) the rest of the digits, or by rounding off? What test would you give your calculator to tell which way it does this?

1. Pick any 3-digit number and write it down.

2. Repeat its digits in the same order to form a 6-digit number (like 123123, for example). Key this number into your calculator.

A.4

3. Divide your number by 7.

4. Divide your answer by 11. How do you do this without reentering the answer?

5. Divide the last number by 13. What do you notice about the result? Do you think that it is just a coincidence?

6. Pick another 3-digit number and repeat steps 2–5.

7. Try to beat the system; see if you can pick a 3-digit number that doesn't work this way. What might you try? Why?

8. Can you actually prove that the pattern you see *works every time*? How might you try to do this?

The Two Minus Signs

The calculator has two minus signs. The one on the gray key looks like $\boxed{-}$ and the one on the white key looks like $\boxed{(-)}$. The gray one, on the right, is for subtraction. It is grouped with the keys for the other arithmetic operations. To subtract 3764 from 8902, for example, you would key in

$$8\ 9\ 0\ 2\ \boxed{-}\ 3\ 7\ 6\ 4\ \boxed{\text{ENTER}}$$

Go ahead; do it. Do you get 5138?

The white minus key, to the left of the ENTER key at the bottom, is for making a number negative. It is grouped with the digit keys and the decimal point. To add the numbers -273, 5280, and -2116, for example, you would key in

(-) 2 7 3 + 5 2 8 0 + (-) 2 1 1 6 ENTER

Try it. Notice that the display shows these negative signs without the parentheses, but they are smaller and raised a little. To see the difference between this negative sign and the subtraction sign, try subtracting the negative number -567 from 1234. Here are the keystrokes:

1 2 3 4 − (-) 5 6 7

The display should look like this:

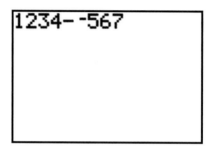

Raising to a Power

To raise a number to a power, press ^ (just above the division sign) just before entering the exponent. Thus, to compute 738^5, press

7 3 8 ^ 5 ENTER

The screen should look like Display A.5.

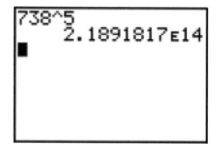

Display A.5

The Menu Keys

Many keys bring a menu to the screen. A menu is a list of functions—things that the calculator is ready to do for you. For instance, each of the keys across the row that starts with MATH (except for CLEAR) brings up a menu. Don't worry about what all those lists say; just look at the menus for the MATH button as you read the rest of this paragraph. Notice that it is actually a double menu. There are two cursors on it, shown as dark blocks. The one in the top left corner can be moved along the top line by using the ◄ and ► keys. Each time you move it to a new place on the top line, the menu below changes. The items in each lower menu are reached by using the other cursor, which can be moved up and down along the left side of the screen by using the ▲ and ▼ keys.

Once you have put the cursor on the choice you want, you actually make the choice by pressing ENTER . This makes the calculator go back to its "home" screen and display your choice. To make the calculator do what you have chosen, press ENTER again.

1. **How many separate calculator functions can be reached through the menus of the** MATH **key?**

2. **How many separate calculator functions can be reached through the menus of the** MATRIX **key?**

A.5

Entering Data in a List

The data handling tools are found through the statistics menu.

- Turn your calculator on and press STAT . You'll see a menu that looks like Display A.6.

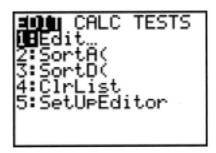

Display A.6

- To enter data, make sure that the top cursor is on EDIT and the left cursor is on **1:**. Then press ENTER . Your screen display should look like Display A.7, with the cursor right under **L1**.

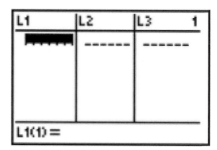

Display A.7

Note that if the display shows numbers in the **L1** column, you'll have to clear the data memory. You can highlight each number and press DEL , but there are two ways to clear the whole list at once.

Without leaving this display, use the ▲ and ◄ keys to move your cursor to the top of the column and highlight **L1**. Press CLEAR and then the ▼ key. List L1 should be cleared.

or

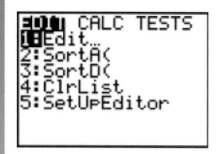

Go back to the **STAT** menu. Press 4 . When **ClrList** appears, press 2ND [L1]then ENTER ; **Done** will appear. Now go back to the **STAT** screen and choose **1:Edit**.

If you are missing a list in L1 to L6, go back to the **STAT** menu and press 5 and ENTER . This will reset the calculator to List 1 through 6.

- Now it's time to enter the data. Let's use a set of test scores {90, 85, 95, 87, 86, 92, 88, 75, 81, 92}. The calculator stores in its memory each data number you enter, along with an **L1** label for that entry. The first number is called **L1(1)**, and the second is called **L1(2)**, and so on. We'll ignore the **L2** and **L3** labels for now. Key in the first data number, then press ENTER . Notice that **L1(2)** now appears at the bottom of the screen. Key in the second data number and press ENTER ; and so on, until you have put in all the data. If you make a mistake, just use the arrow keys to move the cursor to your error, type over it correctly, then move back to where you were.

At this point, the calculator has all your data stored in a way that is easy to use, and the data will stay stored even after the calculator is turned off.

Summaries of 1-Variable Data

It is easy to get summary information about data that is stored in a single list.

- Bring up the **STAT** menu.
- Move the top cursor to **CALC**. The side cursor should be on **1:1-Var Stats**. Press ENTER.
- **1-Var Stats** will appear on your screen. Enter the list you want the calculator to summarize. For instance, if you want a summary of the data in list **L1**, press 2nd [L1]; then press ENTER.

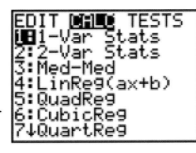

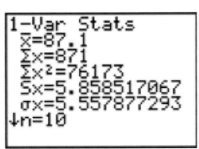

That's all there is to it! A screen full of information will appear. Sections 1.3–1.7 in Chapter 1 of Year 1 explain how to interpret that information.

Putting Data in Size Order

The TI-84 Plus has a built-in program that will put your data in size order automatically. Let's order the test scores that you just entered.

1. Go to the **STAT** menu and choose **2:SortA(** then press ENTER.

2. Tell the calculator to sort the **L1** list by pressing 2ND [L1] then ENTER. Your calculator screen should now say DONE.

3. To see what it has done, reopen List 1 (using STAT 1:Edit). Your data should now be listed in ascending order—that is, from smallest to largest as you read down the list. The **A** in **SortA** stands for ascending order.

Now go back to the **STAT** menu and choose **3:SortD(** then press ENTER. Tell the calculator to sort the **L1** list again. (Press 2ND [L1] ENTER.)

A.6

1. When the screen says **Done**, what has your calculator done? Look at **L1** again to help you answer this question.

2. What does the **D** in **SortD(** stand for?

Once the data are in size order, it is easy to find the median. For example, if you have 21 data items in all, the median is just the 11th one in the sorted list. Scroll through the data (using the ▾ key) until you find **L1(11)**. Its value is the median. If you have 20 data items, the median is halfway between the 10th and 11th items in the sorted list. Scroll through the data until you find **L1(10)** and **L1(11)**. Then calculate the number halfway between them.

Finding the mode is just as easy. Count repeated items in this list. The one that is repeated the most times is the mode.

The Graph Window

This kind of calculator is called a graphing calculator because it can *draw graphs*. The screen on a graphing calculator can show line drawings of mathematical relationships. It does this with two kinds of coordinate systems—*rectangular coordinates* or *polar coordinates*. In this section we shall use only rectangular coordinates; polar coordinates will appear much later. If you are not familiar with the idea of a rectangular coordinate system, you should review the first section of Chapter 3 in Year 1 now.

Your calculator leaves the factory with standard coordinate axes built in. To see what they look like, turn on your calculator and press GRAPH (in the upper right corner). You should see a horizontal and a vertical axis crossing the middle of the screen. The horizontal axis is called the *x*-axis, and the vertical axis is called the *y*-axis. If your screen doesn't show this, press ZOOM and choose **6:ZStandard**. Examine this display carefully; then answer the following questions.

A.7

1. Assuming that the dots along each axis mark the integer points, what is the largest possible value on the *x*-axis? On the *y*-axis?

2. What is the smallest possible value on the *x*-axis? On the *y*-axis?

3. Does it look as if the same unit of measure is being used on both axes?

4. Why do you suppose the spacing between the units is not exactly the same everywhere on an axis? Do you think that this might cause a problem?

The standard coordinate axis setting can be changed in several ways. This is done using the menu that appears when you press WINDOW. Try that now. You should get Display A.8.

```
WINDOW
 Xmin=-10
 Xmax=10
 Xscl=1
 Ymin=-10
 Ymax=10
 Yscl=1
 Xres=1
```

Display A.8

Xmin and **Xmax** are the smallest and largest values on the *x*-axis (the horizontal axis); **Ymin** and **Ymax** are the smallest and largest values on the *y*-axis (the vertical axis).

Xscl and **Yscl** are the scales for marking off points on the axes. The setting 1 means that each single integer value on the axis is marked. To see how the scale value works, change **Xscl** to 2. Move the cursor down, using ▼, then just key in 2 in place of 1. Now press GRAPH. What change do you notice? Now go back to the **WINDOW** menu (press WINDOW) and change **Yscl** to **5**. Return to the graph (press GRAPH). What has changed?

The **Xres51** line indicates the resolution of the graph. It can be set to an integer from 1 to 8. At **Xres51**, it evaluates a function at each of the 94 pixels on the *x*-axis. At **Xres58**, it evaluates the function at every eighth pixel.

Change the **WINDOW** settings so that they look like Display A.9 (on the next page). Then look at the graph and answer these questions.

A.8

1. Where on the screen is the origin of the coordinate system?

2. Does it look as if the same unit of measure is being used on both axes?

3. Does it look as if the spacing between the units is the same everywhere on an axis?

4. What happens when you press ▲ then ▼?

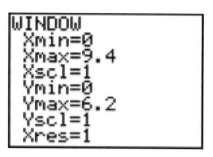

Display A.9

If you have worked through the previous questions, you found that pressing ▲ then ▼ puts a cross exactly in the middle of your screen and two numbers at the bottom. The cross is the cursor for the graphing screen, and the numbers are the coordinates of the point at its center. In this case, the cursor is at **(4.7, 3.1)**. It can be moved to any point on the graph by using the four arrow keys ▲, ▼, ◀, ▶ at the upper right of the keypad.

A.9

Move the cursor to the point **(4, 3)**. How far does the cursor move each time you press ◀ or ▶? How far does it move each time you press ▲ or ▼? Now move the cursor directly down to the bottom of the screen. What are the coordinates of the lowest point you can reach?

These new **WINDOW** settings are better than the standard one in some ways, and worse in others. Let's look again at the standard coordinate system and compare it with the one we just saw. To get back to the standard settings, press ZOOM, then press 6 to choose **ZStandard**. The standard coordinate axes should appear immediately.

A.10

These questions refer to the standard coordinate axes.

1. Where is the cursor to begin with? How do you find it if you can't remember?

2. Try to move the cursor to the point **(4, 3)**. How close can you get to it?

3. How far does the cursor move each time you press ◀ or ▶?

4. How far does it move each time you press ▲ or ▼?

5. Move the cursor directly down to the bottom of the screen. What are the coordinates of the lowest point you can reach?

6. In what ways is this coordinate system better than the one we set up for the previous set of questions? In what ways is it worse?

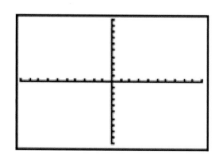

7. How might we fix the bad features of this system without losing the good ones?

Another useful **WINDOW** setting is **8:ZInteger** in the **ZOOM** menu. When you press ⑧, coordinate axes appear, but they are still the standard ones. Press ENTER to get the Integer settings.

These questions refer to the **Integer** coordinate axes.

A.11

1. Try to move the cursor to the point (4, 3). How close can you get to it?

2. How far does the cursor move each time you press ◄ or ►?

3. How far does it move each time you press ▲ or ▼?

4. Why is this setting named Integer?

5. In what ways is this coordinate system better than the one we set up for the previous set of questions? In what ways is it worse?

6. How might we fix the bad features of this system without losing the good ones?

To plot a point (mark its location) on the graphing screen, you will need to go to the point-drawing part of the **DRAW** menu. To do this, you should be on the graph screen. If you are not, press GRAPH. Then press 2ND [DRAW] and move the top cursor to **POINTS**.

```
DRAW POINTS STO
1:ClrDraw
2:Line(
3:Horizontal
4:Vertical
5:Tangent(
6:DrawF
7↓Shade(
```

DRAW Menu

```
DRAW POINTS STO
1:Pt-On(
2:Pt-Off(
3:Pt-Change(
4:Pxl-On(
5:Pxl-Off(
6:Pxl-Change(
7:Pxl-Test(
```

POINTS Menu

Choose **1** to make the ENTER key mark cursor locations. If you want to mark some points and erase others, choose **3**. This lets the ENTER key change the state of any point the cursor is on; it will mark one that isn't already marked, and will unmark one that is. If you have plotted too many points and you want to start over, you can go to the **DRAW** menu and enter **1** for **ClrDraw**. This will wipe out everything you have plotted and return to the standard coordinate settings. If you were using different coordinate settings, you will have to redo them in the **WINDOW** menu.

Problem Set: Appendix A

1. What **WINDOW** settings do you need in order to put the origin at the upper right corner of your screen? What can you say about the coordinates of the points that can be plotted on this screen?

2. What **WINDOW** settings do you need in order to put the origin at the upper left corner of your screen? What can you say about the coordinates of the points that can be plotted on this screen?

3. Choose the Integer setting for the coordinate axes and plot the points **(30, 14)**, **(−5, 20)**, **(−26, −11)**, and **(6, −30)**. Then write the coordinates of two points that lie within the area of the graph window but cannot be plotted exactly with this setting.

4. Find **WINDOW** settings to form a coordinate system such that the points **(120, 80)** and **(−60, −40)** are within the window frame.

   (a) How far does the cursor move each time you press ◄ or ►?

   (b) How far does it move each time you press ▲ or ▼?

   (c) Can you put the cursor exactly on **(120, 80)**? If not, how close can you come? Plot this point as closely as you can.

   (d) Can you put the cursor exactly on **(−60, −40)**? If not, how close can you come? Plot this point as closely as you can.

   (e) Can you put the cursor exactly on **(0, 0)**? If not, how close can you come?

5. Find **WINDOW** settings to form a coordinate system such that the cursor can be put exactly on the points **(20, 24.5)** and **(−17.3, −14)**.

   (a) What is the initial position of the cursor?

   (b) How far does it move each time you press ◄ or ►?

   (c) How far does it move each time you press ▲ or ▼?

   (d) Can you put the cursor exactly on **(0, 0)**? If not, how close can you come?

Drawing Histograms

Drawing a histogram is easy. All you have to do is choose a few numbers to tell the calculator how wide and how tall to make the bars. Turn your calculator on and press WINDOW. The screen should look like Display A.10, maybe with different numbers.

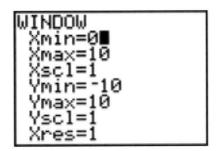

Display A.10

The numbers in this **WINDOW** list tell the calculator how to set the horizontal (X) and vertical (Y) scales.

- **Xmin**, an abbreviation of X *minimum*, is the smallest data value the picture will show. You should set it at some convenient value less than or equal to the smallest value in the data set you wish to plot.

- **Xmax**, an abbreviation of X *maximum*, is the largest data value the picture will show. Set it at some convenient value greater than or equal to the largest value in your data set.

- **Xscl**, an abbreviation of X *scale*, says how to group the data. It is the size of the base interval at the bottom of each bar of the histogram. For instance, **Xscl=10** will group the data by 10's, starting from the value of **Xmin** that you chose.

- **Ymin** is the smallest frequency of any data group. It is never less than 0, which usually is a good choice for it.

- **Ymax** represents the length of the longest bar. Choose a convenient number that is not less than the largest frequency of any data group, but not much larger.

- **Yscl** determines the size of the steps to be marked on the vertical (frequency) scale. For small data sets, set it to 1. If your setting for **Ymax** is much larger than 10, you might want to set **Yscl** larger than 1. A little experimenting will show you how to choose a helpful setting.

- Leave **Xres=1**.

Now your calculator is ready to draw a histogram.

- Press [2ND] [STAT PLOT], highlight **1:** and press [ENTER].
- Select settings from each row by moving the cursor to them with the arrow keys and pressing [ENTER] each time.
  - Select On.
  - Select the histogram picture.
  - Set **Xlist** to the list containing your data (**L1**, **L2**, etc.).
  - Set **Freq:1**.

Now press [GRAPH] — and there it is!

Drawing Boxplots

The TI-84 Plus calculators can draw boxplots. All they need are the data and a few sizing instructions. Here's how to do it.

- Turn the calculator on, press [STAT] and choose **1:Edit...** from the **EDIT** menu. Check which list contains the data you want to use. Let's assume it's in L1.
- Press [WINDOW] and set the horizontal **(X)** and vertical **(Y)** scales. If you have forgotten how to set your **WINDOW**, refer to "The Graph Window" section. Choose convenient numbers for the **X** range—**Xmin** less than your smallest data value and **Xmax** greater than your largest data value, but not too small or too large. You don't want the picture to get squeezed into something you can't see well! Also set **Xscl** to some convenient size.
- The Y settings don't matter as much. **Ymin=−2** and **Ymax=3** work well for boxplots.
- Press [2ND] [STAT PLOT], highlight **1:** and press [ENTER]. Select these settings from each row by moving the cursor to them with the arrow keys and pressing [ENTER] each time.

  On; the boxplot picture; **L1** for **Xlist**; 1 for **Freq**

- Now press [GRAPH] — and there it is!
- To read the five-number summary, press [TRACE] and use the [◄] and [►] to display the five numbers one at a time.

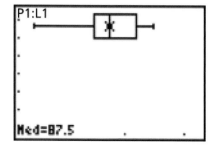

Graphing and Tracing Lines

If you want the calculator to graph a line or a curve, you must first be able to describe the line or curve by an algebraic equation. Once you have the equation for what you want to draw, you must put it in the form

$$y = [\text{something}]$$

For a straight line, that's not a problem; we often put the equation in this form, anyway. For some other kinds of curves, putting them in this form can be a little messy. In this section we shall deal only with straight lines.

All graphing begins with the $\boxed{Y=}$ key. When you press this key for the first time, you get the screen in Display A.11.

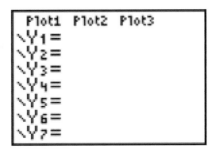

Display A.11

These lines allow you to graph as many as ten different algebraic equations. The subscript number gives you a way to keep track of which equation goes with which picture on the graph. To see how the process works, we'll make the first example simple—two straight lines through the origin.

Key in **−.5X** on the **Y₁=** line, *using the* $\boxed{X,T,\Theta,n}$ *key to make the* **X**; then press $\boxed{\text{ENTER}}$.

Key in **−.25X** on the **Y₂=** line.

Be sure to use the $\boxed{(-)}$ key for the negative sign. If you don't, you'll get an error message when you ask for the graph. If you want to wipe out one of these equations and redo it, just move the cursor back to the equation and press $\boxed{\text{CLEAR}}$.

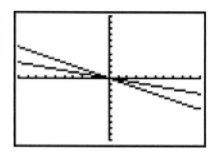

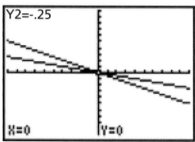

Now your work is done. Press GRAPH and just watch as the calculator draws the lines. If you forget which line goes with which equation, or if you want to see the coordinates of the points along your lines, press TRACE and then move the cursor with the ◄ and ► keys. When you do this, the coordinates of the cursor's position appear at the bottom of the screen. The equation appears in the upper left hand corner. In this example, when you press TRACE you will be on **Y₁= −.5X**, the first of the two lines we entered. Try it. To switch from one line to another, use the ▲ and ▼ keys. Notice that, in this case, either of these keys gets you to the other line. That's because we are only graphing two equations. If we were graphing more than two, these keys would move up and down the *list of equations*, regardless of where the graphs appeared on the screen.

There is a way to remove the graph of an equation from the screen without erasing the equation from your list. For example, let us remove the line **Y₁= −.5X** from the picture. Go back to the Y= list. Notice that the = sign of each equation appears in a dark block. This shows that the graph of this equation is turned on. To turn it off, move the cursor to the = sign and press ENTER. The dark block will disappear. To turn it back on, put the cursor back on = and press ENTER again.

Approximating Data by a Line

This section refers to a situation that commonly arises in the analysis of two-variable data. Such data can be represented as points on a coordinate plane, and it is often useful to know if the pattern of points can be approximated by a straight line. A common way of doing this is called *least-squares approximation*. An explanation of this process and its use appears in Chapter 4 of Year 1. This calculator section provides a simple example of how to get the TI-84 Plus to give you a least-squares approximation of a set of data.

Let's look at a very small, simple data set. The process is exactly the same for bigger, more complicated data sets. Here are four points of two-variable data.

$$(1, 2) \ (2, 3) \ (3, 5) \ (4, 6)$$

If you plot these points on a coordinate plane, you will see that they don't all lie on the same line. Don't just take our word for it; make a sketch! The calculator uses the least-squares method to find automatically the line of "best fit." Section 4.3 (in Chapter 4) describes how this method works and what best fit means. These are the instructions for getting the calculator to do all the tedious work for you.

First of all, you need to have the data entered in two *separate data storage lists*. You get to these lists by pressing [STAT] and choosing **1:Edit...** from the **EDIT** menu. When you press [ENTER], you should get Display A.12.

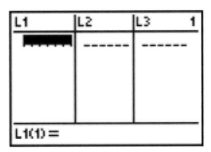

Display A.12

If the columns already contain data that you don't want, you can clear them out. For instructions to clear the lists, refer to the Entering Data on a List section of this Appendix.

Enter the first coordinate of each data point into list **L1**; put its second coordinate in list **L2**. The four data points of our example should appear as shown in Display A.13.

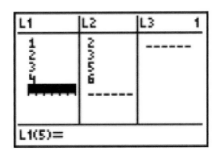

Display A.13

Now we are almost done. Press [STAT] and go to the **CALC** menu. Choose **4:LinReg(ax+b)**. When you press [ENTER], the screen will display an algebraic description of the line of best fit. For our example, it looks like Display A.14 (on the next page).

- The second line, **y=ax+b**, just tells you that the information is for slope-intercept form. Notice that the TI-84 Plus uses a, not m, for the slope here.

- The third line says that the slope is **1.4**.

- The fourth line says that the y-intercept is **.5**.

Note that the last two lines may show the correlation coefficient r, and the coefficient of determination r^2. If your calculator doesn't show these lines, press [2ND] [CATALOG] scroll down to **DiagnosticOn**, and press [ENTER] twice. The screen should say **Done**. Then choose **LinReg(ax+b)** again. The correlation coefficient is discussed in your textbook in Section 4.3 of Year 1. In case you are curious about it, here is a little more information. The correlation coefficient is always a number between -1 and 1, inclusive. 1 and -1 stand for a perfect fit, with all points exactly on the line. (1 is for lines with positive slope; -1 is for lines with negative slope.) The closer r is to 0, the worse the fit.

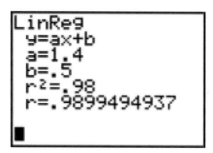

```
LinReg
 y=ax+b
 a=1.4
 b=.5
 r²=.98
 r=.9899494937
■
```

Display A.14

Putting together this information about our example, we see that the least-squares line is described by the equation

$$y = 1.4x + .5$$

Graph the line $y = 1.4x + .5$. Are any of the four data points on it? How can you be sure?

A.12

Using Formulas to Make Lists

Sometimes it is useful to make a new list of data from an old one by doing the same thing to each data value. For instance, you might want to add a fixed number to each value, square each value, or find the distance of each value from some particular number. Instead of computing the new list one entry at a time, you can do it all at once if you can express your process as a formula.

Here's how the process works.

- Go to the **STAT** menu. Select **1:Edit...** then enter a list of data in **L1** and clear the other lists.
- To add 5 to each entry in **L1**, move the cursor over to the second column, then up to the heading, **L2**. The bottom line of your display should read **L2=** (without any number in parentheses).

- The trick here is to let the symbol **L1** stand for each element of the list **L1**. That is, we make **L1** *a variable*. Key in **L1+5** ; the bottom of your screen should read **L2=L1+5** .

- Now press ENTER and watch the entire column for **L2** fill out automatically!

- To list in **L2**, the square of each entry in **L1**, put the cursor on **L2** (at the top of the column). Then enter **L1^2** (or **L1*L1**).

- Now let us list in **L3** the midpoint between the **L1** entry and the **L2** entry. Put the cursor on **L3** (at the top of the column). Now key in **(L1+L2)/2** and press ENTER.

A.13

1. List at least ten data values in **L1**.

2. Write a formula to list in **L2** the distance between 17 and each entry in **L1**. Remember: Distances are never negative numbers. Then use it.

3. Write a formula to list in **L3** the square of the difference (which may be negative) between each entry in **L1** and 17. Then use it.

4. Write a formula to list in **L4** the square root of each entry in **L3**. Then use it.

5. How are columns **L2** and **L4** related? Explain.

Drawing Circles

To draw circles directly on a graph, use **9:Circle(** in the **DRAW** menu. (The **DRAW** menu appears when you press 2ND [DRAW].) **2:Line(** can be used to draw segments, which lets you add radii, diameters, and other segments to your drawings of circles.

Before beginning, clear out any functions in your **Y=** list or make sure that all the functions on your **Y=** screen are turned off. If they are not, their graphs will appear when you draw circles and segments. Also make sure that all **STAT PLOTS** are turned off.

Follow these instructions to draw a circle directly on a graph.

1. From the **ZOOM** menu, choose **ZStandard** (to clear any unusual **WINDOW** settings). Then choose **8:ZInteger**, which displays the graph window. Then press ENTER.

2. From the **DRAW** menu, choose **9:Circle(**.

3. Choose a point for the center by moving the cursor to this point and pressing ⌈ENTER⌉.

4. Choose the radius for your circle by moving the cursor this many units away from the center and pressing ⌈ENTER⌉.

You can continue to draw circles by repeating the last two steps. To clear the screen before drawing a new circle, use **1:ClrDraw** in the **DRAW** menu. If you want to stop drawing circles, press ⌈CLEAR⌉.

Follow the steps above to draw each of these items.

A.14

1. A circle with center (0, 10) and radius 5

2. A circle with center (12, −7) and radius 15

3. Four circles with center (0, 0)

You can also draw a circle from the Home Screen (the calculator's primary display window) by following these instructions. You can use this same method to draw circles from a program.

1. From the Home Screen, choose **9:Circle(** from the **DRAW** menu.

2. Input the coordinates of the center, followed by the radius; then press ⌈ENTER⌉. For example, if you enter **Circle(0,10,5)**, the calculator will draw a circle with center at (0, 10) and radius 5, using whatever **WINDOW** setting was last used.

3. To return to the **Home** Screen, press ⌈CLEAR⌉.

1. Draw a circle with center (3, 2) and radius 7 directly from the Home Screen. If your graph does not look like a circle, how can you adjust the graph **WINDOW** so that it does?

A.15

2. Draw four concentric (circles with the same center but different radii) circles around (0, 0) directly from the Home Screen. Earlier you were asked to draw circles directly on a graph. Which method is easier for you? Why?

Sequences

On your graphing calculator, you may have noticed four letters ($\boxed{X,T,\Theta,n}$) on the key that you press to get **X**. The letter n is used when you are in sequence mode. In Chapter 6 of Year 1, you will read about sequences and you will be asked to describe these sequences by using a recursive definition. This definition is what you will use on the calculator. Let's look at the sequence 1, 4, 7, 10, …. If you wanted to find the 10th term in the sequence using your calculator, you would enter the number 1 and press $\boxed{\text{ENTER}}$. Next, if you press $\boxed{+}\boxed{3}$ you would see that the calculator added 3 to the previous answer. If you then press $\boxed{\text{ENTER}}$, you would notice that the calculator "remembered" to add 3 automatically.

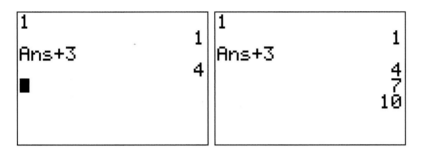

Display A.15

You would continue to hit $\boxed{\text{ENTER}}$ until you get to the 10th term. This would be tedious if you needed to find the 50th term, but if you used your algebra skills, this task would be done in less time. Another method that you could use is the calculator's sequence mode. You will find this option on the fourth line of the **MODE** menu. Go to that screen and select **SEQ**. Now, press $\boxed{Y=}$ and you will see the screen shown below.

```
Plot1 Plot2 Plot3
 nMin=1
\u(n)=■
 u(nMin)=
\v(n)=
 v(nMin)=
\w(n)=
 w(nMin)=
```

Display A.16

nMin=1 starts the counter, n, at 1. The next line, u(n)=, defines the sequence recursively. What operation is being performed on the previous term? In this case, 3 is being added to the previous term. This is done by typing **u(n-1)+3**. The letter **u** is found above the **7** key. So, you press $\boxed{\text{2ND}}$ $\boxed{7}$. This is followed by **(**

and the **n** found on the $\boxed{\text{X,T,}\Theta,n}$ key and finally **-1)+3)**. The next line that appears is **u(nMin) =**. This is where you will put your initial value. This value represents u(1), the first term of the sequence, because **nMin= 1**. If you use the sequence from above, you would enter the value 1 as the first term. All you need to do is enter 1 (the calculator will add the brackets). Your screen should look like the following:

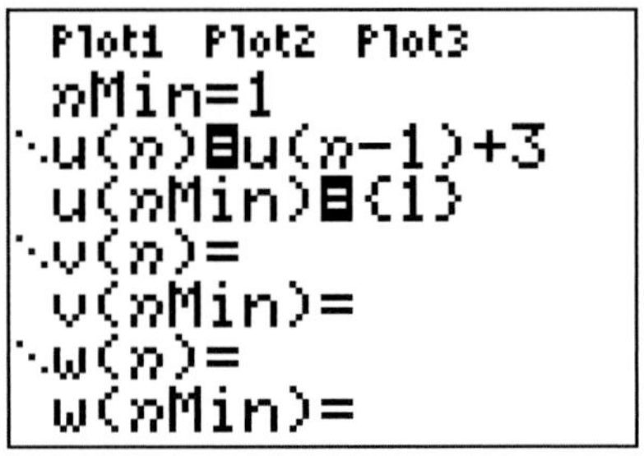

```
Plot1  Plot2  Plot3
nMin=1
\u(n)Bu(n-1)+3
 u(nMin)B{1}
\v(n)=
 v(nMin)=
\w(n)=
 w(nMin)=
```

Display A.17

If you go to the table, you will find the screen shown below. By scrolling down, you can find any value of n that you like. Due to the fact that the function is defined recursively, scrolling down takes a little longer. If you go to **TBLSET**, set **Indpnt** to **Ask**, and select **TABLE**, you can enter the value 50 to quickly get the answer.

Why does the value of $n = 0$ yield **ERROR** as a result? Think about how you define your first term.

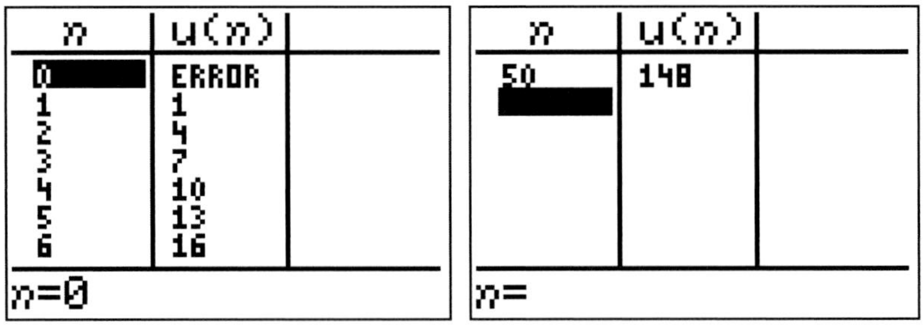

n	u(n)			n	u(n)	
0	ERROR			50	148	
1	1					
2	4					
3	7					
4	10					
5	13					
6	16					
n=0				n=		

Display A.18

If you go to the graph of the function, you will notice that the points are all in the first quadrant and appear to form a line. You can select $\boxed{\text{TRACE}}$ and use the right arrow to get the various values for n. See Display A.19.

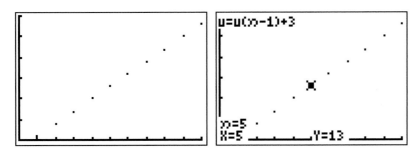

Display A.19

The sequence mode allows you to define up to three sequences at a time in the three functions **u(*n*)**, **v(*n*)** and **w(*n*)**.

Another way to list the elements of a sequence is through the **OPS** menu within the **LIST** menu. The command is seq(rule, variable, initial value of variable, final value of variable, increment). For the previous problem, you would do the following:

First, go back to function mode by going to the **MODE** menu and choosing **FUNC** on the fourth line. Second, press [2ND][STAT] to get the **LIST** menu and use the right arrow to get the **OPS** menu. Third, press **5** to select **seq(**. In this case the rule needs to be written in the explicit form, not in the recursive form. In Chapter 6 of Year 1, you will read about how to convert from recursive to explicit form. For this problem the explicit form will be $S_x = 3x - 2$. Lastly, you would enter **seq (3X–2, X, 1, 10, 1)**. Your screen should then look like this:

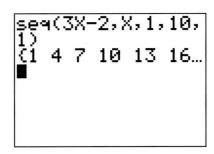

Display A.20

If you use the right arrow, you can see all of the elements of the list. You can store this information in a list by inserting [STO▸][2ND][1] (for [L1]) at the end of the initial command. The ten items will now be in [L1]. A quicker way to do this is to press [2ND][ENTER]. This brings back the initial command. Now, press [STO▸][2ND][1] and [ENTER]. The sequence will appear on the main screen again as well as in list 1.

You have just read about three methods that are used to produce sequences. Try the following problems using all three methods.

1. List the first ten even natural numbers.
2. Determine the 20th element of the sequence 3, 7, 11, 15, ...
3. Which method do you find easiest to use?

Regression Equations Revisited

In Chapters 4 through 8 of Year 1, you will look at data involving two variables. There are times when it is important for you to determine an equation that will allow you to estimate a value given a specific input. In Chapter 4, you will read about the least-squares regression method for linear data as well as the median-median line. Let's look at the least-squares line method. If you were given the following set of data: (1, 3), (2, 5), (3, 7), (4, 10), (5, 12) and (10, 25), what would the linear equation be that best fits this data? You may recall that the steps include putting the x-values into list 1 and the y-values into list 2. This would be followed by using the **LinReg(ax+b)** command from the **STAT CALC** menu.

Step 1: Input data into **L1** and **L2**.

Step 2: Go to the **STAT** menu, arrow over to **CALC**, select **LinReg(ax+b)**, and press ENTER followed by **L1, L2**.

Try this now.

What if you wanted to see how this looks? Remember, you can go to **STAT PLOT** and graph the points by turning on **Plot1**. Adjust the **WINDOW** appropriately and then graph. You should see the following screens:

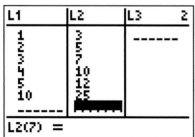  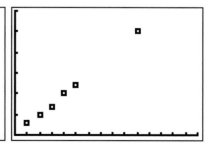

Display A.21

What if you wanted to determine the equation of the line and graph it all in one step? You would need to put the equation into **Y1**. In other words, store the **LinReg** equation in **Y1**. **Y1** is located in **Y-VARS** of the **VARS** menu. In order to get **Y1**, press **VARS**, arrow over to **Y-VARS**, choose **1:Function** (because a linear equation is a function) and then **Y1**. Now that you know how to find **Y1**, let's try graphing the line.

Enter the following on the main screen: **LinReg(ax+b)** [L1] [,] [L2] [,] , **Y1** [ENTER]

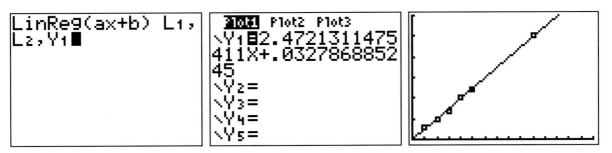

Display A.22

The three screens above show you the main screen, the **Y=** screen (which indicates that you have a graph in **Y1** and shows that **PLOT1** is on), and finally, the graph of the points and the regression equation.

You are not limited to using regression equations that give lines. From the **STAT CALC** menu, you will see a number of different types of regression equations. You will eventually become familiar with the appearance of each of these graphs, and you will be able to determine which best fits the data.

```
EDIT CALC TESTS          EDIT CALC TESTS
1:1-Var Stats            8↑LinReg(a+bx)
2:2-Var Stats            9:LnReg
3:Med-Med                0:ExpReg
4:LinReg(ax+b)           A:PwrReg
5:QuadReg                B:Logistic
6:CubicReg               C:SinReg
7↓QuartReg               D:Manual-Fit
```

Display A.23

The two screens above show 11 methods of calculating regression equations. In addition, there is a method called **Manual-Fit** that gives you a means for determining a linear equation that fits the data. Let's use the data (2, 1), (3, 6), (4, 13), (5, 22), and (6, 33). Enter this data into **L1** and **L2** and graph it on an appropriate window. You should have a graph screen similar to Display A.24.

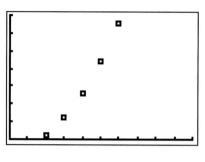

Display A.24

Let's look at a few of the regression equations. Remember that you can determine the equation and graph it all in one step. Let's see how a nonlinear function may work. Try **CubicReg**, **ExpReg**, and **PwrReg** on your own. Do they resemble the following?

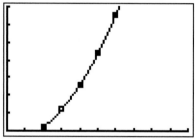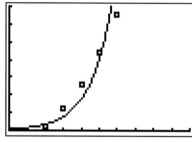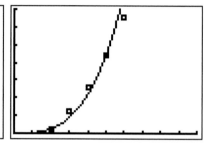

Display A.25

Try **QuadReg**. Notice that it is the same as **CubicReg**. If you look carefully at the equations, you will see that they are the same equation. Each of the above graphs fits the data relatively closely. Because you were only using a few points that were close together, you need to be careful about how you interpret the data and how you make inferences from the result that you chose.

TBLSET, CALC, and TABLE Menus

There is a lot of information that can be determined about a function from the tools on the graphing calculator. In Chapter 8 of Year 1, you will read about quadratic equations. How can your calculator help you understand this and other functions? Look at the function $y = x^2 + x - 6$. Clear your calculator and go to the **Standard WINDOW**. Next, enter this function into **Y1** and graph it.

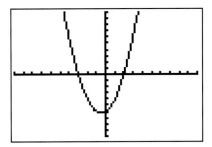

Display A.26

You may wonder what the values of x are when the graph crosses the x-axis (called the zeros), what the coordinates of the vertex are, or what the value of y is for a given x. If you look at the **CALC** menu (located above the **TRACE** menu), you will see the following screen:

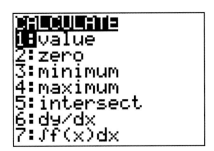

Display A.27

Items 1 through 3 will help answer your questions. If you choose **value**, you will see the following screen:

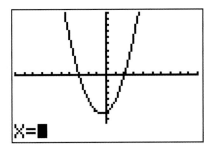

Display A.28

If you enter a number, it will appear beside the **X**. When you press ENTER, you will get the y-value for that given x input. Enter 4. This will give Display A.29.

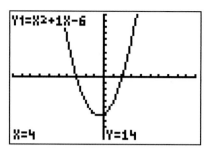

Display A.29

The one problem that this approach has is that the value of x has to be within the boundaries of the screen. It does not matter if the point is on the screen (enter 7 and you have a y-value of 50. The point (7, 50) is not on the screen). One method of dealing with this problem is to expand the boundaries of your window. Another method is to look at the **TABLE**. You will need to set up the table. If you are only going to look at integers, then you want the table to list only integers for your x-values. Press [2ND] **[TBLSET]**. You will see the **TABLE SETUP** screen.

TblStart needs a starting value. Δ**Tbl=** needs an incremental value (how much you want to increase from the previous term). **Indpnt** lets you choose to have the table automatically generated or "asks" for a result based on an x-value that you entered. If **Depend** is on **Auto**, it will fill in the y-values automatically. If **Depend** is on **Ask**, it will not show y-values. You need to scroll down the x-list and then move to the y-list. When you press [ENTER], the corresponding y-value appears for that x-value. This method enables you to check your computational skills.

Returning to the problem, you have to start the table at 0 with increments of 1. Set your **TBLSET** to look like the first screen shown below. When you finish, go to **TABLE** and you will see the second screen shown below.

Display A.30

If you scroll up or down, you will notice more values for x. What values for x have a result of 0? By scrolling, you should see that there are two. One is the x-value 2 and the other is -3. Take a look at the y-values above and below the zeros. You will see that one is positive and the other is negative. You will often find a sign change around a zero unless the zero is a local minimum point on the x-axis.

Is there another way to find the zeros? If you look back on the **CALC** menu, you will find **2:zero**. To use this command, you will need to set a left boundary and right boundary around the zero. Only one zero can be found and only within the interval that you define. First, make sure you are in the **Standard WINDOW** setting, then go to the **CALC** menu and select **zero**. You should see the first screen below or something very close to this. You are being asked to enter the left bound (boundary) of the zero. Your cursor should begin flashing. Using your left arrow, move the cursor to an x-value to the left of the zero and press ENTER. You are now being asked to supply the right bound. Move the cursor to the right of the zero that you are looking for and press ENTER. Finally, you are asked to "guess." This means that you should move your cursor close to the zero and press ENTER. Did you get $x = -3$?

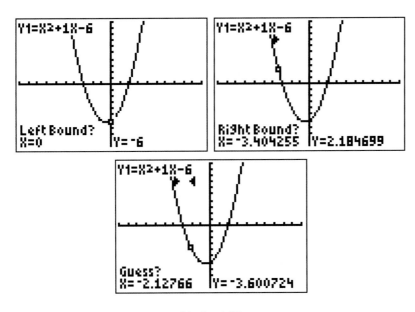

Display A.31

In order to get the other zero, you need to get the left and right bound around that zero. Try it. You should have something that looks like the following three screens.

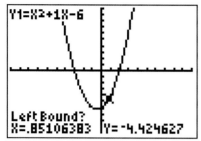 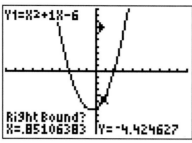 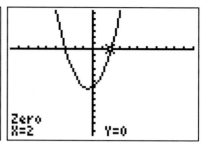

Display A.32

The table method is useful when the zeros are integers, but when you have a zero that is not an integer, the **CALC** method is better. You will also be learning the algebraic method, which may be a better approach.

In the above example, notice that the vertex is the lowest point of the graph. Looking at the **CALC** menu, you see the words **Minimum** and **Maximum**. These operations find the lowest point of a graph over a given interval or the highest point over a given interval. Again, you will be asked to set a left bound, a right bound, and a guess as to where the minimum or maximum point is located. For the current problem, you should find the minimum point.

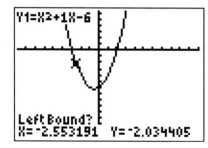 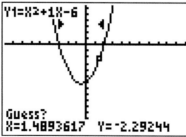 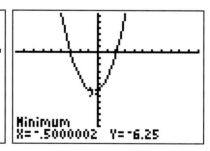

Display A.33

You can also use the **TABLE** menu to find a minimum or maximum point. Look at the x- and y-values around the vertex of the problem above. Go to **TblSet** and set the initial value to -3 at increments of 1. Display A.34 should appear.

X	Y1	
-3	0	
-2	-4	
-1	-6	
0	-6	
1	-4	
2	0	
3	6	
X= -3		

Display A.34

What do you notice about the y-values? You should see that they decrease from 0 to -6 and then increase from -6 to 6. This pattern indicates that there is a low point somewhere between $x = -3$ and $x = 3$ and more specifically between $x = -1$ and $x = 0$, as both yield a y-value of -6. How can you find the x-value between -1 and 0 that would give you the low point? The key is in the **TblSet** menu. The increment value can be adjusted. Set the initial value to -1 and adjust the increments to 0.1. What do you see?

X	Y1	
-1	-6	
-.9	-6.09	
-.8	-6.16	
-.7	-6.21	
-.6	-6.24	
-.5	-6.25	
-.4	-6.24	
X= -1		

Display A.35

The y-values decrease from -6 to -6.25 and then increase again. At $x = -.6$ and $x = -.4$, you have the same y-value. Because parabolas are symmetric, the low point must be halfway between these two values at $x = -.5$ with $y = -6.25$. There are times that you will need to change the increment to a finer value such as 0.01 or smaller depending on the accuracy that you need. Using the **Maximum** or **Minimum** function might work better in these cases.

Systems of Equations or Points of Intersections

In mathematics, you will need to find a common point of a system of two equations. Look at the following linear equations.

$$2x + 3y = 9$$
$$3x - y = 1$$

You cannot enter these equations into the graphing calculator in this form. You will have to convert to slope-intercept form and enter them into **Y1** and **Y2** and then press **GRAPH**. You should see the following on your calculator:

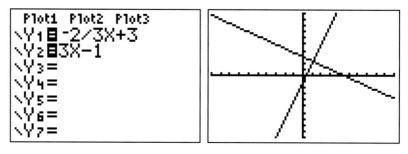

Display A.36

Go back to the **CALC** menu and you will see the **intersect** function. This finds the intersection point of two given graphs. First, the calculator "asks" you to identify the two graphs. You can toggle between graphs using the up and down arrow keys. Once the two graphs are selected, you are directed to move the cursor near the point of intersection. Press ENTER and the calculator will give you the intersection point. After doing so, you should see the screens below. The final screen gives the point of intersection which is approximately (1.0909, 2.2727). If there are only two linear functions on the screen, then the commands are rather simple. You can just select **intersect** and press ENTER three times and you have the solution screen.

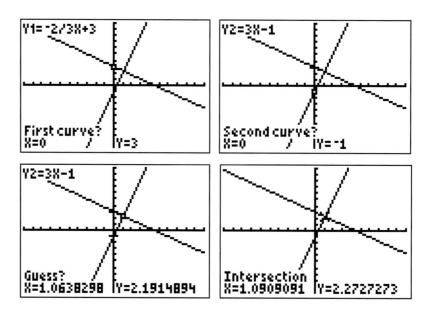

Display A.37

Another method of finding this point of intersection is to look at the **TABLE**. In the first screen of Display A.37, you can see that the intersection is somewhere in quadrant 1. By setting the **TblSet** menu to an initial value of 0 and increments of 1, you will see the following table:

X	Y1	Y2
0	3	-1
1	2.3333	2
2	1.6667	5
3	1	8
4	.33333	11
5	-.3333	14
6	-1	17

X=0

Display A.38

You now have the *y*-values for each of the functions. Take a moment and look at these *y*-values. Do you notice anything as the *x*-value increases? You may notice that **Y1** is decreasing and **Y2** is increasing. Compare the two. What occurs between $x = 1$ and $x = 2$? The *y*-value of the first graph is higher than the *y*-value of the second graph up until $x = 1$. At $x = 2$, the *y*-value of the second graph is now higher than the *y*-value of the first graph. Thus, they must have crossed in between. Do you remember how to refine a search using the **TABLE**? Go back to **TblSet** and change the initial value to 1 and increments of 0.1.

X	Y1	Y2
1	2.3333	2
1.1	2.2667	2.3
1.2	2.2	2.6
1.3	2.1333	2.9
1.4	2.0667	3.2
1.5	2	3.5
1.6	1.9333	3.8

X=1

Display A.39

Looking at the new table, where does the change take place? At $x = 1$, **Y1** is larger than **Y2**. At $x = 1.1$, **Y1** is less than **Y2**. So, somewhere between this interval is the point of intersection. Refine your search by decreasing the increments to 0.01 with an initial value of $x = 1$. You will notice that the change takes place between $x = 1.09$ and $x = 1.1$. You could close in further on the point of intersection by changing the increments to 0.001 beginning at $x = 1.09$. For many problems a solution of (1.09, 2.27) may be refined enough, but in some areas of mathematics you need to have more significant digits in your solution.

X	Y₁	Y₂
1.04	2.3067	2.12
1.05	2.3	2.15
1.06	2.2933	2.18
1.07	2.2867	2.21
1.08	2.28	2.24
1.09	2.2733	2.27
1.1	2.2667	2.3

X=1.1

Display A.40

To use this method, the equations have to be written in the form of $y =$ [something]. If you have more than one equation, you need to be careful in selecting the graphs that you want. Finally, the point of intersection needs to be on the screen.

Appendix B: Using a TI-Nspire Handheld

The Texas Instruments Nspire™ handheld has two models. One contains a computer algebra system (CAS) and will do symbolic algebraic manipulations. The other does not contain a CAS system, but will do numeric algebraic solutions. The non-CAS model can also function as a TI-84™, if desired, by using its interchangeable keypad. When you wish to use your Nspire as a TI-84 calculator, refer to Appendix A.

TI-Nspire is a "document" based handheld. Companion software is also available for a computer. You can create documents either on the handheld or the computer and transfer the documents between the two pieces of hardware. If you are composing documents on a computer, the documents should be composed in the "handheld view," so that you can see what the documents will look like when they are sent to the handheld. A "presentation" view choice is also available for documents that you do not plan to transfer to a handheld.

Each document can contain multiple problems. Each problem can consist of multiple pages. And each page can contain multiple applications. We will simply look at creating documents containing one problem with a single application on each page. The applications on a page can be chosen from the following five types:

- Calculator
- Graphs and Geometry
- Lists and Spreadsheet
- Notes
- Data and Statistics

The Calculator Application

First, we will look at the calculator application. This will allow you to use your handheld as a calculator.

Press the **home** key on your handheld (the key with the little house on it). You should see the first screen in Display B.1. Select **6:New Document.** You may be asked to save a current document (if one is open on the handheld). After saving the current document if you choose to, you will then have five application choices for the first page in your new document. The second screen in Display B.1 should appear. If it does

B.1

not automatically appear, press **home** and then **1** to obtain it. You might also be prompted to press **menu** to obtain it.

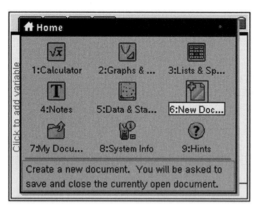
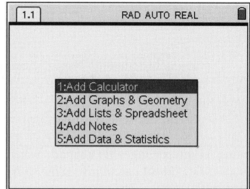

Display B.1

After you select **1** to **Add Calculator**, you will see a blank screen. The cursor is waiting for you to enter something. Try entering $3^2 \times 13 \div 12$. Press **enter**. You should see the first screen shown in Display B.2.

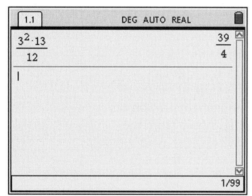
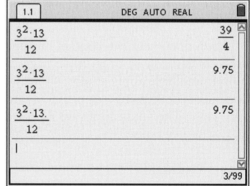

Display B.2

Notice that the handheld is returning an "exact" value for the fraction and not a decimal approximation. If you want to see a decimal approximation, there are several ways to obtain one. You can press the **ctrl** key and then the **enter** key to get it. You also could have placed a decimal point somewhere in the entry line indicating that you want a decimal result and the handheld will then return one. Another way is to change the handheld defaults to always return a decimal approximation. The first two options are shown in the second screen in Display B.2. The decimal result located in line 2 was obtained by using the **ctrl** and **enter** keys. The handheld copied the exact answer from line 1 and changed it to a decimal when **ctrl** and then **enter** were pressed. Line 3 shows the result of typing 13 with a decimal point instead of without.

The calculator tool menu is very extensive. If you press **menu** when you are in a calculator application, you will see the screen in Display B.3. If you use your **arrow** keys to explore these menus, you will see some of the many things that you can do with the calculator application.

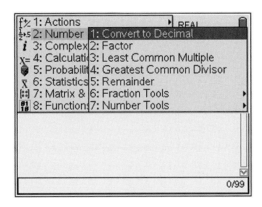

Display B.3

One-Variable Statistics

Single-variable statistics is introduced very early in **MATH** *Connections* and continues to be important for the remainder of the program (and in your life).

Let's look at some data. Suppose that ten of your classmates just took a special test to measure their physical fitness. On a scale of 1-10, with 10 being the most fit, these are the scores that they received: {3, 3, 4, 5, 6, 7, 8, 8, 8, 10}. To perform a single-variable statistics analysis of this data, try the following steps.

Press the **home** key on your handheld. You should see the screen in Display B.4.

B.2

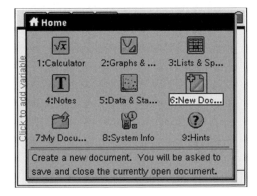

Display B.4

Select **6:New Document.** You may be asked to save a current document if one is open on the handheld. After saving the current document (or not), you will then have five application choices for the first page in your new document. The screen in Display B.5 should appear.

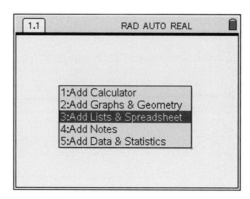

Display B.5

Since we want to enter this data into a list or spreadsheet, choose **3:Add Lists & Spreadsheet.** After making this choice, you will see the screen in Display B.6.

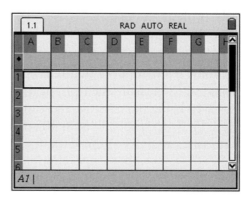

Display B.6

Enter the data into column A and the screen should look like Display B.7.

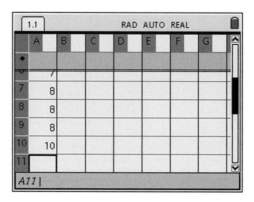

Display B.7

Now if you press **menu,** then use the down arrow key on the **NavPad** to highlight **4:Statistics,** and then the right arrow key to select it, you should see the screen in Display B.8.

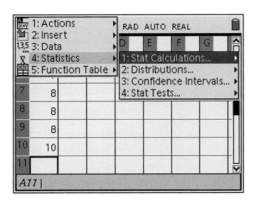

Display B.8

After choosing **1:Stat Calculations** (either by pressing the **pointer/hand** key in the center of the **NavPad,** just pressing the **enter** key, or pressing **1**), you should see the screen in Display B.9.

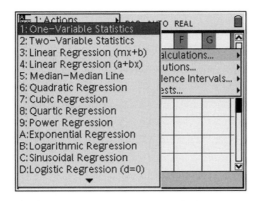

Display B.9

Choose **1:One-Variable Statistics** and the screen in Display B.10 should appear.

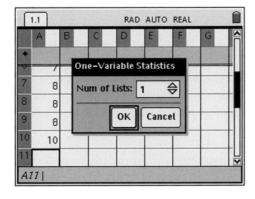

Display B.10

Use the **tab** key to move to the **OK** button, and then press the **enter** key to select it. The screen in Display B.11 should appear.

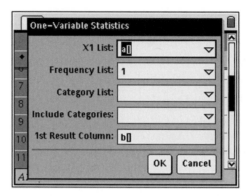

Display B.11

Again, just use the **tab** key to get down to **OK** and press the **enter** key to select it. The single-variable statistics will be calculated for the data in column A and the results will be stored in columns B and C. You should see the following screen.

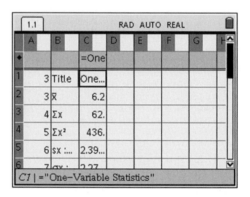

Display B.12

If you use your arrow keys to scroll around in this data, you will see that the typical one-variable statistics information is all there. Notice what appeared in the cell located at column C and the diamond row. **=One…** is a formula that the handheld has placed there for you. We can tell that it is a formula because it starts with an = symbol. This information is important for you to know later on.

B.3

How did the students do on the physical fitness test? What was the mean? What was the median? Were they the same? What does that tell you?

Moving Point Lesson

An example of a simple three-page (lesson) document is presented below.

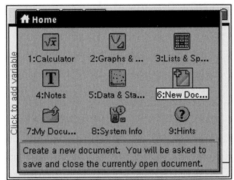
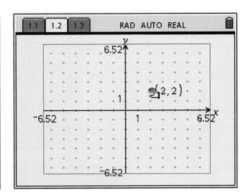

Display B.13

These three pages in the document were created by choosing the Notes application for pages 1.1 and 1.3. Page 1.2 was created by choosing the Graphs and Geometry application option. On page 1.2, an appropriate window was set. The grid was turned on (show grid) and a point was "constructed." The coordinates for the point were attached to it. When you grab and move the point, the coordinates of the point change as the point moves around the coordinate system.

Normally, your teacher might create a document like this for you and transfer it to your handheld. You would use the **ctrl** and **NavPad** (right and left) arrow keys sequentially to move from page to page in the document. Because you need to know how to create a document, see if you can duplicate this document on either your handheld or your computer. When you are comfortable with this simple document, you will be ready to create more complex ones.

On the next page you will find specific directions for duplicating this document on the handheld.

Press the **home** key on the handheld. You will see the screen in Display B.14.

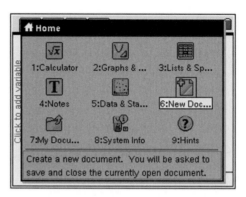

Display B.14

Select **6:New Document**. Again, you may be asked to save a current document if one is open on the handheld. After making a selection, you will have five application choices for the first page in your new document.

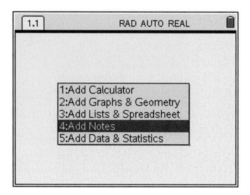

Display B.15

Select **4:Add Notes** to add the first note page. Type the notes on the page as shown in page 1.1 of Display B.13. To add the next page, press **home** and then **2:Add Graphs & Geometry** since we want this page to have a graph. As a shortcut, you can press **ctrl** and then **I** to bring up the insert page menu.

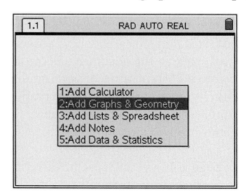

Display B.16

You should see the screen in Display B.17. This will be page 1.2 in your document.

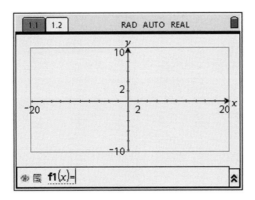

Display B.17

Press **menu,** and then select **2:View** (either by pressing **2** or by pressing the down arrow to highlight it, followed by the right arrow to select it). Next, select **5:Show Grid.** Your handheld screen should look like Display B.18 before you choose **Show Grid.**

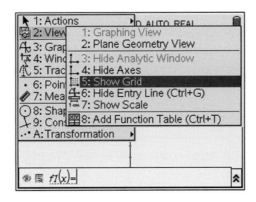

Display B.18

After you select **Show Grid,** you should see the screen shown in Display B.19.

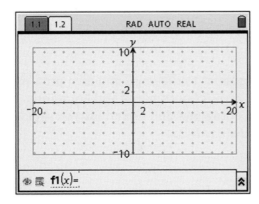

Display B.19

Press **menu, 6:Points & Lines,** and then select **1:Point.** Prior to selecting a point, the screen should look like Display B.20.

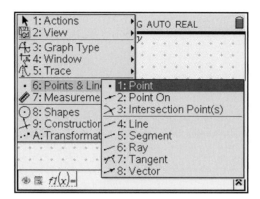

Display B.20

Use the arrow keys on the **NavPad** to place the point where you want it to be. See if you can place it on a grid point. Then press the **pointer/hand** key in the center of the **NavPad** or **enter** to place the point. Since you do not want to construct another point, press the **esc** key to leave the "add a point" environment. You will see the square with the point in it disappear from the upper left hand corner of page 1.2 when you press **esc,** letting you know that you left the "add a point" environment.

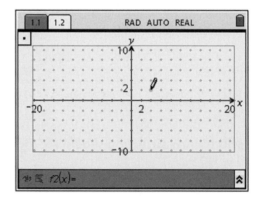

Display B.21

Move the pointer to the point and then press **menu, 1:Actions,** then **6:Coordinates and Equations.** Prior to selecting Coordinates and Equations you should see the screen in Display B.22.

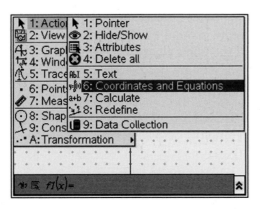

Display B.22

After you select **6:Coordinates and Equations** you will see
the coordinates of your point shown in light gray on the
screen. Move the pointer finger to the point you placed
on the grid and then press the **pointer/hand** key in the
center of the **NavPad** to label that point. Use the arrow keys
to place the light gray label near the point so that you can
see both the point and the label. Press the **pointer/hand**
key again to drop the label near the point. The label will
now show up as a darker black. Press **esc** to leave the
"Coordinates and Equations" environment. The point
should appear with its coordinates labeled. You should
see a screen similar to the one shown in Display B.23.
Do not worry if your screen doesn't look exactly like this
one. What is important is that you can place a point
somewhere on a coordinate system (or the grid) and attach
a coordinate label to it.

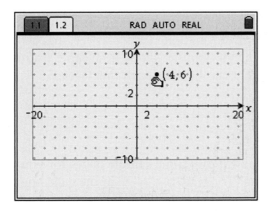

Display B.23

To grab the point and move it, use the **NavPad** arrows
to move close to the point until you see the open hand
icon trying to grab the point. Press **ctrl** and then the
pointer/hand key in the center of the **NavPad** to close the

hand on the point. Then use the arrows on the **NavPad** to move the point around the coordinate system. Notice how the label of the point changes as you move it around the screen. When you are finished moving the point, press the **esc** key to stop grabbing and dragging the point.

Page 1.3 is created by pressing the **home** key, then **4:Notes**, and then typing the desired notes onto the page.

After you have created this three-page document, you may want to save it. The handheld makes it easy for you to do this. When you try to create a new document you will be prompted to save the current document. You will have an opportunity to name this current document and then to save it so that it will not be lost. If you just want to save it without creating a new document, press **ctrl**, **Home**, **1**, and then **3**. A shortcut for these four steps is to press **ctrl** and then **S** like you might do to save a file on a computer. It might be good to save this first document with a brief description and your initials. A suggestion for a name is "mov pt jd" (assuming that your name is either John or Jane Doe).

B.5

Can you answer the questions posed on page 1.3 in this lesson? How did the signs of the x and y coordinates change as you moved the point from quadrant to quadrant? What happened when the point was on the x-axis? What happened when the point was on the y-axis?

Now that you see how the construction of a point can be linked with the coordinates of that point, use your imagination. You can construct any geometric object or graph any function. You can then grab the object or graph and move it. The selected measurements and equation labels that are attached to it will change with the motion. Let's look at another example of the many things that can be done with this feature.

Moving Line

B.6

Display B.24 shows some sample pages for you to try duplicating. Try graphing a line in the coordinate plane. Attach its equation to it. Grab the line and see how the equation changes.

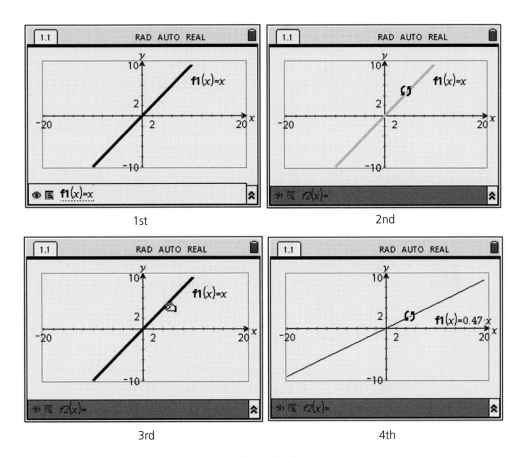

1st   2nd

3rd   4th

Display B.24

If you need help, here is how these pages were created. The function **f1(x) = x** was typed into the function box at the bottom of the Graphs and Geometry screen. This function was then entered by pressing the **enter** key and then the **esc** key to leave the "typing a function" environment (see the first screen in Display B.24). The arrow keys were used to point to the line (away from the origin) which allowed for the option of the rotational motion (see the second screen in Display B.24). **Ctrl** and then the **pointer/hand** keys were used to close the hand on the line in order to grab the line (see the third screen of Display B.24). The arrow keys were then used to rotate the line (notice how the equation has changed in the fourth screen of Display B.24). The **esc** key is used to leave the "rotational motion" environment.

Describe how the coefficient of the *x*-variable changed as you rotated the line. Was it ever positive? Was it ever negative? Was it ever 0? What is the significance of this coefficient?

B.7

Now try grabbing the line closer to the origin. You need to be certain that you are choosing the line and not the coordinate axis. After you use **ctrl** and the **pointer/hand** key to grab the line, and then the arrow keys to move the line up or down, you should see screens like the ones shown in Display B.25.

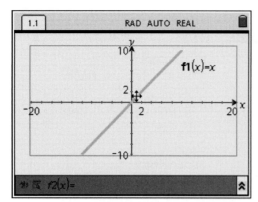
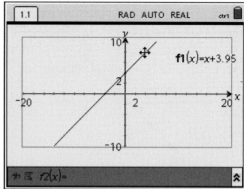

Display B.25

What happens to the equation of the line as you move the line up or down? What is the significance of this change?

B.8

Two-Variable Statistics

Imagine that you and your friend sometimes play a game called "What is my pattern?" Your friend just sent you the data in Display B.26 and challenged you to find a pattern for it (if one exists). Your friend deliberately left out the output values for 6 and 8. Part of the game is to see if you can figure out what those values should be.

input	0	1	2	3	4	5	6	7	8
output	−9	−6	−3	0	3	6		12	

Display B.26

B.9

Let's use the two-variable statistics ability of your handheld to see if we can figure out the pattern. By now you probably know how to start a document on your handheld, so we will just review the initial steps without showing all of the screens. First, press **home**, then **6.** Save the current document if you want to when you are prompted to do so. Second, select **3:Add Lists & Spreadsheet.** Enter your "input" data in column A and the "output" data in column B. Do not enter the input values of 6 and 8 because you do not have output values to go with them. After you have entered the data, you should see the first screen in Display B.27. Type the word "input" in the space next to the letter A and the word "output" in the space next to the letter B. This gives a *list name* to the data in each column. You can use *almost* any name to describe the data lists that you have entered. You may not use names that are reserved variables on the handheld, such as "**ans**" or "**Log.**" You will get an error message if you try to use a reserved name or variable.

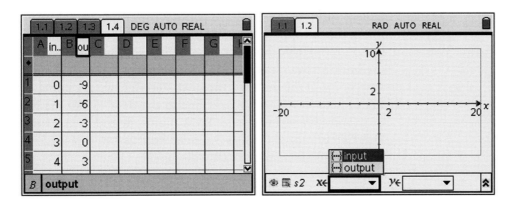

Display B.27

To create a scatter plot of your data, press **home** and
2:Add Graphs & Geometry. Then press **menu, 3,** and **4**
to select **Scatter Plot.** Use the **pointer/hand** key and click
on the rectangle for the *x*-list. Choose input for your *x*-list.
Repeat these steps for your *y*-list. You should see your
data plotted. If you do not see it, press **menu, 4,** then **9** for
Zoom-Data.

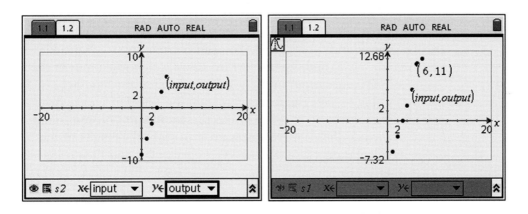

Display B.28

B.10

What do you think about this data? Does it look linear?
What do you think would happen if you added the input
value of 6 with a guess for the output value that goes with
it to the spreadsheet page? Try it. Remember that you use
the **ctrl** and left and right arrow keys to go from page to
page in a document. What happened to the scatter plot
when you added data to the spreadsheet? The second screen
of Display B.28 shows a guess of 11 for output with a 6 for
input. Was that a good guess? To show the coordinates,
turn **trace** on by pressing **menu, 5,** and then **1.** You can
then use the right and left arrows to trace the points.

B.11

Unless your guess for 6 gave you the result you were looking for, go back to the Lists and Spreadsheet page and remove it. You remove both values by moving to them and pressing the **back arrow/clear button**. We do not want a "bad" data point in the data for the next step that we are going to do. Let's fit a least-squares line to the data. Go to the Lists and Spreadsheet page. Press **menu, 4,** and then **1** for **Stat Calculations**. Choose **3:Linear Regression (mx+b)**. The screens in Display B.29 will appear.

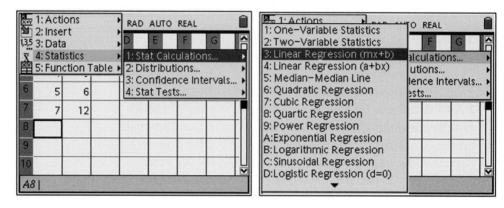

Display B.29

After choosing **Linear Regression**, you will see the first screen in Display B.30. You can use the **pointer/hand** key (to select) and the **tab** key (to move) to choose input in the *x*-list and output in the *y*-list. Notice that the handheld is going to save the regression equation into **f1** for you. You will also need to type **c[]** into the **1st Result Column** to tell the handheld where you want it to store the results of the calculations. Use the **tab** key to get to **OK** and then press **enter** to select it.

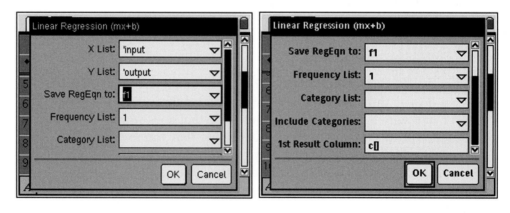

Display B.30

After you press **OK** you should see the first screen in Display B.31. Scroll around in it.

What do you think about the r^2 and the r values? What is the linear equation that the handheld produced to fit the data?

B.12

Go back to the graph screen (page 1.2) and select **menu, 3, 1** for **Function**. You can use the arrow keys to see that the handheld has saved the linear equation in **f1(x)** as mentioned before. Use the up and down arrows to select **f1(x)** and then press **enter** to graph it. You should see the graph and the data points both graphed as shown in the second screen of Display B.31. Remember to press **esc** to leave the "graph a function" environment so you can navigate on the graph screen. If the function label is obstructing your view of the graphs, remember that you can grab it and move it to a different place on the screen. The (x, y) label can also be grabbed and moved so that you can see it better. In this case, notice that it is a (input, output) label because that is what you chose as names for the lists.

B.13

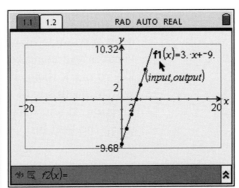

Display B.31

What do you think the pattern is for your friend's data? You should now be able to "trace" along the function to find the missing output values for 6 and 8. What do you think the missing values are? Are the values that you get when you trace consistent with the values that the function (equation) gives you?

B.14

Geometry and Measurements

It is possible to create a geometric object and then take measurements on it. We will start with a triangle so that you can see how this works.

Do all of the steps to open a new document. These are: **home, 6,** save (or not), and **2:Add Graph & Geometry.** After you obtain a graphing page, select **menu, 2:View,**

B.15

4:Hide Axes, menu, 2:View, then **6:Hide Entry Line.** As you do this, you should see the screens in Display B.32.

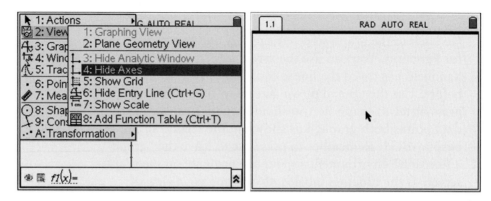

Display B.32

The second screen in Display B.32 is the "geometric" area of the Graphs & Geometry application, not the "analytic" area. They are both on the same work area and you can work with either one or both at the same time. Now, we are going to press **menu, 8,** and **2** to choose **Triangle.** You draw a triangle by choosing a location for each of the three vertices and using either the **pointer/hand** key or the **enter** key to mark them. If you want to label the vertices, the best way to do this is to type in a label right after you select the location. If you decide to label them later, you can do so by using the **text** box (**menu, 1, 5**).

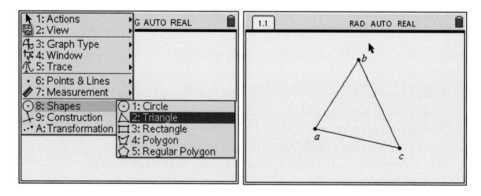

Display B.33

Now we are going to measure each angle. To do this, press **menu, 7** and then **4** for **Angle.** Measure each angle by using the **pointer/hand** key on three vertices with the angle that you want to measure as the second (middle) click. This is the same way that you would name an angle. Order doesn't matter as long as the vertex of the angle that you are measuring is the middle selection. You will see the measure of the angle appear in a gray color. After you have selected the last vertex (for each angle), use the arrow keys to place the measurement near the angle. Make sure the first digit in the angle measurement is near the angle so it will also move if the point is moved. Then press **enter** or the **pointer/hand** key to drop the measurement. It will turn to a darker shade of black.

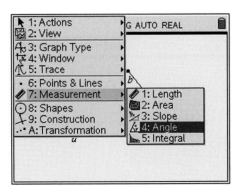
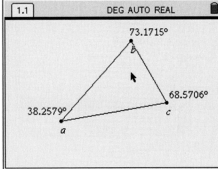

Display B.34

The default setting for the angle measurement is in radians. If you want to have the handheld indicate degrees, press **home**, **8**, and then **1** for **Document Settings**. After you select **Degrees** and **Apply to System**, the measurements will change to degrees.

Let's add up the interior angles of this triangle to see what the sum is. Select **menu**, **1**, and then **5** for **Text**. Move the text symbol to a good location and select it. Type **s=a+b+c** in the box and then press **enter** to attach it to the page. Don't forget to press **esc** when you are done to leave the "text" environment.

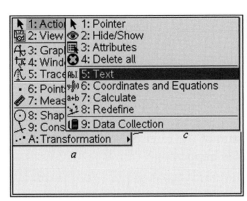
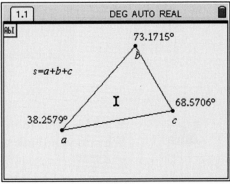

Display B.35

To attach the measurements to the equation, follow these steps: Select **menu**, **1**, and then **7** for **Calculate**. Move the pointer to the formula and when it blinks, select it. As you move away from it, you will be asked for the measurement of the first variable. Move to the measurement (not the label) and when it blinks, select it. Continue in this manner until *a*, *b*, and *c* have all been selected. After selecting *c*, you will see 180° appear in a gray color. Use your arrow keys to move it near the equation and press **enter** to drop it. If you want, you can use the **Text** option again to label it *s* =.

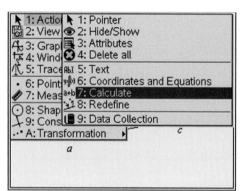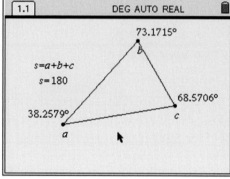

Display B.36

Now grab any vertex of the triangle to change its shape. Display B.37 shows a possible result.

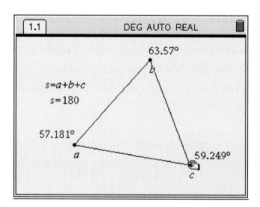

Display B.37

B.16

What happens to the sum of the interior angles? Why do you think this is happening?

Glossary 1a & 1b   Glosario 1a & 1b

ENGLISH	SPANISH	VISUAL
	A	

absolute temperature scale
(Kelvin scale) A scale calibrated where water boils at 373° and freezes at 273°. The scale starts at absolute zero and has the same size degrees as the Celsius scale.

escala absoluta de temperatura
(Escala Kelvin) Una escala calibrada donde el agua hierve a 373° y se congela a 273°. La escala comienza en el cero absoluto y tiene los mismos grados a la escala Celsius (centígrados).

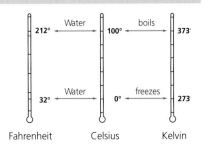

absolute value The (nonnegative) distance of a number from 0.

valor absoluto La distancia (no negativa) de un número desde 0.

$$|7| = 7 \qquad |-7| = 7 \qquad |0| = 0$$

acronym A type of abbreviation for a string of words.

acrónimo Un tipo de abreviatura para una serie de palabras.

AWOL, ASAP, RSVP

algorithm A step-by-step procedure, often used to solve equations more quickly.

algoritmo Un procedimiento progresivo, usado regularmente para solucionar ecuaciones rápidamente.

<u>Steps in an Algorithm</u>
$42.25 = 0.09u + 8.50$
$42.25 - 8.50 = 0.09u + 8.50 - 8.50$
$33.75 \div 0.09 = 0.09u \div 0.09$
$375 = u$

arithmetic sequence
A sequence where the difference between any two successive terms of the sequence is constant.

secuencia artimética
Una secuencia donde la diferencia entre cualesquiera dos términos sucesivos de la consecuencia es constante.

$2, 5, 8, 11, 14, \ldots$

Associative Law of Addition
$(a + b) + c = a + (b + c)$

Ley asociativa de la adición
$(a + b) + c = a + (b + c)$

$(19 + 6) + 4 = 19 + (6 + 4)$

Associative Law of Multiplication
$a(b \cdot c) = (a \cdot b)c$

Ley asociativa de la multiplicación
$a(b \cdot c) = (a \cdot b)c$

$19(6 \cdot 4) = (19 \cdot 6)4$

axis One of the reference lines in a coordinate system.

eje Una de las líneas de referencia en un sistema de coordenadas.

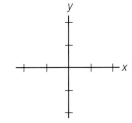

Glossary/Glosario

B

bar graph A picture of data using the length of bars relative to some scale to show the number of times each label occurs.

gráfica de barra Un dibujo de datos usando la longitud de barras con relación a alguna escala para demostrar el número de veces que cada situación ocurre.

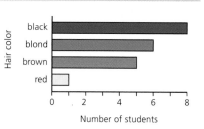

$2^4 = 2 \cdot 2 \cdot 2 \cdot 2 = 16$

base The number that is multiplied the number of times indicated by its exponent.

base El número que es multiplicado el número de veces que es indicado por su exponente.

biased (experiment) An experiment or event in which one or several outcomes are more likely to occur than others.

influenciado (experimento) Un experimento o evento donde es posible que uno o varios resultados ocurran más que otros.

bimodal (data set) A set made up of two distinct data groupings that are relatively far from each other.

bimodal (conjunto de datos) Un conjunto compuesto de dos grupos distintos de datos que están relativamente lejos uno de otro.

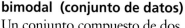

boxplot A five-number summary in picture form.

diagrama de bloques Un gráfico que representa lo que es conocido como las cinco números claves de un grupo de datos numéricos.

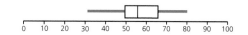

branch An arrow that represents a choice on a tree diagram.

rama Una flecha que representa una opción en un diagrama de árbol

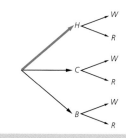

C

category data Data that can be classified into groups and titled—labels, names, etc.

categoría de datos Los datos que pueden ser clasificados en grupos y nombrados—etiquetas, nombres, etc.

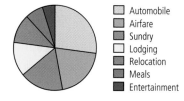

Celsius temperature scale A scale calibrated where water boils at 100° and freezes at 0°.

escala de temperatura Celsius (centígrados) Una escala calibrada donde el agua hierve a 100° y se congela a 0°.

coefficient A number or variable that precedes a variable in a product.

coeficiente Un número o variable que precede a una variable en un producto.

$5x = 8z$

common monomial factor (or CMF) The greatest common divisor of all the terms in a polynomial.

factor monomio común (o FMC) El factor divisor común más grande de todos los términos en un polinomio.

$8x^2 - 12x^2 + 24x$
$CMF = 3x$

common ratio The ratio of any term to the previous term in a geometric sequence; the number each term is multiplied by to get the next term in a geometric sequence.

proporción común La proporción de cualquier término al término previo en una secuencia geométrica; el número por el cual cada término es multiplicado para obtener el término próximo en una secuencia geométrica.

For 3, 6, 12, 24, 48, ..., the common ratio $r = 2$.

commutative A term that means a different order of variables or constants in an expression or an equation.

conmutativo Un término que significa un orden diferente de variables o constantes en una expresión o una ecuación.

Commutative Law of Addition $a + b = b + a$

Ley conmutativa de la adición $a + b = b + a$

$5 + 8 = 8 + 5 = 13$

Commutative Law of Multiplication $a \cdot b = b \cdot a$

Ley conmutativa de la multiplicación $a \cdot b = b \cdot a$

$5 \cdot 8 = 8 \cdot 5 = 40$

complement (of a set) The set of elements not in that set, but in the universal set.

complemento (de un conjunto) El conjunto de elementos que no se encuentran en ese conjunto, pero sí en el conjunto universal.

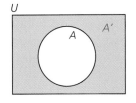

complete branch A path of branches from the starting point to an end point of a tree diagram.

rama completa Un trayecto de ramas desde un punto de comienzo hasta un punto final de un diagrama de árbol.

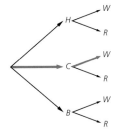

completing the square A method of solving quadratic equations of the form $ax^2 + bx = k$.

completando el cuadrado Un método para solucionar ecuaciones cuadráticas de la forma $ax^2 + bx = k$.

$x^2 + 8x = -12$
$x^2 + 8x + 16 = -12 + 16$
$(x + 4)^2 = 4$
$x + 4 = \pm 2$
$x = \pm 2 - 4$
$x = -2 \text{ or } -6$

composite (function) The function that results from applying one function to the range of another function.

compuesta (función) La función que resulta de la aplicación de una función al alcance de otra función.

$$f(x) = 2x + 3 \quad g(x) = x^2 - 4x + 1$$
$$f(g(x)) = f(x^2 - 4x + 1)$$
$$f(g(x)) = 2(x^2 - 4x + 1) + 3$$
$$f(g(x)) = 2x^2 - 8x + 5$$

compound interest Paying interest on interest previously earned.

interés compuesto Interés pagado en interés ganado previamente.

$1500 + 4\%$ int. $= 1500 + 60 = 1560$
$1560 + 4\%$ int. $= 1560 + 62.40 = 1622.40$
$1622.40 + 4\%$ int. $= 1622.40 + 64.90 = 1687.30$

constant A number, letter, or symbol that represents one value only.

constante Un número, letra o símbolo que representa un valor solamente.

$$y = mx + b$$
$m = $ slope $\qquad b = y\text{-intercept}$
$y = 4x + 1 \quad m = 4 \quad b = 1$

convention An agreement to do something in a particular way.

convención Un acuerdo de hacer algo de una manera particular.

coordinate Each of the numbers or letters used to identify the position of a point in a coordinate system.

coordenada Cada uno de los números o letras usados para identificar la posición de un punto en un sistema de coordenadas.

$$(7, 4)$$
x-coordinate, y-coordinate

coordinate system A graphical method that uses two or more numbers or letters to locate a position in space. Sometimes called the Cartesian coordinate system after the French scholar René Descartes who first used this system, or a rectangular coordinate system because the axes cross at right angles.

sistema de coordenadas Un método gráfico que usa dos o más números o letras para localizar una posición en el espacio. Algunas veces llamado el sistema de coordenadas Cartesiano por el erudito francés René Descartes quien usó este sistema por primera vez, o un sistema de coordenadas rectangular porque los ejes se cruzan en ángulos rectos.

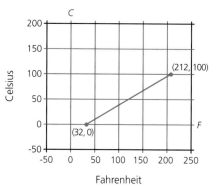

correlation coefficient (symbolized by the variable r) Rates the way a regression line fits its data on a scale from 0 to 1 or -1, where $r = 1$ or -1 means that all the data points lie right on the line.

correlación coeficiente (simbolizado por la variable r) Evalúa la manera en que una línea de regresión ajusta sus datos en una escala de 0 a 1 ó -1, donde $r = 1$ ó -1 significa que todos los puntos de datos caen justo en la línea.

cross multiplication A method to rewrite a proportion without fractions by setting equal to each other the products of the terms diagonally across from each other.

multiplicación cruzada (productos cruzados) Un método para reescribir una proporción sin fracciones colocando uno al lado del otro los productos de los términos equivalentes diagonalmente opuestos.

If $\frac{a}{b} = \frac{c}{d}$, then $ad = bc$.

D

---

data Factual information.

datos Información actual.

NCAA Men's Baseball Champions, 1970-2006			
Year	Winning college	Year	Winning college
1970	USC	1989	Wichita State
1971	USC	1990	Georgia
1972	USC	1991	LSU
1973	USC	1992	Pepperdine

defined on A function is *defined on* a particular set if that set is in the domain of the function.

definida en Una función *es definida en* un conjunto determinado si ese conjunto se encuentra en el dominio de la función.

degree (of a polynomial) The degree of a polynomial is equal to the highest power of the variables in the polynomial.

grado (de un polinomio) El grado de un polinomio es igual a la potencia mayor de las variables en el polinomio.

$3x^4 - 2x^3 + 8x^2 + 4x - 7$ is a 4th degree polynomial.

density The mass divided by the volume of any matter.

densidad La masa dividida por el volumen de cualquier materia.

$$density = \frac{mass}{volume}$$

dependent variable A variable that represents the range elements (the "output") of a function.

variable dependiente Una variable que representa los elementos de alcance (la "salida") de una función.

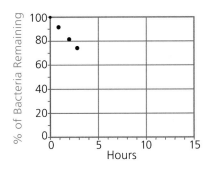

deviation The difference between a data value and some measure of center, such as the mean.

desviación La diferencia entre el valor de un dato y alguna medida del centro, tal como la media.

$$x \qquad x - \bar{x} \qquad |x - \bar{x}|$$
variable   deviation   value of deviation

difference (of functions) The function obtained by subtracting the two images for each domain element.

diferencia (de funciones) La función obtenida por medio de la resta de dos imágenes para cada elemento del dominio.

$$(f - g)(x) = f(x) - g(x)$$

difference (of two sets) The set of elements in the first set that are not in the second set.

diferencia (de dos conjuntos) El conjunto de elementos en el primer conjunto que no se encuentran en el segundo conjunto.

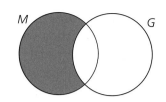

difference of squares A quadratic equation in the form $x^2 - k^2$, which can be factored to $(x - k)(x + k)$.

diferencia de cuadrados Una ecuación cuadrática en la forma de $x^2 - k^2$, la cual puede ser factorizada a $(x - k)(x + k)$.

$$(x^2 - 16) = (x - 4)(x + 4)$$

disjoint (sets) Two or more sets that have no elements in common.

disjuntos (conjuntos) Dos o más conjuntos que no tienen ningunos elementos en común.

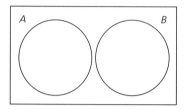

Distributive Law for multiplication over addition
$$a(b + c) = ab + ac$$
$$(a + b)c = ac + bc$$

Ley Distributiva para la multiplicación sobre la adición
$$a(b + c) = ab + ac$$
$$(a + b)c = ac + bc$$

$$5(6 + 7) = 5 \cdot 6 + 5 \cdot 7$$
$$(5 + 6)7 = 5 \cdot 7 + 6 \cdot 7$$

for multiplication over subtraction
$$a(b - c) = ab - ac$$
$$(a - b)c = ac - bc$$

para la multiplicación sobre la sustracción
$$a(b - c) = ab - ac$$
$$(a - b)c = ac - bc$$

$$4(3 - 6) = 4 \cdot 3 - 4 \cdot 6$$
$$(4 - 3)6 = 4 \cdot 6 - 3 \cdot 6$$

domain (of a function) The set of first elements of a function; the set of elements to which a function is applied.

dominio (de una función) El conjunto de los primeros elementos de una función; el conjunto de elementos a los cuales se aplica la función.

dotplot A data display in which each data item is shown as a dot above its value on a number line.

diagrama de puntos Una demostración de datos en la cual cada dato es mostrado como un punto sobre su valor en una línea numérica.

E

element Each object in a set.

elemento Cada objeto en un conjunto.

$$A = \{5, 7, 9, 11, 13\}$$

ellipsis The symbol [...] used to indicate something is missing or omitted.

elipsis El símbolo [...] usado para indicar que se ha omitido o falta algo.

$$B = \{1, 2, 3, ..., n\}$$

empty set The set with no elements.

conjunto vacío El conjunto sin elementos.

$$C = \{ \} \text{ or } C = \varnothing$$

end behavior (of a function)
The value of the function or the value that the function is approaching when x is extremely large or small.

comportamiento final (de una function) El valor de la función o el valor que la función está alcanzando cuando x es extremadamente grande o pequeño.

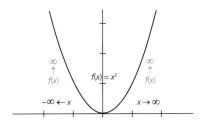

equal functions Functions with the same domain that assign the same image to each domain element.

funciones equivalentes Funciones con el mismo dominio que asignan la misma imágen para cada elemento del dominio.

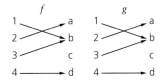

equally likely (events) Events that have the same probability of occurring.

igualmente probables (eventos) Eventos que pueden ocurrir con la misma probabilidad.

The chance of getting a heads or tails when flipping a fair coin are equally likely events.

equation A symbolic statement that two quantities are equal.

ecuación Una declaración simbólica de dos cantidades que son iguales.

$$15a + 2b = 24$$

even function A function where $f(x) = f(-x)$.

función par Una función donde $f(x) = f(-x)$.

$$f(x) = 3x^6 - 6x^4 + x^2$$

event A subset of a sample space.

evento Un subconjunto de una muestra de espacio.

experiment Any situation with an uncertain outcome.

experimento Cualquier situación con un resultado incierto.

exponent The small, raised number, or power, that tells how many times a base is multiplied by itself.

exponente El número pequeño y elevado o potencia, que dice cuántas veces una base es multiplicada por sí misma.

$$3^5$$

exponential decay The description of a function in the form $y = a^x$, where $0 < a < 1$; y decreases as x increases.

decremento exponencial La descripción de una función en la forma $y = a^x$, donde $0 < a < 1$; y disminuye según x aumenta.

$$y = 0.95^2 = 0.9025$$
$$y = 0.95^3 = 0.8574$$
$$y = 0.95^4 = 0.8145$$
$$y = 0.95^5 = 0.7738$$

exponential function A function in which the independent variable is used as an exponent.

función exponencial Una función en la cuál la variable independiente es usada como un exponente.

$$f(x) = 1.09^t \cdot 100,000$$

exponential growth The description of a function in the form $y = a^x$, where $a > 1$; y increases as x increases.

incremento exponencial La descripción de la función en la forma $y = a^x$, donde $a > 1$; y aumenta mientras x aumenta.

$$y = 50^2 = 2500$$
$$y = 50^3 = 125,000$$
$$y = 50^4 = 6,250,000$$

exponentiation An operation of arithmetic where the base (a number or variable) is raised to an exponent (power).

exponenciación Una operación aritmética donde la base (un número o variable) es elevada a un exponente (potencia).

$$a \cdot a \cdot a \cdot a \cdot a = a^5$$

extrapolation A procedure used to predict values of a variable in an unobserved interval (outside the interval) from observed values inside the interval. Backward extrapolation is when an estimate is made to the left of the region of data points; forward extrapolation, or forecasting is when an estimate is made to the right of the region of data points.

extrapolación Un procedimiento usado para predecir valores de una variable en un intervalo no observado (fuera del intervalo) de valores observados dentro del intervalo. Extrapolación retrasada es cuando un estimado es hecho a la izquierda de la región de puntos de datos; extrapolación anticipada, o pronosticada es cuando un estimado es hecho a la derecha de la región de puntos de datos.

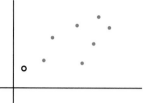
Backward extrapolation

Forward extrapolation—forecasting

F

factorial For any natural number n, the product of all consecutive positive integers from 1 to n.

factorial Para cualquier número natural n, el producto de todos los enteros positivos consecutivos de 1 a n.

$$4! = 4 \cdot 3 \cdot 2 \cdot 1$$
$$n! = n \cdot (n - 1) \cdot (n - 2) \cdot \ldots \cdot 2 \cdot 1$$

Fahrenheit temperature scale A scale calibrated where water boils at 212° and freezes at 32°.

escala de temperatura Fahrenheit Una escala calibrada donde el agua hierve a 212° y se congela a 32°.

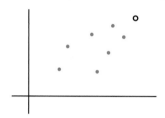

finite (set) A set that can be counted; i.e., there is an end to the number of elements it contains.

finito (conjunto) Un conjunto que puede ser contado; por ejemplo, hay un final para la cantidad de elementos que contiene.

$\{100, 200, 300, \ldots, 1000\}$

$\{a, b, c, d\}$

first differences The difference between successive values of a function for a sequence of equally spaced domain values.

primeras diferencias La diferencia entre valores sucesivos de una función para una secuencia de valores de dominio separados igualmente.

first quartile The median of the "first half" of a data set; the median of the data that is less than the median of the entire data set.

primer cuartil La mediana de la "primera mitad" de un conjunto de datos; la mediana de los datos que es menos que la mediana de todo el conjunto de datos.

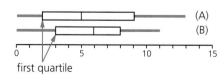
first quartile

five-number summary The minimum, first quartile, median, third quartile, and maximum numbers of a set of numerical data.

resumen de cinco números El mínimo, primer cuartil, mediana, tercer cuartil y los números máximos de un conjunto de datos numéricos.

Five-number summary:
53, 65.5, 78.5, 88.5, 97

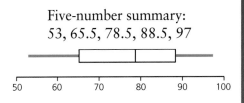

forecasting A procedure used to predict future events such as sales, the weather, etc., based on known data.

pronóstico Un procedimiento usado para predecir eventos futuros como son las ventas, el clima, etc., basándose en datos conocidos.

Forward extrapolation—forecasting

frequency The number of times a value appears in a data set.

frecuencia El número de veces que un valor aparece en un conjunto de datos.

The category "9" has a frequency of 1.

function Any process or rule that assigns to each element of a first set exactly one element from a second set.

función Cualquier proceso o regla que asigna a cada elemento del primero conjunto exactamente un elemento del segundo conjunto.

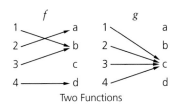

Two Functions

function composition The process of following one function by another, so that the images from the first function are in the domain of the second.

función de composición El proceso de seguir una función por otra, de manera que las imágenes de la primera función se encuentran en el dominio de la segunda.

$f(x) = 2x + 3 \quad g(x) = x^2 - 4x + 1$

$f(g(x)) = f(x^2 - 4x + 1)$

$f(g(x)) = 2(x^2 - 4x + 1) + 3$

$f(g(x)) = 2x^2 - 8x + 5$

Fundamental Counting Principle If one of k actions can be taken in n_1 ways, a second action can be taken in n_2 ways, a third action can be taken in n_3 ways, and so on, then there are

$$n_1 \cdot n_2 \cdot n_3 \cdot \ldots \cdot n_k$$

ways to take all k actions.

Principio fundamental de conteo Si una de k acciones puede ser tomada de n_1 maneras, una segunda acción puede ser tomada en n_2 maneras, una tercera acción puede ser tomada en n_3 maneras, y así sucesivamente, entonces hay

$$n_1 \cdot n_2 \cdot n_3 \cdot \ldots \cdot n_k$$

maneras de tomar todos las acciones k.

G

geometric sequence A sequence where the ratio of any two successive terms of the sequence is constant

secuencia geométrica Una secuencia donde la proporción de cualesquiera dos términos sucesivos de la secuencia es constante.

3, 6, 12, 24, 48, …

graph A pictorial representation of a set of points in a coordinate system.

gráfica Una representación gráfica de un conjunto de puntos en un sistema de coordenadas.

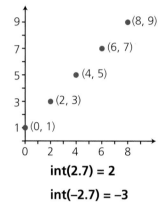

greatest integer function The function that matches each real number with the greatest integer that is less than or equal to that real number. Written as **int(** on TI calculators.

función entera más grande La función que es igual a cada número real con el entero más grande que es menor o igual a ese número real. Representado como **int(** en las calculadoras TI.

int(2.7) = 2

int(–2.7) = –3

growth function A function that expresses the amount of something at a particular time based on how much there was just before that time.

función de crecimiento Una función que expresa la cantidad de algo en un momento determinado basado en cuánto había de esa cantidad antes de ese momento.

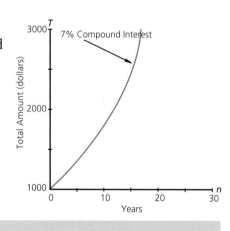

H

histogram A graphical display of measurement data that uses rectangles to show the frequency of data items in successive numerical intervals of equal size.

histograma Una presentación gráfica de datos de medidas que usa rectángulos para mostrar la frecuencia de artículos de datos en intervalos numéricos sucesivos de igual tamaño.

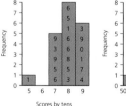

image (of an element) The element in the range of a function that is assigned to a given domain element.

imagen (de un elemento) El elemento en el alcance de una función que es asignado a un elemento de dominio dado.

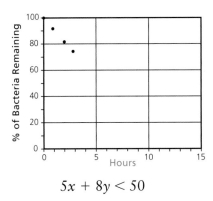

The image of 2 is a.

independent variable A variable that represents the domain elements (the "input") of a function.

variable independiente Una variable que representa los elementos del dominio (la "entrada") de una función.

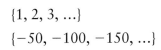

inequality An algebraic statement which says that two numbers or expressions representing numbers are not equal.

desigualdad Una declaración algebraica la cual dice que dos números o expresiones representando números no son iguales.

$5x + 8y < 50$

infinite (set) A set that is not finite or cannot be counted; i.e., there is no end to the number of elements it contains.

infinito (conjunto) Un conjunto que no es finito o no puede ser contado; por ejemplo, ho hay un final para la cantidad de elementos que contiene.

$\{1, 2, 3, ...\}$
$\{-50, -100, -150, ...\}$

interpolation A procedure used to estimate values of a variable between two known values.

interpolación Un procedimiento usado para estimar valores de una variable entre dos valores conocidos.

See "linear interpolation"

interquartile range The numerical difference between the first and third quartiles of a data set.

amplitud intercuartil La diferencia numérica entre el primer y el tercer cuartil de un conjunto de datos.

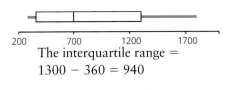

The interquartile range =
$1300 - 360 = 940$

intersection (of sets) The set of elements common to two or more sets.

intersección (de conjuntos) El conjunto de elementos comunes a dos o más conjuntos.

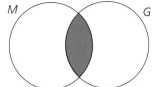

interval notation A way to represent a range of numbers between two endpoints. Parentheses are used to indicate that an endpoint is not included and brackets are used to indicate that an endpoint is included.

notación de intervalo Una manera de representar una gama de números entre dos puntos finales. Se usan paréntesis para indicar que un punto final no está incluido y los corchetes son usados para indicar que un punto final está incluido.

$[4, 9)$ indicates numbers from 4 (including 4) up to 9 (not including 9).

K

Kelvin temperature scale (absolute temperature scale) A scale calibrated where water boils at 373° and freezes at 273°. The scale starts at absolute zero and has the same size degrees as the Celsius scale.

escala de temperatura Kelvin (escala de temperatura absoluta) Una escala calibrada donde el agua hierve a 373° y se congela a 273°. La escala comienza en cero absoluto y utiliza la misma escala de grados que la escala Celsius (centígrados).

kilowatt One thousand watts of electrical power.

kilovatio Mil vatios de energía eléctrica.

kilowatt-hour (kWh) The amount of electrical energy used in one hour.

horas kilovatio La cantidad de energía eléctrica usada en una hora.

L

label data Category data; data that are not numerical.

datos rotulados Categoría de datos; datos que no son numéricos.

See "category data"

laws governing equality
If $a = b$, then $a + c = b + c$.
If $a = b$, then $a - c = b - c$.
If $a = b$ and $c \neq 0$, then $a \div c = b \div c$.

leyes que gobiernan a las desigualdades
Si $a = b$, entonces $a + c = b + c$.
Si $a = b$, entonces $a - c = b - c$.
Si $a = b$, entonces $a \cdot c = b \cdot c$.
Si $a = b$ y $c \neq 0$, entonces $a \div c = b \div c$.

$a = b, c = 5$	$a + 5 = b + 5$
$a = b, c = 7$	$a - 7 = b - 7$
$a = b, c = 12$	$a \cdot 12 = b \cdot 12$
$a = b, c = 2$	$a \div 2 = b \div 2$

leading coefficient The coefficient of the variable term with the highest power.

coeficiente mayor El coeficiente del término variable con la potencia mayor.

$3x^4 - 2x^3 + 8x^2 + 4x - 7$ has a leading coefficient of 3.

least common denominator (or LCD) The least common multiple of the denominators.

denominador común mínimo (o DCM) El mínimo común múltiplo de los denominadores.

LCD of $\frac{3}{5}$ and $-\frac{4}{7}$ = LCM of 5 and 7 = 35

least common multiple (or LCM) The smallest possible number or algebraic quantity that is a multiple of each term.

mínimo común múltiplo (o MCM) El número menor o cantidad algebraica que es un múltiplo de cada término.

Multiples of 15 = 15, 30, 45, 60, 75, 90, 105, 120, ...
Multiples of 24 = 24, 48, 72, 96, 120, ...
LCM of 15 and 24 = 120

least-squares line (or regression line) A straight line that minimizes the sum of the squares of the vertical distances from the line to the points of a given data set in a coordinate plane.

recta de mínimos-cuadrados (o línea de regresión) Una línea recta que minimiza la suma de los cuadrados de las distancias verticales de la línea a los puntos de un conjunto de datos dados en un plano de coordenadas.

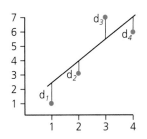

like terms Terms with the same variables raised to the same powers.

términos parecidos Términos con las mismas variables elevadas a la misma potencia.

$2x^2y$ and $\frac{1}{3}x^2y$

line of symmetry A line that divides a graph in half so that each half is a mirror image of the other.

línea de simetría Una línea que divide una gráfica por la mitad de manera que cada mitad es un reflejo exacto de la otra.

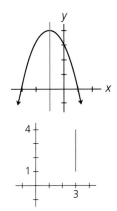

line segment A piece of a line that is between two points.

segmento de línea Un pedazo de una línea que está entre dos puntos.

linear equation An equation that can be put in the form $y = ax + b$ or $x = k$.

ecuación lineal Una ecuación que puede ser puesta en forma de $y = ax + b$ o $x = k$.

$T = 0.09u + 8.50$

linear function A function that can be put in the form $f(x) = ax + b$ or $x = a$, where a and b are constants.

función lineal Una función que se puede escribir en la forma de $f(x) = ax + b$ o $x = a$, donde a y b son constantes.

$f(x) = -2x + 4$

linear interpolation A procedure used to estimate values of a variable between two given points in a scatterplot by using the values of the points that lie on a straight line joining the two given points.

interpolación lineal Un procedimiento usado para estimar los valores de una variable entre dos puntos dados en un diagrama de dispersión usando los valores de los puntos que caen en una línea recta uniendo los dos puntos dados.

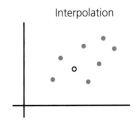

Interpolation

M

mathematical law A statement that is true for all values for which it is defined.

ley matemática Una declaración que es cierta para todos los valores para la cual es definida.

mean The sum of a collection of numerical data divided by the number of data items.

media La suma de una colección de datos numéricos dividido por la cantidad de datos.

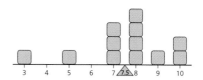

mean absolute deviation The mean (average) of all the distances between the individual data items and the mean of a data set.

desviación absoluta media La media (promedio) de todas las distancias entre los artículos individuales de datos y la media de un conjunto de datos.

measurement data Data that are numbers being used to count or measure things.

medición de datos Datos que son números siendo usados para contar o medir cosas.

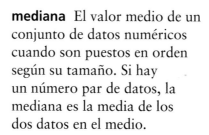

median The middle value of a set of numerical data when the data are arranged in size order. If there is an even number of data items, the median is the mean of the two middle data items.

mediana El valor medio de un conjunto de datos numéricos cuando son puestos en orden según su tamaño. Si hay un número par de datos, la mediana es la media de los dos datos en el medio.

1, 1, 2, 3, 4, 5, 6, 7, 79

median-median line A method for determining a best-fit line to a set of data.

línea mediana-mediana Un método para determinar la línea más apropiada en un conjunto de datos.

midpoint The point at the center of a line segment. $\left(\frac{x_1 + x_2}{2}, \frac{y_1 + y_2}{2}\right)$ is the formula for the midpoint of a line segment with endpoints (x_1, y_1) and (x_2, y_2).

punto medio El punto en el centro de un segmento de línea. $\left(\frac{x_1 + x_2}{2}, \frac{y_1 + y_2}{2}\right)$ es la fórmula para el punto medio de un segmento de línea con extremos (x_1, y_1) y (x_2, y_2).

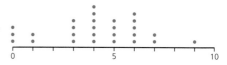

mode The category in a data set that occurs most often.

modo La categoría en un conjunto de datos que ocurre más frecuentemente.

The data item "3" is the **mode**.

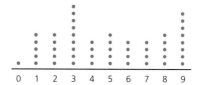